Fire engineering

CIBSE Guide E

CIBSE

Typeset by CIBSE Publications Department

Printed in Great Britain by Henry Ling Ltd., The Dorset Press, Dorchester DT1 1HD, UK.

Note from the publisher

This publication is primarily intended to provide guidance to those responsible for the design, installation, commissioning, operation and maintenance of building services. It is not intended to be exhaustive or definitive and it will be necessary for users of the guidance given to exercise their own professional judgement when deciding whether to abide by or depart from it.

Foreword

This edition of CIBSE Guide E: *Fire engineering* is a fully updated version of the first edition. It has two completely new sections dealing with firefighting (section 9) and fire safety management (section 12).

The art of fire engineering has evolved and changed since the first edition of Guide E was published in 1997; computers are much more powerful, allowing greater use of analytical techniques such as computational fluid dynamics, and there are now a vast number of websites relating to fire engineering, which means much faster and wider dissemination of ideas.

In 1998, the Institution of Fire Engineers was certified as a nominating body of the Engineering Council, thereby providing a professional 'home' for chartered fire professionals. More recently, the Association of Fire Consultants has been formed by the major fire consultancies within the UK.

This Guide has been updated to take account of recent research and current legislation, and has made reference, where possible, to the latest publications and websites at the time of going to press. However, the pace of change is so fast that any published guidance will quickly be out-of-date. Therefore I would ask that users of this Guide open their minds and explore new techniques not yet covered in this Guide.

Finally, I should like to extend my thanks to all of the professional fire consultants listed below who have given their valuable time and expertise to this project and worked so hard to make this new edition of Guide E possible.

Martin Kealy
Chairman, CIBSE Guide E Steering Committee

Guide E Steering Committee

Martin Kealy (Chairman) (WSP Fire Engineering, part of WSP Group plc)
John Barnfield (Tenos Fire Safety Engineering Consultants)
Peter Bressington (Arup Fire)
Mike Dennett (consultant)
John Hopkinson (Faber Maunsell Ltd)
Margaret Law (consultant)
Alan Porter (Warrington Fire Research Ltd)
Terry Watson (GEM Consultants)
Corinne Williams (FRS, BRE)
Ken Butcher (Secretary) (CIBSE)

Principal authors, contributors and acknowledgements

Section 1: Introduction

Principal author (second edition):
Martin Kealy (Chairman) (WSP Fire Engineering, part of WSP Group plc)

Section 2: Legislation, standards and strategy

Principal author (first and second editions):
Peter Bressington (Arup Fire)

Acknowledgements:
Institute of Building Control

Section 3: Building designation

Principal author (first and second editions):
John Hopkinson (Faber Maunsell Ltd)

Acknowledgements:
British Standards Institution

Section 4: Means of escape and human factors

Principal author (second edition):
John Barnfield (Tenos Fire Safety Engineering Consultants)

Contributor (second edition):
Sue Pearce (Qequality)

Authors and contributors (first edition):
Harry Hosker (formerly Building Design Partnership)
John Barnfield (Tenos Fire Safety Engineering Consultants)
Jonathan D Sime (Jonathan Sime Associates)

Section 5: Compartmentation and spread of flame

Principal author (first and second editions):
Alan Porter (Warrington Fire Research Ltd)

Acknowledgements:
British Standards Institution

Section 6: Alarm, detection and emergency lighting

Principal author (second edition):
Simon Robinson (WSP Buildings Ltd)

Contributor (second edition):
Shane Tate

Authors and contributors (first edition):
Linton Rodney (Chubb Alarms Ltd)
Graham Faulkner (Chubb Alarms Ltd)

Section 7: Fire and smoke ventilation

Principal author (second edition):
Martin Kealy (WSP Fire Engineering, part of WSP Group plc)

Contributors (second edition):
Gerard Sheridan (Fire Design Solutions, formerly of Buro Happold FEDRA)
Andy Riley (Fire Design Solutions)

Principal authors and contributors (first edition):
Mick Green (Buro Happold FEDRA)
Graeme Hansell (Michael Slattery Associates)
Hugh Mahoney (Nu-Aire Ltd)
Martin Kealy (WSP Fire Engineering, part of WSP Group plc)

Section 8: Fire suppression

Principal author (second edition):
Terry M Watson (Gem Consultants)

Contributor (second edition):
Bob Whiteley (Wormald Ansul UK)

Acknowledgements:
British Standards Institution
Loss Prevention Council

Authors and contributors (first edition):
Terry M Watson (Gem Consultants)
Peter Bressington (Arup Fire)
David Boughen (Chubb Fire)

Section 9: Firefighting

Principal author:
Mike Dennett (consultant)

Contributor:
Terry M Watson (Gem Consultants)

Section 10: Fire dynamics

Principal authors (first and second editions):
Martin Kealy (WSP Fire Engineering, part of WSP Group plc)
Margaret Law (consultant)

Contributor (second edition):
John Klote (John H Klote Inc)

Acknowledgements:
National Fire Protection Association (USA)

Contributors (first edition):
Gordon Butcher (consultant)
Geoffrey Cox (Fire Research Station)
Graeme Hansell (Michael Slattery Associates)
Frank Mills (consultant)
Alan Porter (Warrington Fire Research Ltd)
Philip Thomas (consultant)
Chris Trott (Ove Arup & Partners)
Peter Warren (Fire Research Station)

Section 11: Fire safety management

Principal author:
Corinne Williams (FRS, BRE)

Acknowledgements:
Martin Shipp (FRS, BRE)

Section 12: Fire safety on construction sites

Principal author (first and second editions):
John Hopkinson (Faber Maunsell Ltd)

Acknowledgements:
Peter Bressington (Arup Fire)

Editor

Ken Butcher

CIBSE Publishing Manager

Jacqueline Balian

Acknowledgements

Permission to reproduce extracts from British Standards is granted by BSI under licence number 2003DH0221. British Standards can be purchased from BSI Customer Services, 389 Chiswick High Road, London W4 4AL. Telephone: +44 (0)20 8996 9001. Email: customerservices@bsi-global.com

Extracts from Crown copyright publications are reproduced by permission under licence number C02W0002935.

Contents

1 Introduction

1.1 About this Guide

CIBSE Guide E: *Fire engineering* was first published in 1997 and, because fire safety engineering is a fast developing discipline, it has been updated to take into account new knowledge and the latest fire safety engineering techniques.

The Guide has been written by experienced fire engineers representing the main engineering consultancy firms in the UK, it is intended to give practical advice on fire engineering. Since publication of the first edition, Guide E has been widely used and is referred to in British Standards as an authoritative guidance document.

Some of the sections have been greatly modified and there are new sections on firefighting and the management of fire safety.

1.2 What is fire engineering?

The term fire engineering is widely misused and not well understood; there are two main types fire engineering:

— *fire protection engineering*: where the engineer is responsible for design of fire systems such as automatic fire suppression and fire detection systems

— *fire safety engineering*: where the engineer is responsible for design of fire strategies including location and number of stairs, design of smoke control regimes and designed structural fire protection measures.

This Guide deals with both types of fire engineering.

BS 7974: *Application of fire safety engineering principles to the design of buildings. Code of practice*[1] addresses fire safety engineering and has replaced BS DD 240[2]. However, at the time of writing (March 2003), BS 7974 does not contain a complete set of the methodologies to go with the framework. Guide E can be used for that purpose.

1.3 Fire safety engineering approach

There are two ways of demonstrating compliance with the Building Regulations. One is to follow the prescriptive guidance given in codes of practice and Approved Document B[3] and the other is to use a fire engineering approach.

Approved Document B states that:

> Fire safety engineering is a recognised method of achieving adequate fire safety in a building. It takes into account the entire fire safety engineering package and is sometimes the only viable method of achieving a satisfactory standard of fire safety in large or complex buildings.

Therefore not only is it clear that one need not follow the guidance published in the various British Standards and Approved Document B but, for some buildings, it is essential not to follow prescriptive codes.

For example, prescriptive guidance will limit travel distances to, say, 45 m. In buildings such as airports and other large buildings this is impractical as it imposes restriction on building design. A fire safety engineering alternative method would look at the time taken to escape and compare that with the time for conditions to cease being tenable. This Guide will assist engineers to calculate escape times and tenability criteria and to make the judgement as to whether the performance criteria required by the regulations have been met.

There are three main fire safety engineering approaches:

(a) *Equivalency* (or *comparative approach*): whereby it is demonstrated that the design provides a level of safety equivalent to that which would have been obtained by applying prescriptive codes.

(b) *Deterministic approach*: in which the objective is to show that on the basis of the initial (usually 'worst credible case') assumptions, some defined set of conditions will not occur. Where there is any doubt regarding the reliability of the input data a conservative approach should be adopted. This may require the use of explicit safety factors to compensate for uncertainties in the assumptions.

(c) *Probabilistic approach*: the objective of which is to show that the likelihood of a given event occurring is acceptably small. This is usually expressed in terms of the annual probability of occurrence of the unwanted event (e.g. a probability of an individual death through fire of 10^{-6}, or one per million). It must be recognised that, whatever measures are taken, risks can never be reduced to zero.

1.4 Benefits of a fire engineering approach

Guidance documents such as Approved Document B[3] and British Standards cannot take into account the peculiarities of every single building design. The larger and more complex the design the more difficult and more costly it is to ensure that the design meets the requirements of the prescriptive codes. The main benefits that fire engineering alternatives can bring are:

— increased design flexibility

— reduction in construction and/or running costs

— measures more suited to the building use.

1.5   Purpose of this Guide

It is intended that this Guide will be used in conjunction with established codes to provide guidance to practitioners. It will also be of interest to designers and authorities who, whilst not directly concerned with fire engineering, need to understand the advice offered to them by specialists. The Guide will be of value to students embarking on careers in the professions related to fire safety and to practising designers who wish to enhance their knowledge through continuing professional development.

1.6   Contents of this Guide

1.6.1   Section 1: Introduction

Section 1 discusses what fire safety engineering is and the benefits that it offers to designers. It also provides an overview of its structure and contents, and highlights changes from and additions to the previous edition.

1.6.2   Section 2: Legislation, standards and strategy

This section defines fire safety objectives of both life safety and property protection and explains the current approach of legislation and fire insurers. It describes the consultative procedures which may be employed as an alternative approach to achieving the fire safety objectives of the client, the design team and the appropriate authorities. It recognises the need to develop the theoretical and analytical base at an early stage. It also considers the legal considerations, with reference to the relevant codes and standards and sets down the designer's role and the client's requirements. Section 2 identifies the need for a fire strategy report and suggests a basis for such reports. It also discusses quantified risk assessment (QRA) and its application in fire engineering.

The version of section 2 contained in this edition of the Guide addresses issues raised by the terrorist attacks that took place in the USA on 11 September 2001, particularly concerning insurance. It also takes account of changes in UK legislation and now includes an international perspective.

Recent changes in legislation to allow the use of Approved Inspectors is also addressed.

1.6.3   Section 3: Building designation

Section 3 addresses the manner in which buildings are classified in the context of fire precautions. It includes

extracts from published data and identifies factors that have implications to building types, together with a check list of items to be considered following purpose group classification. It also contains a section on risk profiling and references the BS 5588: Part 7[4] for atrium design.

1.6.4   Section 4: Means of escape

Section 4 covers the basic principles of means of escape and explains the underlying assumptions of established codes. It includes information on escape strategy, behaviour of people, occupancy types and capacities, escape and response times, travel speeds and distances, capacities of escape routes, escape for people with disabilities, lifts, escalators and information systems, together with comments on established codes and standards. Section 4 also gives guidance on means of escape design using the a code-based approach, as well as a fire safety engineering approach.

1.6.5   Section 5: Compartmentation and spread of flame

For England and Wales, the Building Regulations[1] relate compartmentation solely to the protection of occupants, however this section also considers compartmentation for property protection. It discusses the statutory requirements relating to compartmentation and the requirements for the enclosing elements. It considers the challenges of modern building designs and the need to provide compartment sizes larger than those for conventional buildings, together with the relationship of compartment size to sprinklers.

The fire engineering approach is addressed with the three questions:

— Does the building need to be compartmented?

— How big can a compartment be?

— What standard of fire resistance is needed?

1.6.6   Section 6: Alarm, detection and emergency lighting

This section covers both manual fire alarm systems and automatic fire detection systems, and provides the basic requirements for the design and application of fire detection systems. It is not offered as an alternative to BS 5839: Part 1[6]. It defines the intentions of the systems with respect to both property protection and life protection. Guidelines are given with respect to zoning of systems together with descriptions of specialist systems, location and selection of detectors.

This section has been modified to include detailed practical guidance on the design of emergency lighting taking into account recent changes in legislation.

1.6.7   Section 7: Fire and smoke ventilation

This section describes the objectives of smoke ventilation systems. The various factors affecting the design of smoke ventilation systems are described, including the effect of sprinklers and external wind effects. Alternative approaches to pressurisation of stairs and lobbies are also described.

1.6.8   Section 8: Fire suppression

Section 8 considers the principal fixed systems for fire suppression within buildings.

Within the section dealing with automatic sprinklers there is a new section on early suppression fast response (ESFR) sprinklers designed for high ceilings, third party certification and residential sprinklers. There is also a new section that addresses the detail and specification of water mist systems.

Detailed design guidance is given for the design of gaseous systems. This section also compares the various design properties of the main gases including ozone depletion potential (ODP) and minimum design concentrations.

1.6.9   Section 9: Firefighting

Section 9 is a new section and reflects the need to address all the relevant fire issues when using an engineered approached for building design.

This section describes the methods used to fight fires and the system requirements to ensure that firefighting operations are able to be initiated quickly and completed effectively.

1.6.10   Section 10: Fire dynamics

Fire dynamics describes the complex subject of fire behaviour and provides the reader with a basic understanding of the processes which govern fire development. This section addresses the available techniques for calculating the parameters at the design stage of a project and the effect of sprinklers on fire size and smoke. Whilst section 7 covers smoke ventilation, the basics of smoke production and movement are covered in section 9. The formulae and engineering relationships for smoke control given in this section are drawn from TM19: *Relationships for smoke control calculations*[7], and have been updated using new data from full-scale fire tests.

1.6.11   Section 11: Fire management

Section 11 is a new section, and reflects the importance that is attached to the proper management of a building with respect to fire safety.

1.6.12   Section 12: Fire safety on construction sites

Since publication of the first edition of Guide E, the Health and Safety Executive (HSE) has published its own guidance to fire safety in construction work[8]. Many of the recommendations in the previous edition of Guide E have been incorporated in the HSE guidance.

Section 12 has been re-titled and a new section added on the designer's responsibilities in respect of fire safety on construction sites.

1.7   Other sources of information

It is hoped that this Guide will provide an invaluable reference source for those involved in the design, installation, commissioning, operation and maintenance of buildings when considering fire precautions. However, it does not claim to be exhaustive. It contains many references to other sources of information which should be carefully consulted in conjunction with Guide E.

References

1   BS 7974: 2001: *Application of fire safety engineering principles to the design of buildings. Code of practice* (London: British Standards Institution) (2001)

2   DD 240: 1997: *Fire safety engineering in buildings* (London: British Standards Institution) (withdrawn)

3   *Fire Safety* The Building Regulations 2000 Approved Document B (London: The Stationery Office) (2000) (amended 2002)

4   BS 5588: *Fire precautions in the design, construction and use of buildings*: Part 7: 1997: *Code of practice for the incorporation of atria in buildings* (London: British Standards Institution) (1997)

5   The Building Regulations 2000 Statutory Instruments 2000 No. 2531 (London: The Stationery Office) (2000)

6   BS 5839: *Fire detection and alarm systems for buildings*: Part 1: 2002: *Code of practice for system design, installation, commissioning and maintenance* (London: British Standards Institution) (2002)

7   *Relationships for smoke control calculations* CIBSE TM19 (London: Chartered Institution of Building Services Engineers) (1995)

8   *Fire safety in construction work — Guidance for clients, designers and those managing and carrying out construction work involving significant fire risks* (London: HSE Books) (1997)

2 Legislation, standards and strategy

2.1 The concept of fire engineering

2.1.1 Introduction

Fire safety engineering is a relatively new discipline and, although there are specialist fire safety engineers, designers from other disciplines will often be asked to provide a major input into the way in which the fire safety strategy is developed. As an alternative to prescriptive approaches, fire safety engineering offers a flexible alternative to prescriptive approaches especially when designing for unusual or 'difficult' buildings. A fire safety engineering approach that takes into account the total fire package can provide an alternative approach to fire safety. It may be the only viable way to achieve a satisfactory standard of fire safety in some large and complex buildings.

The use of fire safety engineering allows beneficial effects to be recognised. For example, the use of fast response sprinklers can reduce the design fire size which may in turn lead to a more economic smoke control system design or reduced structural fire protection.

The concept of fire engineering provides a framework which enables designers to demonstrate that the functional requirements of legislation are met, or bettered, even though the design solutions adopted fall outside the recommendations of prescriptive codes and guidance.

To achieve this objective the first step is to understand the functional requirements underlying the prescribed standards. Small departures can then be accepted without a full fire engineering analysis. For example, adding fully automatic fire detection may allow an increase in escape travel distance or an increase in compartment size due to the early alarm and earlier contact with the fire service.

However, where there is a greater difference between the building design and the guidance offered by codes, then analytical techniques which demonstrate the control of fire growth, control of smoke spread and the movement of people may be required to prove the overall fire safety strategy. The first step in preparing such an analysis is to define the building geometry, functional planning, construction materials, and the general use of the building. The outline steps are given in Figure 2.1.

Whilst many aspects of the analysis may be quantified, others will require subjective judgement and will be subject to discussion with the building control and fire authorities. They may include, for example, the consequences of fire (which will be subject to construction standard and maintenance) or people movement (subject

to a motivation or mobilisation time which may be improved with training or stewarding).

2.1.2 International overview

There has been a growing trend internationally to use and accept a fire engineering approach as a legitimate alternative to prescriptive codes. The adoption of this approach has led to a greater understanding of fire safety design in general, as it is often the case that the objectives behind prescriptive codes are not fully understood.

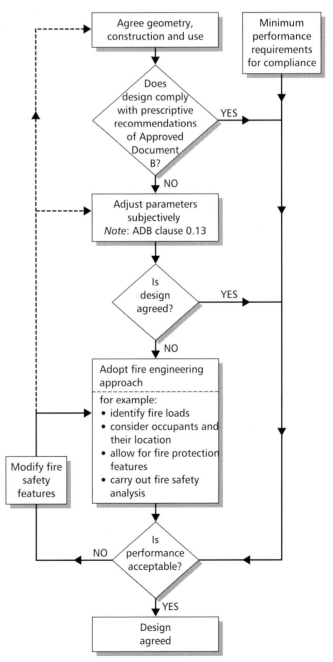

Figure 2.1 Main steps in fire engineering analysis

Countries such as Australia and New Zealand have in place performance-based codes which permit greater flexibility to applied solutions as they set down a framework and criteria for designers and approving authorities. Other countries such as Hong Kong, USA and Singapore are moving toward a formal performance-based code regime whilst in the meantime accepting fire engineering solutions on a project specific basis. It should be noted that the level of acceptability will vary between countries depending upon the level of conservatism within the approving authorities and awareness of fire engineering in the design community. It would be a mistake to assume that criteria which applies to the UK would automatically apply to all other countries. Firefighting and access, management, maintenance, population density and behaviour, and infrastructure are among those areas where economic, cultural and environmental factors will impact.

For certain occupancy types NFPA codes* (which are considered international codes) provide guidance for fire safety design. Within each of these codes, fire engineering is permitted as an alternative to the prescriptive guidance. Often the greatest challenge in using fire engineering is the level of acceptability on the part of the approving authorities. This is particularly the case where there are few precedents and the authority feels uncomfortably exposed to criticism for allowing a 'non-standard' design. This situation can lead to uncertainty within the design team and concern over meeting key programme dates. It is prudent to discuss fire engineering solutions with the authority at a very early stage to gauge reaction and the likely level of acceptability.

The prescriptive codes that apply in each country vary in approach and extent of coverage. In some countries there is very little in the way of codes and it is in such situations that the application of a fire engineering approach or the adoption of the NFPA codes will help.

2.1.3   United Kingdom

The Building Regulations in England and Wales[1] and, since 1994, Northern Ireland[2] are set in functional terms, see sections 2.3.1.1, 3.4.1.1 and 3.4.1.3. That is, in England and Wales, requirements B1–B5 set down the goals for fire safety. Guidance on meeting the requirements of Schedule 1 of the Regulations is given in Approved Document B[3] (see section 2.3.1) and, for Northern Ireland, in Technical Booklet E[4]. In Scotland, prescriptive requirements are set down in the Building Standards (Scotland) Regulations[5], see sections 2.3.1.1 and 3.4.1.2. These Regulations are supplemented by the *Scottish Executive Technical Standards*[6]. Fire safety is also covered by various British Standards (see section 2.4.1).

Where a building design is straightforward and conventional, then it would normally be expected that designers would apply the prescriptive approach of Approved Document B and the associated British Standards with little or no need to vary the detailed recommendations. However, where an innovative design is being proposed or a difficult refurbishment or a large complex space is being considered, then a fire safety strategy may need to be developed that is not in accordance with Approved

Document B but which, nevertheless, meets the functional requirements B1–B5 of the Building Regulations (or their equivalent in Northern Ireland, see sections 3.3.13). (Note that in Scotland, compliance with the Regulations[5,6] may be achieved by means other than the prescriptive requirements, provided that these can be shown to satisfy 'the relevant standards', see section 3.3.1.2.)

Paragraph 0.13 of Approved Document B[3] lists the factors which should be taken into account and suggests measures which can be considered in arriving at an overall fire safety strategy.

Factors that should be taken into account include:

(a)   the anticipated risk of a fire occurring

(b)   the anticipated fire severity

(c)   the ability of a structure to resist the spread of fire and smoke

(d)   the consequential danger to people in and around the building.

Measures that can be considered and incorporated to a greater or lesser extent, as appropriate in the circumstances, include:

(a)   the adequacy of means to prevent fire

(b)   early fire warning by an automatic detection and warning system

(c)   the standard of means of escape

(d)   provision of smoke control

(e)   control of the rate of growth of a fire

(f)   the adequacy of the structure to resist the effects of a fire

(g)   the degree of fire containment

(h)   fire separation between buildings or parts of buildings

(i)   the standard of active measures for fire extinguishment or control

(j)   facilities to assist the fire service

(k)   availability of powers to require staff training in fire safety and fire routines, e.g. under chapter 40 of the Fire Precautions Act 1971[7] (as amended), and the Fire Precautions (Workplace) Regulations 1997 (Amended), or registration or licensing procedures

(l)   consideration of the availability of any continuing control under other legislation that could ensure continued maintenance of such systems.

2.2   Consultation and consensus

2.2.1   General

The aim of the consultation process is to realise the fire safety objectives as agreed between the client, the design team, the insurers and the authorities.

---

* National Fire Protection Association (NFPA), 1 Batterymarch Park, P.O. Box 9101, Quincy, Massachusetts, USA 02269-9101 (www.nfpa.org)

A building may be considered to be acceptable if the design and construction standards meet the requirements of the Building Regulations as approved by the local building control authority and the developer/owner. Where there is an element of judgement and/or opinion then approval will be based on consensus between the parties.

The primary objective of the fire safety design is to achieve an adequate level of life safety with consideration for property protection. The protection of property and contents is not specifically addressed in the codes and standards. Consequently, where non-life safety issues are to be covered, the fire strategy should identify measures intended to meet these objectives.

It is important that a consultative procedure be established as soon as possible as design decisions will be affected by the input from the various authorities. This is particularly the case where a fire safety engineering approach is adopted and the fire safety strategy is not based upon the recommendations of Approved Document B[3], British Standards or other recognised codes of practice.

2.2.2 Consultation with fire safety authorities

There are two main public authorities with which designers, developers and occupiers of buildings may have to deal in connection with fire safety:

— the building control authority (or approved inspector)

— the fire authority.

Building control authorities are responsible for enforcing the requirements of the Building Regulations. These Regulations are concerned with building work and the requirements for structural fire precautions, means of escape and access for the fire brigade in case of fire (Part B of the Schedule). They apply to most buildings. Technical supporting information is given in one of the Approved Documents; fire matters are covered in Approved Document B[3] (ADB). There is no legal obligation to comply with the ADB but, if there was seen to be a contravention of the Regulations not complying with the ADB this would be more likely to establish liability.

The fire authority is responsible for matters relating to Fire Certificates and regulations made under the Fire Precautions Act 1971[7] (as amended) and the Fire Precautions (Workplace) Regulations 1997 (Amended), which concern the safety of certain buildings once occupied. Generally, there is an obligation on the occupier to apply for a fire certificate and, if the fire authority is satisfied that adequate measures are in place, a fire certificate will be issued. The Fire Precautions (Workplace) Regulations 1997 (Amended) incorporates the requirements of the European Framework and Workplace Directives. The requirements are designed to impact only where necessary to ensure the safety of employees in case of fire. One major feature of this legislation is the obligation on the employer to carry out a fire risk assessment.

The applicant needs to know the requirements of both authorities at the design and construction stages. There is a risk that in dealing with two enforcing bodies the applicant may receive different interpretations of the requirements from the two sources and this may lead to confusion between guidance and requirements. For this reason one authority only should take the leading role and, by consultation with the other authority at appropriate times, should be able to channel all the necessary information to the applicant.

During the design and construction phases of a project the building control authority (or approved inspector) is the lead authority and is the applicant's primary reference. The building control authority interprets and enforces the requirements of the Building Regulations[1]. Enquiries for guidance on other matters, including the fire authority's requirements for certification, should also be channelled through the building control authority (see *Building regulations and fire safety procedural guidance*[8]).

For buildings designated under the Fire Precautions Act[7], on completion of the building the lead passes to the fire authority for matters relating to the building in use, such as Fire Certificates. The fire authority will also be consulted by licensing/registration authorities about fire safety matters concerning premises that need to be licensed or registered although the fire authority is not generally the licensing or registration authority. Note that licensing and/or registration conditions are also likely to refer to matters other than fire safety.

Building work which complies with the requirements of the Building Regulations[1] with respect to means of escape and structural fire safety will be satisfactory in these areas for the purposes of fire certification. However, there are other measures such as fire alarms, detection systems (other than in domestic situations), and means of fighting fires which are not covered by the Regulations (although they are features of the process leading to fire certification about which the fire authority can make requirements). Fire certification matters should be taken into account in the design and construction phases, although certification only becomes necessary on occupation of the building.

It is expected that changes to the regulatory procedures will be proposed in 2003 through a new regulatory reform Act. It is thought that the Fire Authority will be the continuing authority with all designated buildings not being subject to the statutory bar.

2.2.3 Consultation with other parties

In addition to the requirements for life safety there will be varying degrees of property protection to consider and therefore the client (and where applicable) the insurance company should be consulted. Specialised industrial and storage areas may require certification by the Health and Safety Executive.

2.2.4 Crown immunity

Currently, many buildings belonging to the Crown enjoy immunity from both the Building Regulations[1] and the Fire Precautions Act[7]. In these cases the government department responsible for the particular building will seek advice on the fire safety standards required. These standards will not be less stringent than those required by Approved Document B[3] and may include a greater protection of property due to security and insurance considerations. The government department responsible may appoint an external body to act as a building control authority. This body would consult with the Crown Premises Inspection Group of the Home Office Fire Service Inspectorate on matters relating to certification, rather than the local fire authority.

2.2.5 Exemption for educational buildings

In England and Wales, the requirements of the Building Regulations[1] do not apply to any building required for the purposes of a school or educational establishment which has been erected, or will be erected according to plans which have been approved by the Secretary of State for Eduction and Skills or the Secretary of State for Wales. This exemption also applies to buildings erected according to plans approved under Section 14 of the Education Act 1980[9] or under regulations made under Section 17(4) of that Act.

Guidance on fire safety in educational buildings is contained in Building Bulletin 7: *Fire and the design of educational buildings*[10], published by the Department for Education and Employment (now the Department for Education and Skills).

2.3 Legal considerations

2.3.1 Building Regulations

2.3.1.1 General

The Building Regulations[1] and Approved Document B: *Fire safety*[3], which compliments the Regulations, apply to England and Wales only. Different regulations exist for Scotland and Northern Ireland; the Building Standards (Scotland) Regulations[5] were revised in 1990. The Building Regulations (Northern Ireland)[2] were amended in 2000.

In England and Wales, the functional requirements of the Building Regulations are encompassed in Requirements B1–B5. The following notes indicate the general intent of each of these requirements and provide some guidance on the main items referred to in the corresponding sections of Approved Document B.

— B1: *Means of Escape*: to ensure that there are a sufficient number and capacity of routes to enable people to escape to a place of safety in the event of a fire. Routes will be sufficiently protected from fire, adequately lit and suitable signed. Approved Document B defines a notional building population, maximum travel distances to protected routes and minimum capacities of escape routes related to population.

— B2: *Internal Fire Spread (linings)*: to limit the spread of flame over internal surfaces. Approved Document B considers classifications in accordance with British Standards and applies the appropriate classification to building use, space use and position in the building (e.g. assembly building or corridor).

— B3: *Internal Fire Spread (Structure)*: to limit the effects and size of fire. Approved Document B considers appropriate periods of fire resistance for structures and compartment walls to limit collapse and compartmentation size relative to risk or hazard. Services which penetrate fire resisting walls must not compromise the performance of these elements.

— B4: *External Fire Spread*: to limit the risk of fire spread from one building to another. Approved Document B approaches this aspect on the basis of building spacing, proportion of elevation which is non-fire resisting, compartmentation and risk or hazard.

— B5: *Access and Facilities for the Fire Service*: to ensure that the fire service has means of fighting fires and mounting rescue operations when necessary. Approved Document B gives appropriate measures for internal or external access dependent on site layout or building height. There are particular recommendations for ventilation and (possibly) sprinklering of basements.

The above requirements may be re-expressed in more general terms and be expanded to include some of the wider interests of the developer/owner, as follows:

— Given the function and purpose of the building or installation, that the design should not present an unacceptable risk of fire developing and spreading.

— Occupants will have time to reach a place of safety without being affected by heat or smoke from a fire.

— The fire will not spread to adjacent property.

— The fire will not spread beyond the compartment of origin.

— Fire brigades will be able to gain access, mount rescue operations and protect property without undue risk to their health or safety.

— Damage to building contents will be limited.

Whilst the above items do not substantially alter the Building Regulation statements there are three important points that should be noted:

— For means of escape, the distance and capacity depend upon the time available for escape, see section 4.7.

— The safety of firefighters is an increasingly important consideration.

— The use of the word 'will' is significant in that where analyses are used, they need to be sufficiently conservative to produce reliable conclusions. Otherwise conclusions are to some extent subjective and judgmental.

In terms of practical design development it would be unusual to be required to analyse in detail a complete building, room by room. Normally, a particular issue would be considered and analysed in the context of other parts of the building which conform to the requirement of Approved Document B and the appropriate British Standards. For the purposes of this section a 'complete' approach is described below.

(a) Consider the most probable location of a significant fire developing.

(b) Consider the most probable worst case arrangement of combustible materials for the use and life of the building; survey data[11] may be used.

(c) Identify rate of fire development[12], temperature rise and smoke production by calculation.

(d) Estimate activation of detection and suppression systems. Activation of sprinklers should identify a limiting fire size.

(e) Consider the movement of the following during an appropriate period of fire development and burning:

— *people*: population, location, method of alarm, response time, rate of movement, protection and safety of route

— *smoke*: natural distribution, mechanical plant influenced distribution

— *fire*: conduction through barriers (*Note*: insulation values), convection through gaps and openings, radiation between connecting spaces.

(f) Continue analysis to ensure safety and structural stability, including consideration of firefighting.

(g) Check stability of external wall cladding to ensure no increase in exposure for spread to adjacent properties.

(h) Consider further analyses where the developer and/or owner wishes to consider factors such as property damage.

Where necessary the above steps could be repeated for sections of a building where conditions vary e.g. different numbers of people, differing fire loads, larger or smaller compartments. Special factors that may need to be introduced in the above analytical sequence include especially hazardous materials and toxicity of smoke.

2.3.1.2 Appeals procedure

If there is disagreement over the proposed fire safety measures between the applicant and the local authority the applicant can seek a determination from (i.e. an appeal to) the Department of the Environment under The Building Act 1984[13]. This procedure applies in England and Wales. Other procedures apply in Scotland and Northern Ireland.

2.3.2 Fire Precautions Act

2.3.2.1 General

The Fire Precautions Act 1971[7] is the principal instrument for the control of fire safety in occupied premises and is designed to ensure the provision of adequate general fire safety, means of escape and related fire precautions in premises within its scope.

The fire authority is the enforcing authority for this Act and issues Fire Certificates where applicable and should be consulted directly for designated premises, see section 2.2.2. An existing Fire Certificate issued under the Factories Act 1961[14] or the Offices, Shops and Railway Premises Act 1963[15] is also deemed to be a Fire Certificate under the Fire Precautions Act providing there has been no material change to the premises.

The occupier must inform the authority where a material change is proposed which affects the fire safety provisions within an existing building which already possesses an existing Fire Certificate. If changes fall within the terms of the Building Regulations an application should be made to the building control authority, as well as the fire authority.

2.3.2.2 Fire Certificates

Fire safety falls into two specific categories:

— fire safety in the home (not considered in this Guide)

— fire safety at work.

Fire safety precautions in places of work are controlled mainly by the Fire Precautions Act 1971[7], as amended by the Fire Safety and Safety of Places of Sport Act 1987[16]. The Fire Precautions Act requires certain designated premises namely factories, offices, shops, hotels and boarding houses, and railway premises to have a Fire Certificate and will contain information on means of escape, firefighting, and means for giving warning in case of fire.

A Fire Certificate is required:

— where more than 20 people are employed, or 10 if higher than ground floor

— in hotels and boarding houses where sleeping accommodation is for more than six people above the first floor or below the ground floor.

Figure 2.2 indicates the main steps involved in obtaining a Fire Certificate and Figure 2.3 illustrates in more detail the consultation procedure which takes place between the designer, building control and the fire authority.

A Fire Certificate is a unique document tailored to suit the particular circumstances of individual premises. However, some items appear on every Certificate. These include the following:

— uses of the premises covered by the Fire Certificate

— means of escape in case of fire

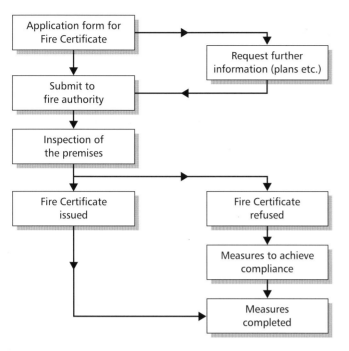

Figure 2.2 Outline procedure for obtaining a Fire Certificate

— means of ensuring that the means of escape can be safely and effectively used at all material times, e.g. escape lighting

— type, number and location of all firefighting equipment and fire alarms

— for factories, particulars of any explosive or highly flammable materials which may be used or stored on the premises.

Premises which manufacture, use or store certain highly hazardous materials are subject to the requirements imposed under the Fire Certificates (Special Premises) Regulations 1976[18], and must have a Fire Certificate issued by the Health and Safety Executive.

2.3.2.3   Additional guidance

In the case of existing premises the Home Office and Scottish Office have published a number of guides to assist occupiers and/or owners and fire authorities to ensure consistency of approach in compliance with the *Fire Precautions Act*.

The relevant guides are:

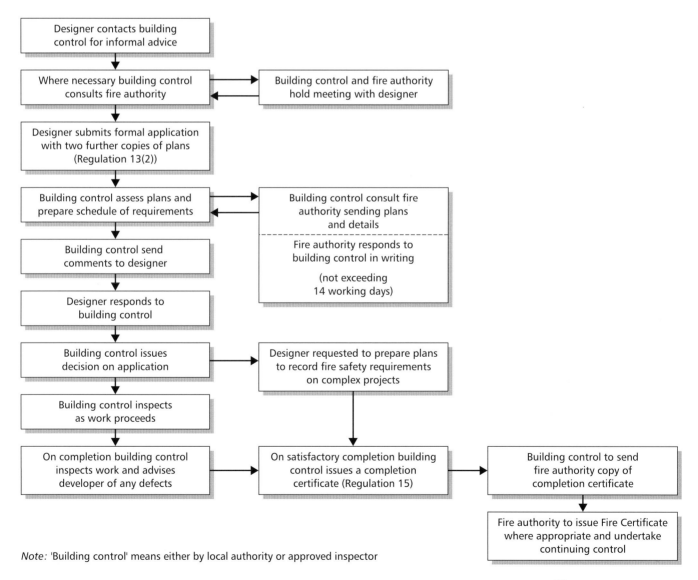

Note: 'Building control' means either by local authority or approved inspector

Figure 2.3 Fire and building regulations — procedural guidance (reproduced from *IBC Approved Document B Workbook*[17] by kind permission of the Institute of Building Control)

— *Code of Practice for Fire Precautions in Factories, Offices, Shops and Railway Premises not required to have a Fire Certificate*[19]

— *Guide to Fire Precautions in Premises used as Hotels and Boarding Houses requiring a Fire Certificate*[20]

— *Guide to Fire Precautions in existing Places of Work requiring a Fire Certificate — Factories, Offices, Shops and Railway Premises*[21].

2.3.3   Other statutory requirements

There is other legislation pertaining to fire safety in buildings. In the case of legislation enforced by other authorities, i.e. that which involves a licensing or registration function, it is normally a requirement that the fire authority be consulted.

In many cases, legislation is either accompanied by guidance documents or refers to other published information, these guidance documents usually provide the detailed technical information required by the designer.

The most important Acts relevant to fire safety include:

— Health and Safety at Work etc. Act 1974

— Factories Act 1961

— Fire Precautions Act 1971

— Fire Safety and Safety of Places of Sports Act 1987

— Public Health and Building Acts

— Housing Act 1985

— Local Government Act 1985

— Petroleum Act 1928

— Registered Homes Act 1984

— Education Acts

— Cinemas Act 1985

— Fireworks Acts 1951 and 1964

— Local Government Acts

2.4   Codes and standards

In addition to the statutory requirements previously discussed there are a number of codes which provide guidance on the subject of fire safety.

2.4.1   British Standards

There are a number of British Standards which deal with various areas of fire safety including equipment specification, system design specification, selection guidance and codes of practice for fire precautions. For example, Approved Document B[3] refers the designer to the BS 5588[22] series for guidance on fire precautions in different occupancy groups.

Approved Document B also cites BS 5588: Part 10[22] as an example of an overall approach to fire safety. However, it should be noted that 'an overall approach to fire safety' is not necessarily the same as a fire safety engineering

approach. Although the various parts of BS 5588 contain some recommendations based on fire engineering principles, the use of this British Standard does not in itself constitute a fire engineering solution.

It should be noted that BS 5588 is a code of practice and therefore is not mandatory. It offers an approach to fire precautions for particular occupancies but it does not preclude the use of alternative approaches.

2.4.2   Home Office guides

The Home Office has produced a number of guides which recommend fire precaution measures and provide guidance to designers, building control and fire officers. The objective of the guides is to set acceptable standards of safety and encourage consistency of enforcement, while at the same time leaving scope for flexibility and the exercise of professional judgement. Home Office guides, see section 2.3.2.3, have no statutory force but their provisions have been compiled for consistency with legislation such as the Building Regulations[1], the Fire Precautions Act 1971[7] and the Health and Safety at Work etc. Act[23]. In addition, where appropriate, reference should be made to the Home Office's *Guide to fire precautions in existing places of entertainment and like premises*[24].

2.4.3   National Fire Protection Association (NFPA) codes

NFPA codes are the American standards covering fire matters and may be useful in providing guidance for fire safety design in the UK since they contain important advice on fire load, smoke control, egress from buildings and specialised occupancies. It has been found that when adopting a fire engineering approach, building control and fire officers normally accept equations taken from the relevant NFPA codes.

2.4.4   London District Surveyors Association (LDSA) guides

The LDSA has issued the following guides to cover buildings within the London area:

— *Fire Safety Guide No 1: Section 20 Buildings*[25]

— *Fire Safety Guide No 3: Phased evacuation from Office Buildings*[26]

— *Model Technical Regulations for Places of Public Entertainment*[27]

2.4.5   Building Research Establishment (BRE) reports

The Building Research Establishment publishes reports which address various aspects of fire safety. These reports can assist the designer by providing criteria for design and specific design guidance. These include *Aspects of fire precautions in buildings*[28] (BR 137), *Guidelines for the construction of fire-resisting structural elements*[29] (BR 128) and *Design principles for smoke ventilation in enclosed shopping centres*[30] (BR 186).

2.5   Design implications

2.5.1   General

Whatever particular expertise the designer possesses, or whichever discipline the designer is from, it is important that he/she has an understanding of all aspects of fire safety. It is unlikely that the designer will have a detailed knowledge of this subject but it is essential to appreciate the way in which the elements of the fire safety strategy are inter-related. For example, provision of means of escape from a building is primarily the responsibility of the architect, sometimes with advice from a fire safety engineer. However, the building services engineer will provide the design for the emergency lighting, the fire detection system and the smoke extract systems, all of which are related to the way in which safe evacuation is accomplished. Therefore it is important that the services design for fire safety is not undertaken in isolation but reflects the objectives of the fire safety strategy.

The building services engineer will often provide the pivotal role in the design team when the fire safety strategy and its effect on building design is being developed. Specialist advice may also be required on evaluating the overall fire engineering package especially where unusual building features require a non-standard approach. Specialist design advice may also be required, for example, where working drawings for sprinkler systems are required. This is because building insurers and building control authorities recognise only those sprinkler installers approved by the Loss Prevention Council.

Specialised advice may be sought from equipment manufacturers but care should be exercised to relate it to the overall fire safety strategy.

It is important that designers consider the implications of fire safety on the building design at a very early stage. To this end the preparation of a fire safety strategy which considers fire precautions as a whole is a valuable and necessary way of setting out design policy. However, it does mean that the fire safety strategy becomes the key document when negotiating fire safety matters with the fire officer or building control authority.

In addition to the discussions with the authorities on fire precaution measures relating to life safety, the client's view on the protection of the property and its contents should be sought. The client, or the client's insurers, may require enhanced fire precaution measures to minimise losses and to obtain reduced insurance premiums.

The wide range of codes, standards and regulations applicable to fire safety, see section 2.4, is constantly increasing and individual publications are frequently amended or revised. Designers may not have all relevant information readily to hand but must be aware of, and have access to these publications. Further information is available through product data and articles in fire safety journals, which keep the designer up-to-date with new developments in fire safety matters.

The designer should aim to harmonise the need for fire safety with both building use and aesthetic considerations. Fire protection measures do not have to be intrusive; the development of miniature or concealed sprinklers, slim body detectors and unobtrusive fire curtains are examples of architecturally sympathetic design solutions.

Construction sites represent a significant fire risk, see section 12: *Fire safety on construction sites*, due to the nature of the work, the storage of flammable materials and the likelihood that the fire protection measures are not yet in place. Consideration should be given to ways in which fire precaution measures can be completed as the building progresses. It may be that the fire systems design incorporates features which will allow phased commissioning. For example, temporarily converting a wet sprinkler system to alternate wet/dry operation so that the sprinkler system is effective in an office building which is under construction during the winter months.

2.5.2   Extreme events

Following the destruction of the World Trade Center in New York on 11 September 2001, many questions have been asked about the resilience of tall buildings to withstand extreme events.

Codes and standards have evolved to provide for safe buildings. Safety is thought of as an absolute — the expression 'as safe as houses' implies zero risk — but safety is relative and there is always more that can be done to make buildings and their occupants safer. Disasters often trigger the re-examination of standards and it may be that codes will be revised in an attempt to address some of the issues that result from such events. Codes and standards have generally served people well over the years but they were designed to protect people from 'normal' hazards.

Codes and standards have been developed to provide reasonable protection to the occupants of a building in conventional fire scenarios. Even in the UK, for example, the basic design rules that exist today were developed shortly after the Second World War. Wartime devastation was in people's minds, but the regulations were not developed to address such attacks but to provide for safety in a peacetime environment.

Existing fire regulations work together as a package; compartmentation contains the fire, sprinklers ensure that the fire does not develop to breach the compartmentation, and protected shafts enable people to escape safely when, by necessity, they have to escape past the fire. For large structures, such as high-rise buildings, phased evacuation (see section 4.3.4.2) is the favoured procedure.

Risk analysis techniques can play an important role in determining what 'enhancements' should be considered. In general terms the following fire safety issues may be subject to evaluation:

—   use of phased and simultaneous evacuation

—   use of lifts for evacuation when the building has not been impacted

—   overall target time for building evacuation

—   better adhesion and/or greater robustness of fire protecting materials

—   sophisticated evacuation management regimes

—   better training and selection of fire marshals

—   greater robustness of escape stairs.

2.6   Client/building occupier's role

The client plays a pivotal role in forming the fire safety strategy and often determines the extent of the fire precautions, particularly in respect of property protection. When the fire safety strategy is formulated it will include not only design parameters and objectives but will also explain the way in which the fire management of the building will operate.

This means that the scope of the fire safety strategy may go beyond that of a design brief to form the basis of a fire safety management procedure for the building, once occupied. Fire management procedures will include escape, fire containment, automatic detection and suppression systems and communications. Fire management procedures will set out the maintenance and test procedures, together with the action to be taken in the event of fire.

With greater dependence on automatic suppression systems, full and regular fire safety audits, in which all the fire safety systems and components are reviewed, are essential. The normal fire safety procedures will specify staff training requirements, covering both induction training for new staff and regular refresher training for all occupants. Such training should be more than mere 'fire drills' and should include training in fire prevention and perhaps firefighting as well as fire evacuation. The Fire Protection Association, a division of the Loss Prevention Council issues numerous guides to assist those developing fire manuals and training.

The second part of the fire strategy will cover the action to be taken if ignition occurs; the design team can assist in the pre-planning of such action. The fire management policy must outline the responsibilities and duties of the staff, indicating which tactics should be attempted in what eventualities (e.g. refuge or egress, fire extinguishment or fire containment). Such a pre-planned response to a fire emergency can be used as the basis for training but it should be revised as fire safety audits reveal new risks or changes in the use of the building.

It is the responsibility of the occupier to comply with any conditions attached to the Fire Certificate and keep up-to-date any insurance record sheets for test and maintenance of fire systems.

2.7   Insurance standards

As well as satisfying the requirements of the authorities for life safety in buildings, consideration may also need to be given to property protection. It is important that advice, and approval, be sought from the insurers at the earliest possible stage if the insurer of the proposed building is already known. In the case of speculative buildings it is unlikely that an insurance company will be nominated by the client. In these circumstances the client

should be made aware of the likely differences between life safety measures required by the Building Regulations[1] and the Fire Precautions Act[7] and enhanced property protection standards.

The Loss Prevention Council (LPC) has sought to provide guidance for designers and insurance companies through its *Code of Practice for the Construction of Buildings*[31]. The code is applicable to new industrial and commercial buildings but the principles may also be applied when upgrading existing buildings. The LPC also publishes codes of practice for sprinkler systems[32] and fire alarm systems[33].

From the insurers' viewpoint, the fire requirements of the Building Regulations[1] do not adequately control the compartment size and construction, especially for large industrial, factory and warehouse buildings. The main emphasis of the regulations is on the early stages of fire and its effect on the safety of the building occupants, prevention of fire spread to adjoining buildings where life risk is involved and access for the fire brigade.

Property protection is the main objective to the insurer and this calls for higher standards of fire precautions to control fire spread through, and between, buildings and to prevent building collapse. The Loss Prevention Council suggests that these precautions will also improve life safety in the building.

Insurers are also concerned about the effects of fire, in terms of both the direct damage and the potential losses resulting from the interruption of business. The possibility of water and smoke damage to other floors in a building and of fire spreading through windows to other floors is also considered.

Implementation of the *Code of Practice for the Construction of Buildings*[31] will have a significant impact on building design and cost. Designing to the code will result in:

—   small compartment sizes

—   longer periods of fire resistance for the main elements of structure, in particular fire break (i.e. compartment) walls must have a minimum fire resistance of 240 minutes and fire break (compartment) floors should have a minimum fire resistance of 120 minutes

—   the use of non-combustible materials for load-bearing elements, ceilings, linings to roofs, linings to external, fire-break and internal load-bearing walls

—   Class 0 materials for the linings to internal partitions with Class 0 performance being achieved without additional surface treatments, coatings, foil coverings or impregnation treatments

—   no trade-off with sprinklers when considering fire resistance of building elements

—   minimum number of openings and penetrations in fire break walls, fire break floors and other fire resisting elements

—   size limits on openings in fire walls

—   a higher number of cavity barriers in voids

—   stricter control on the design of atria

— restrictions on the use of wood.

It has been suggested by the LPC that the measures contained in its code provide a yardstick to enable insurance companies to set premiums. As with any code it is subject to review and revision and it is likely that its contents will change.

2.8 Fire safety strategy

2.8.1 General

One significant influence on design is the way in which fire safety is incorporated into the structure and services of a building. The designer should have clear objectives in mind when considering fire safety design and its relationship with the overall building design. These objectives will include a number of issues such as:

— cost effectiveness

— function

— aesthetics

— manageability.

All of these aspects should relate to the total design concept.

The purpose of fire safety is to provide protection for people, the building and its contents. The designer should seek to minimise the likelihood of injury or death to building occupants and others, e.g. members of the fire service, while reducing the potential for damage to the building and its contents to an acceptable level. The designer also has a responsibility to consider adjacent buildings and the possible effect of fire on people outside the building. The designer can achieve these objectives in a number of ways; these essential elements make up the fire safety strategy.

2.8.2 Fire safety strategy report

The most effective way of identifying and setting out the tactics for the fire safety design of the building is by compiling a fire safety strategy report. Although some sections will assume a greater or lesser importance depending on the project, one way in which the objectives and design information could be set out is as follows:

(a) *Introduction*: sets out the overall objectives of the fire strategy and the parameters of the report.

(b) *Project*: describes the building or project outlining special features and inter-relationship with other properties.

(c) *Sources of information*: lists the codes, legislation and guidance documents used in the compilation of the report and the features which are based on fire engineering principles.

(d) *Means of escape*: establishes the objectives of the means of escape philosophy and, if necessary, refers to escape times and travel distances.

(e) *Fire spread control*: states the classification of wall and ceiling linings, furnishings and the integrity rating of structure and compartment walls. This section would also contain details of compartment size, external fire spread and cavity barrier position.

(f) *Design fires*: in complex buildings, where necessary, establishes the design fire size by calculation of fire load and type so that the effect of fire and smoke can be assessed. This is particularly important when considering the operation of detectors, smoke extract calculations and the effect of heat on the building structure.

(g) *Facilities for the fire brigade*: describes the facilities which should be made available to the fire brigade including access, and sometimes dry/wet risers, firefighting stairs/lobbies, firefighter's control panel, smoke clearance and point of assembly.

(h) *Fire systems*: including the following, as required:

— *Smoke control*: describes the purpose of the smoke control system where required to maintain clear layer height, limit temperatures or keep escape routes clear or remove smoke in the later stages of a fire.

— *Sprinkler system*: where sprinklers are proposed, states the hazard classification, water supplies, extent of coverage and system standard; identifies special features such as fast response sprinklers used in areas of smoke control.

— *Alarm system*: describes the type and extent of the alarm system; e.g. type and coverage of automatic detectors, manual call points, communication of alarm, technical features of the system, position of panels. Where the alarm system is used to activate dampers, pressurise stairs etc. and also to send a signal to the fire service, suitable reference will be made.

— *First-aid firefighting*: describes the provision of first-aid firefighting equipment available to the occupants of the building. A policy statement may be made for example, that portable fire extinguishers will be positioned throughout the building in accordance with BS 5306: Part 3[34] rather than hosereels.

— *Emergency lighting and signs*: outlines the standards and operating principles.

(i) *Role of management*: clearly defines the management's role. This is an important element in the fire safety strategy which should be clearly defined. Management will play an active part in the prevention of fire by restricting smoking, good housekeeping and security. Management will also be responsible for ensuring that maintenance and testing procedures are in place to ensure that the fire systems within the building will respond to a fire.

The report may contain calculations, sketches and diagrams to support the conclusions and aims of the report. Detailed information would include smoke filling, design fire and egress calculations where these are required.

2.8.3   Interaction of building/system features

There will be features within the overall design of the building which affect the fire strategy, in either supportive or counter-productive ways.

Security considerations are often at odds with the requirements of emergency egress due to the conflict between locked doors and free access to emergency exits. However, security also plays an important role in deterring arson, alerting the management to fire hazards and maintaining access for fire service vehicles.

Methods of construction, materials and structural elements may have levels of intrinsic fire resistance which do not require further fire protection measures. Air-extract systems installed for environmental reasons can be utilised for smoke control or smoke clearance. Voice alarm and evacuation warnings can be incorporated into the public address system providing this system complies with BS 5839: Part 1[35].

2.8.4   Design methods

The fire safety engineering approach is recognised by certain codes and standards, for example Building Regulations Approved Document B[3] suggests that fire safety engineering may be the only viable way to achieve a satisfactory standard of fire safety in some large and complex buildings. Many of the codes produced by the National Fire Protection Association (USA) approve the use of a fire engineering approach.

The areas which the fire engineer will need to address are:

— the anticipated risk of fire occurring

— the anticipated severity of the fire

— the ability of the structure to resist the spread of fire and smoke

— the consequential danger to people in and around the building.

The fire safety design will then be prepared on the basis of an assessment of risk and an analysis of the protection which can be offered by fire safety measures.

2.9   Quantified risk assessment

2.9.1   General

Quantified risk assessment (QRA) is a way of evaluating the risks involved in situations subject to identifiable hazards and then putting useful numbers to that evaluation. It uses a combination of informed judgement, assessment methods, sensitivity analyses and probabilistic mathematics (similar to that used by actuaries for insurance purposes). It leads to discussions on reliability, design

options to reduce unacceptable risks, and risk management, i.e. the strategies for responding to those risks.

In applying QRA methods, it is important to note that the skills involved are akin to the judgement ordinarily exercised by designers. For example, a judgement must be made on the relationships of causes and consequences and 'second order' effects can sometimes dominate the analysis. So, while some of the detailed procedures may seem unorthodox, good designers should find the methods accessible in principle.

In this context, 'hazard' is often (but not always) differentiated from 'risk', as follows:

— 'hazard' is that which can go wrong or which has the ability to cause harm to people, property, systems, etc.

— 'risk' is the frequency of occurrence of the hazard, multiplied by a factor related to its calculated consequences (i.e. the damage likely to be caused).

By this definition, hazards include 'natural' occurrences such as typhoons, riverine flood, soil heave or earth movement, earthquakes and storm surge (against which the Thames Barrier is intended as a countermeasure). They also include fire, material or systems failures, traffic accidents, and bomb blast. All of these hazards are predictable, by reference to historical or statistical records, or by reflection on the activity concerned, its location, context, ways of working, etc.

The 'landmark' projects involving QRA include:

— Three-Mile Island nuclear reactor (1979)

— Flixborough oil refinery (1974)

— Seveso chemical plant (1976)

— Piper Alpha off-shore oil platform (1988)

— King's Cross London Underground station (1987).

The reports on all of these incidents led away from prescriptive design methods towards probabilistic analyses and performance-based design. Increasingly, such considerations are appearing in statutory controls such as those administered by the Health and Safety Executive (HSE). For example, a response to the requirements of the Construction Design and Management Regulations[36] may incorporate these principles.

2.9.2   Application of quantified risk assessment

Currently, there is a much greater awareness on issues of health, safety, environmental impact, etc. than heretofore. There are now many projects that involve appraisals of potential problems relating to these issues and which require the evaluation of alternative approaches. QRA is particularly useful in such situations.

For example, there are a number of large industries, such as nuclear power, chemical engineering, the oil and gas industries, mining, etc., which involve significant and predictable hazards in their normal working arrangements. However, there are also many situations in which the hazards are less serious but where the client is worried about the delay and disruption (and the resulting cost implications) which follow from the consequences of such hazards.

Crucial questions which arise might include:

— What kinds of hazard exist?

— How likely is the hazard to occur, within some specified period?

— What kinds of failure might follow from the potential hazard becoming reality?

— What are the consequences of such a failure?

— How likely is the failure, given the hazard occurring?

— How widespread will be the likely consequent effects?

— How quickly can the organisation return to normal working?

— How acceptable is the risk?

— How can the risk be reduced?

— What are the costs and benefits of reducing the risk?

Provided the hazards are identified, and the consequent risk assessed, it is usually possible to devise strategies for risk management or design solutions which will ensure reasonable safety of the people, and protection for the plant and equipment, involved.

QRA is characterised by the combination of skills from various disciplines and experience of a great variety of applications. Therefore the response may be tailored to respond to the specific problem at hand, allowing an innovatory approach, while ensuring use of the appropriate engineering knowledge and design disciplines.

References

1   The Building Regulations 2000 Statutory Instruments 2000 No. 2531 (London: The Stationery Office) (2000)

2   Building Regulations (Northern Ireland) 2000 Statutory Rules of Northern Ireland 2000 No. 389 (London: The Stationery Office) (2000)

3   *Fire Safety* The Building Regulations 2000 Approved Document B (London: The Stationery Office) (2000) (amended 2002)

4   *Fire safety* The Building Regulations (Northern Ireland) 1990 Technical Booklet E (London: HMSO) (1990)

5   The Building Standards (Scotland) Regulations 1990 Statutory Instruments 1990 No. 2179 (S. 187) (London: HMSO) (1990)

6   *Scottish Executive Technical Standards* (6th Amendment) (Edinburgh: Scottish Executive) (2001)

7   The Fire Precautions Act 1971 (London: HMSO) (1971)

8   *Building regulations and fire safety procedural guidance* (London: The Stationery Office) (2001)

9   The Education Act 1980 (London: HMSO/Department for Education and Employment) (1980)

10   *Fire and the design of educational buildings* (London: HMSO) (1988)

11   Design Guide — Structural Fire Safety (CIB W14 Workshop) *Fire Safety J*. 10(2) (1986)

12   *Smoke management systems in malls, atria and large areas* NFPA 92B (Quincey, Mass. USA: National Fire Protection Association) (1991)

13   The Building Act 1984 (London: HMSO) (1984)

14   The Factories Act 1961 (London: HMSO) (1961)

15   The Offices, Shops and Railway Premises Act 1963 (London: HMSO) (1963)

16   The Fire Safety and Safety of Places of Sport Act 1987 (London: HMSO) (1987)

17   *Fire Safety Building Regulations 1992 (as amended) and Approved Document B Workshop Tutorials — The Second Generation—Workbook* (Epsom: Institute of Building Control) (1995)

18   Fire Certificates (Special Premises) Regulations 1976 Statutory instruments 1976 No. 2003 (London: HMSO) (1976)

19   *Code of Practice for Fire Precautions in Factories, Offices, Shops and Railway Premises not required to have a Fire Certificate* (London: HMSO) (1989)

20   *Guide to Fire Precautions in Premises used as Hotels and Boarding Houses which require a Fire Certificate* (London: HMSO) (1991)

21   *Guide to Fire Precautions in existing Places of Work that require a Fire Certificate — Factories, Offices, Shops and Railway Premises* (London: HMSO) (1993)

22   BS 5588: *Fire precautions in the design, construction and use of buildings*: Part 0: *Guide to fire safety codes of practice for particular premises/applications*; Part 1: 1990: *Code of practice for residential buildings*; Part 4: 1998: *Code of practice for smoke control using pressure differentials*; Part 5: 1991: *Code for firefighting stairs and lifts*; Part 6: 1991: *Code of practice for places of assembly*; Part 7: *Code of practice for the incorporation of atria in buildings*; Part 8: 1999: *Code of practice for means of escape for disabled people*; Part 9: 1999: *Code of practice for ventilation and air conditioning ductwork*; Part 10: 1991: *Code of practice for shopping complexes*; Part 11: 1997: *Code of practice for shops, offices, industrial, storage and other similar buildings* (London: British Standards Institution) (various dates)

23   The Health and Safety at Work etc Act 1974 (London: HMSO) (1974)

24   *Guide to fire precautions in existing places of entertainment and like premises* (London: HMSO) (1990)

25   *Fire Safety Guide No. 1: Section 20 Buildings* (London: London District Surveyors Association) (1997)

26   *Fire Safety Guide No. 3: Phased evacuation from Office Buildings* (London: London District Surveyors Association) (1990)

27   *Technical Standard for Places of Entertainment* (London: London District Surveyors Association) (2001)

28   Morris W A and Read R E H *Aspects of fire precautions in buildings* BRE Report BR 137 (Garston: Building Research Establishment) (date unknown)

29   Morris W A, Read R E H and Cooke G M E *Guidelines for the construction of fire-resisting structural elements* BRE Report BR 128 (Garston: Building Research Establishment) (1988)

30   Morgan H P and Gardner J P *Design principles for smoke ventilation in enclosed shopping centres* BRE Report BR 186 (Garston: Building Research Establishment) (1990)

31   *LPC Code of Practice for the Construction of Buildings* (Garston: Loss Prevention Council) (1992)

32   *Automatic sprinkler installations* (Garston: Loss Prevention Council) (1990)

33   *Automatic fire alarm installations for the protection of property* (Garston: Loss Prevention Council) (1985)

34   BS 5306: *Fire extinguishing installations and equipment on premises*: Part 3: 2000: *Maintenance of portable fire extinguishers. Code of practice* (London: British Standards Institution) (2000)

35   BS 5839: *Fire detection and alarm systems for buildings*: Part 1: 1988: *Code of practice for system design, installation and servicing* (London: British Standards Institution) (1988)

36   The Construction (Design and Management) Regulations Statutory Instruments 1994 No. 3140 (London: HMSO) (1994)

3　Building designation

3.1　Introduction

Fire precautions in buildings can address several aspects, including life safety, control of property and contents damage, business disruption. The use to which a building is put (i.e. its classification) has implications for all of these aspects.

The most important implications arise from building population and the risk to which they are exposed, usually related to fire load. For example, in England and Wales, the Building Regulations[1] are supported by supplementary documentation[2] in which buildings are classified according to specific 'purpose groups', see Table 3.1. Different fire precautions are required for the various purpose groups. The means of detecting, controlling and extinguishing a fire, the provisions for evacuating the building, means of limiting the spread of fire and smoke within the building and their impact on adjacent compartments and structures, and the facilities for firefighting will all be influenced by the building's use.

Authorities differ in their criteria for building designation but, in the context of fire precautions, the main authorities are those concerned with building regulation (including firefighting) and building insurance. Examples of systems of building classification are given in Figure 3.1[3].

3.2　Common factors

There are a number of factors that have implications for most building types. In general, the extremes of these factors call for greater protection and increased fire precautions.

3.2.1　Building height

The fire engineering implications of building height are:

— greater vertical distances through which persons must travel to escape

— increased firefighting difficulties

— greater implications of building collapse.

High buildings are not recommended in certain high life-risk groups, e.g. health care premises.

In some situations protected routes are recommended to assist escape to a place of safety outside the building and lobby protection to stairs is recommended in tall buildings. Phased, rather than simultaneous, evacuation allows increased building height without requiring unmanageably wide stairs, and may reduce the need for total evacuation.

Where firefighting is not possible from the building perimeter due to excessive building height, access within the building can be provided by firefighting shafts. These provide protection for firefighters and include water supply outlets which, in tall buildings, are permanently charged.

Following the destruction of the twin towers at the World Trade Centre in New York, approving authorities, clients, building users, and society in general have expressed concern over the prudence of constructing tall buildings in view of their possible vulnerability to terrorism. The conventional phased evacuation regime designed to minimise disruption in fire is called into question due to the time required for total evacuation. The need or not to construct to withstand such impact and the issues associated with much larger fires and the destruction of fire protection are currently under discussion. Ultimately, society will decide — probably based on a risk analysis — whether or not to continue to build high-rise structures. In the meantime, engineering the fire safety should continue along the well-established lines of a single genuine 'accidental' fire outbreak, phased evacuation via lobbied stairs, voice alarms, sprinkler protection, firefighting access, compartment floors, and increased fire resistance etc. Other features, such as refuge floors, may also be included.

3.2.2　Depth below ground

The implications of depth below ground are:

— there is a possibility of fire products and escaping people using the same route

— the fire hazard below ground is often considered to be greater, with attendant increase of risk

— increased firefighting difficulties

— increased stress during upwards escape.

Basement accommodation often includes storage and hazardous plant. The increased risk to accommodation below ground can be addressed by provision of smoke control systems and sub-compartmentation. Smoke control coupled with sprinkler protection will assist fire control involving higher fire loads.

The movement of people and fire products should ideally be separated, perhaps by smoke extraction at source to keep escape routes clear. People using escape routes in case of fire from upper floors should not have to go below ground level to reach an exit.

Basement areas should be separated from the upper floors by a suitably fire resistant structure. Access for firefighting, by protected pressurised shafts in deep basements, may be required in certain circumstances.

Table 3.1 Classification by purpose group[2] (Crown copyright, reproduced by permission of the Controller of HMSO)

Title	Group	Purpose for which the building or compartment of a building is intended to be used
Residential (dwellings)†	1(a)	Flat or maisonette.
	1(b)	Dwellinghouse which contains a habitable storey with a floor level which is more than 4.5 m above ground level.
	1(c)	Dwellinghouse which does not contain a habitable storey with a floor level which is more than 4.5 m above ground level.
Residential:		
— institutional	2(a)	Hospital, nursing home, home for old people or for children, school or other similar establishment used as living accommodation or the treatment, care or maintenance of people suffering from illness or mental or physical disability or handicap, place of detention, where such people sleep on the premises.
— other	2(b)	Hotel, boarding house, residential college, hall of residence, hostel, and any other residential purpose not described above.
Office	3	Offices or premises used for the purpose of administration, clerical work (including writing, book keeping, sorting papers, filing, typing, duplicating, machine calculating, drawing and the editorial preparation of matter for publication, police and fire service work), handling money (including banking and building society work), and communications (including postal, telegraph and radio communications) or radio, television, film, audio or video recording, or performance (not open to the public) and their control.
Shop and commercial	4	Shops and premises used for a retail trade or business (including the sale to members of the public of food and drink for immediate consumption and retail by auction, self-selection and over-the-counter wholesale trading, the business of lending books or periodicals for gain and the business of a barber or hairdresser) and premises to which the public is invited to deliver or collect goods in connection with their hire, repair or other treatment, or (except in the case of repair of motor vehicles) where they themselves may carry out such repairs or other treatments.
Assembly and recreation	5	Places of assembly, entertainment or recreation; including bingo halls, broadcasting, recording and film studios open to the public, casinos, dance halls; entertainment, conference, exhibition and leisure centres; funfairs and amusement arcades; museums and art galleries; non-residential clubs, theatres, cinemas and concert halls; educational establishments, dancing schools, gymnasia, swimming pool buildings, riding schools, skating rinks, sports pavilions, sports stadia; law courts; churches and other buildings of worship, crematoria; libraries open to the public, non-residential day centres, clinics, health centres and surgeries; passenger stations and termini for air, rail, road or sea travel; public toilets; zoos and menageries.
Industrial	6	Factories and other premises used for manufacturing, altering, repairing, cleaning, washing, breaking-up, adapting or processing any article; generating power or slaughtering livestock.
Storage and other non-residential‡	7(a)	Place for the storage or deposit of goods or materials (other than described under 7(b)) and any building not within any of the purpose groups 1 to 6.
	7(b)	Car parks designed to admit and accommodate only cars, motorcycles and passenger or light goods vehicles weighing no more than 2500 kg gross.

† Includes any surgeries, consulting rooms, offices or other accommodation, not exceeding 50 m² in total, forming part of a dwelling and used by an occupant of the dwelling in a professional or business capacity.

‡ A detached garage not more than 40 m² in area is included in purpose group 1(c); as is a detached open carport of not more than 40 m², or a detached building which consists of a garage and open carport where neither the garage nor open carport exceeds 40 m² in area.

3.2.3   Building area

The implications of increased building area are:

— greater aggregate fire loads

— greater horizontal distances through which persons must travel to escape

— increased firefighting difficulties.

Strict adherence to maximum travel distances will be a determining factor for floor area. Where extended distances are preferred, smoke control or compensating features should be provided.

Sub-compartmentation will divide fire loads but fire control (e.g. venting, sprinklers) may provide an alternative solution. The limits of laid-out firefighting hoses may have a bearing on floor area and 60 m is usually taken as the maximum length for design purposes.

The latest guidance for the England and Wales[2] limits compartment size by area only (except for storage); previously, compartment size was also limited by volume. Volume limits still apply elsewhere.

3.2.4   Building volume

The main effect of building volume is that larger compartments can sustain larger fires.

Extended uncompartmented volumes may result in increased total fire load. Fire development and spread can be controlled by early detection, smoke venting and sprinkler protection but increased volumes do not necessarily imply increased fire load or, therefore, risk. Increased volume may, in fact, extend the smoke filling time.

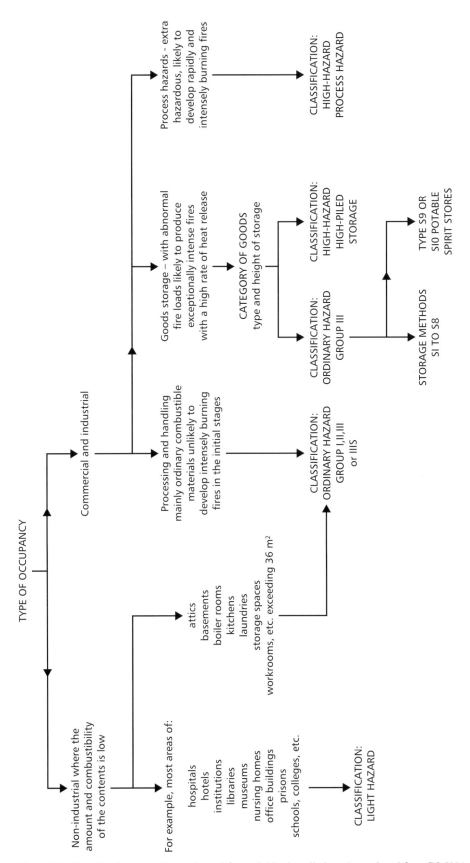

Figure 3.1 Classification according to hazard for sprinkler installations (reproduced from BS 5306: Part 2[3] by permission of the British Standards Institution)

In particular circumstances, the fire load may not be commensurate with the volume (e.g. offices, places of assembly, transport terminals) and lower standards of fire resistance may be appropriate, perhaps coupled with fire containment and smoke control.

3.2.5 Proximity to site boundary and adjacent buildings

The proximity of the building to the site boundary or to adjacent buildings can lead to:

— increased controls on compartmentation

— restrictions on unprotected (i.e. non-fire resisting and combustible) areas of the facade.

UK regulations and guidance[1,4,5] recommend that fire resistance be provided to restrict fire spread across site boundaries. In circumstances where a high life risk is involved, this guidance also requires fire resistance to be provided between buildings on the same site. The division of buildings into compartments provides a means of restricting the area of radiation at the boundary of the building (see section 5). Where such compartmentation conflicts with building occupancy, equivalent provision can be achieved by sprinkler protection since this restricts the fire size. With a life safety sprinkler system, more refined calculations of fire size and the subsequent benefit to the boundary condition can be anticipated.

The proportion of unprotected areas is determined by proximity to the boundary and, broadly, to the nature of the occupancy based on the fire load.

3.2.6 Fire load

The characteristics that contribute to fire hazard include the quantity of combustible materials, their distribution, flammability, smoke production and surface flame spread rates.

Traditionally, various occupancies have identifiable fire loads. The full fire development of these loads result in the standards of fire resistance and limits of compartmentation. Therefore, other measures provided to control fire development and spread should reduce the need for compartmentation (see section 5) whilst at the same time protecting losses.

Standards of enclosure and separation may differ for life safety and property protection purposes, the latter generally being higher when it is assumed that the occupants will have vacated the building during the early stages of a fire. Clearly, the successful action of sprinklers dramatically modifies the impact of fire load on design.

3.2.7 Numbers of people

Large numbers of people may require more emphasis on management to achieve means of escape. There is a tendency towards providing more reliable information to assist people in making the correct decisions in making their exit. This can be achieved by voice alarms or informative displays.

3.2.8 Sleeping accommodation

With sleeping accommodation there is the possibility of disorientation of the occupants on hearing the fire alarm. The response to alarms is affected by the alertness of the occupants at the time that the alarm is sounded and by their knowledge of the building. Therefore, increased detection, protection or fire control can be justified for sleeping accommodation. For example, fire alarms can be suitably located and sufficiently loud to alert sleeping people (see section 6). The reliability of an alarm system has a direct bearing on peoples' response to it and more complex systems can be justified in critical circumstances.

3.2.9 Disadvantaged occupants

Consideration must be given to the special needs of disadvantaged occupants. Fire studies[6] indicate that fires occur most frequently where the occupants are at some disadvantage. These include the physically or mentally handicapped, young or aged persons, the infirm, inebriated persons and the socially disadvantaged. It is recommended that means of escape for the disabled should receive special attention. Guidance on access and exit provision for the disabled is given in Approved Document M[7] and BS 5588: Part 8[8].

3.2.10 Multi-tenancy/multi-occupancy

Where the whole population of a building is not under the same management, there is the possibility of varying standards of care and attention to fire precautions. It is necessary to ensure that the other occupancies are warned in the event of a fire being detected.

The combination of different purpose groups within the same building may call for additional provisions including better fire separation and separate means of escape.

3.2.11 Special building features

Such special features include atria, environmental flues, single stair conditions, open spatial planning and extensive underground spaces.

It is the actual, rather than perceived, problems that arise as a result of the inclusion of unusual features which need to be examined carefully to provide life safety protection.

3.2.12 Life safety and property protection

Life safety protection — which includes both occupants and firefighting personnel — requires different levels of fire precautions to those appropriate to property protection.

Property protection normally requires higher standards of fire precautions. This is often reflected in the call for sprinklers, smoke control and higher standards of fire resistance. In providing for life safety, the issues of property protection are often addressed to a significant degree.

3.2.13 Fire precautions during construction

The fire loads, and the associated risks, can be much greater during construction than in the completed building.

Fires at buildings under construction have emphasised the need to minimise the risk and for increased vigilance. A fire strategy for the construction process incorporating, where possible, the provisions of the completed project will help to minimise overall costs. Fire safety on construction sites is dealt with in detail in section 12.

3.3 Risk profiles

An alternative way of defining the risk to persons in buildings to that outlined in section 3.2, is to adopt a risk profile approach. The risk to which persons may be exposed is a combination of their occupancy group and the likely fire development; a sleeping risk in a hotel is greater than one where persons are awake and familiar with the building. This approach is presented more fully in BS 9999[9]. In summary it divides occupancy into seven life risk categories (also outlined in BS 5588: Part 7[8]), and fire development into four well established growth scenarios. From these divisions, most occupancies can be profiled. Even if BS 9999 is not adopted, the principle of such classification may still be applied. In terms of building design, more flexibility should be expected from the lower risk categories.

3.4 Designing the fire precautions

3.4.1 Fire precautions standards in the UK for life safety

For life safety purposes, fire precautions to an appropriate standard are a requirement of the building regulations in all developed countries but the means of achieving them are varied. At present, standards are not consistent within Europe. Even within the UK there are three systems, i.e. (a) England and Wales, (b) Scotland and (c) Northern Ireland. It is necessary to contact the appropriate building or fire authority to obtain details of the requirements within a particular country.

3.4.1.1 England and Wales

The requirements of the Building Regulations[1] may be met by observing the recommendations contained in Approved Document B: *Fire Safety*[2]. However, the requirements of the Regulations may be met in other ways such as by observing the recommendations of British Standards — particularly BS 5588[8] — or by adopting a fire safety engineering approach, as explained in paragraph 0.11 of Approved Document B.

Local Acts, some of which have facilities for relaxation, may also apply, although most provisions can be met by applying the recommendations given in *Approved Document B*.

3.4.1.2 Scotland

The criteria for compliance with the Building Standards (Scotland) Regulations[4] are set out in Parts D and E of the *Scottish Executive Technical Standards*[10]. The *Technical Standards* are highly prescriptive. However, the Regulations state that compliance may also be achieved 'by any other means which can be shown to satisfy the relevant standards'.

3.4.1.3 Northern Ireland

The functional requirements are set down in the Building Regulations (Northern Ireland) 2000[5]. The associated Technical Booklet E: *Fire safety*[11] provides 'deemed-to-satisfy' measures which, if followed, will ensure compliance with the Regulations.

3.4.1.4 Alternative approaches

In all three of the above legislative areas, there is provision for the consideration of departures from prescriptive solutions.

In England, Wales and Northern Ireland such departures are allowed with the agreement of the local building control officer or by a 'determination' by the Secretary of State for the Environment. The equivalent provision in Scotland is termed a 'relaxation' and is sought through the Secretary of State for Scotland.

3.4.1.5 Fire brigades' requirements

Local fire brigades are concerned with fire precautions in buildings and the approvals process includes provisions for their consultation. Their responsibilities for fire precautions result mainly from the Fire Precautions Act[12] and the Fire Precautions (Workplace) Regulations 1997[13] which deals with occupied buildings, but they also have consultative responsibilities for many issues under the extensive legislation concerning the various occupancies. The extent of this legislation is set down in various publications[14–16]. The consultation procedure is outlined in national procedural guidance[17].

In all cases, the building control department of the local authority or the fire prevention department of the fire brigade will advise on these issues. Generally, building control should be consulted initially for new buildings and the fire authority for occupied buildings. Consultation of both simultaneously may result in confusion of responsibilities. The procedural guidance requires either authority to alert the applicant of the need to consult the other, and to distinguish between 'recommendation' and 'requirement'.

3.4.2 Fire precautions standards outside the UK for life safety

Standards and consultation processes vary considerably outside the UK but, in general, the fire authorities have greater powers than they do in the UK. Therefore, the fire authority is always the best starting point for consultation on requirements and procedures for projects outside the UK. To minimise waste of time and effort, enquiries should be made on the need to also consult other bodies.

3.4.3   Fire precautions standards for property protection, including contents and business disruption

The insurance companies are becoming increasingly concerned with minimising insured risks and their recommendations have a bearing on design. They are concerned both with losses during construction and in the completed building. A code of site fire precautions[18] has been produced by the Loss Prevention Council (LPC) and other codes of practice include appropriate information[19,20]. Standards of construction are contained in another LPC code[21].

Where possible, the particular insurance company should be consulted in the early stages of the design process. However, this may not be possible for speculative developments since the insurer of the completed property may not have been nominated.

3.5   Implications of classification by purpose group

The intention of this section is to provide a checklist of items that should be considered for particular occupancies. Reference will be made to the classifications given in Table D1 of Approved Document B[2], reproduced here as Table 3.1, and Table 4.3.4 in BS 9999[9].

3.5.1   Residential (dwellings)

In dwellings, fire precautions are generally minimal in order to maintain privacy of the individual. The main factors relevant to dwellings are as follows:

—   most deaths by fire occur in dwellings

—   need to maintain privacy

—   separation of dwellings

—   well established and consistent fire load.

Dwellings are divided into three sub-groups which also separates high-rise from low-rise dwellings, including houses in multiple occupation:

(a)   flat and maisonette

(b)   dwelling which contains a habitable storey with a floor level more than 4.5 m above ground level

(c)   dwelling which does not contain a habitable storey with a floor level more than 4.5 m above ground level.

Except for houses in multiple occupation, controls over low-rise dwellings are minimal and are mainly confined to the separation of dwellings from each other, to control fire spread between them, and the need for smoke detectors. Individual dwellings with a habitable storey above 4.5 m require further control by the provision of a protected escape route (unless there is an alternative exit) and escape windows. Approved Document B[2] and BS 5839: Part 6[22] provide guidance on detection and alarm systems relevant to a wide range of residential buildings including large houses, houses in multiple occupation and sheltered housing.

For houses in multiple occupation, reference should be made to *DoE Circular 12/92*[23], which is also relevant to the conversion of existing housing stock into houses in multiple occupation and covers additional requirements for means of escape, including fire detection and alarm systems for houses in multiple occupation having three or more stories above ground.

There is scope for fire safety engineering in unconventional dwellings where protected routes are compromised by an open-plan layout. Provisions may include sprinkler protection and smoke control; smoke detection is recommended in Approved Document B[2]. Such provisions might also be considered during refurbishment or major alterations.

Where dwellings are grouped together, as in flats and maisonettes, increased controls are recommended, particularly with respect to vertical and horizontal separation in order to contain a fire within one dwelling and prevent it from spreading to others. Maintaining this separation is important in the provision of common services and has implications for ductwork and fire-stopping. Protected stairs and firefighting shafts take on increased importance with increased building height, a higher standard being required in single stair situations. The venting of common areas is required as a means of keeping escape and rescue route clear.

There are controls over wall and ceiling surfaces for common areas, and limits on the fire risks opening onto such areas. There are controls on the spread of flame over the external walls and in the sub-division of cavities.

Unconventional designs, particularly in the manner of grouping the dwellings, offer opportunities for fire safety engineering. For example, tall residential blocks in an atrium setting would call for special provisions to offset the loss of physical compartmentation.

For all three groups, the fire load is generally predictable. Also the maximum fire size is known due to the provision of compartmentation.

3.5.2   Residential (institutional)

For residential (institutional) buildings, the key factors are as follows:

—   high life risk

—   occupants may be asleep

—   occupants may be infirm or in other ways disadvantaged

— compartmentation is recommended

— clear advantage of fire detection (subject to reliability)

— well established and consistent fire load

— trained staff may be present.

Sub-division within this purpose group separates the infirm (group (a), which includes health care premises) from the able bodied (group (b), which includes hotels and guest houses).

Greater controls are recommended for purpose group (a) and these are mainly concerned with evacuation procedures, compartmentation and fire detection which can now be provided with minimal false alarms. Health care premises invariably incorporate an abundance of piped and wired services and therefore require particular attention to integrity of the compartmentation.

The historical record of fire incidents in health care premises is generally good but there is concern over the potential for loss of life. In the upgrading of existing premises, there is a strong case for active fire control and informative detection systems. The major fires have occurred in premises catering for the disabled and mentally handicapped and extra provision should be considered for such buildings.

Fatalities and extensive damage have occurred in system-built flat-roofed premises where undivided cavities resulted in hidden fire spread. Guidance on fire precautions design for health care premises is contained in the series of *Firecodes*[24], produced by the Department of Health (NHS Estates).

In the UK, sprinkler protection (i.e. active fire control) is not yet widely adopted for this occupancy, though the benefits are now more forcefully encouraged in guidance. If it were to be adopted there would be clear advantages in the control of fire spread and, as a result, increased opportunities for fire safety engineering. There are also areas where damage to the contents would have serious implications and increased controls are therefore justified. Also, the loss of medical facilities can have serious repercussions.

The Fire Precautions Act[12] arose largely as a result of multiple-fatality fires within buildings in group (b), which includes hotels and boarding houses. Statutory controls for group (b) are lower than those for group (a), being mainly in the areas of compartmentation and detection. Means of escape are more conventional with clear advantages if the normal circulation routes are also those which lead to emergency exits. There is increased interest in providing an appropriate level of emergency lighting.

The provision of an atrium would require additional controls to offset the loss of passive compartmentation. BS 5588: Part 7[8] includes prescriptive guidance for this occupancy but also allows an engineered approach (section 1).

Guidance for fire precautions in existing buildings is available from the Home Office[15]. For new premises in the UK, appropriate guidance is available[2,10,11].

3.5.3 Offices

The key factors are as follows:

— few deaths from fire in offices

— maximum design flexibility

— well established and consistent fire load.

This purpose group offers the greatest flexibility for design in that the risk to life is understood to be low. However, the protection of contents and business disruption take on a greater significance.

Occupants will generally be familiar with the premises and the fire load is well understood. The main emphasis on controls concerns the means of escape. The introduction of an atrium is not always seen as increasing risk, subject to reasonable additional provisions. BS 5588: Part 7: *Fire safety in atrium buildings*[8] is a helpful starting point for design. Note that Approved Document B[2] recommends that compliance with BS 5588: Part 7 is required only where the atrium traverses compartment floors.

3.5.4 Shops and commercial premises

The key factors are as follows:

— historically low life risk

— potentially high life loss

— high contents value

— high occupancy capacity

— high fire load

— designs often involve large volumes and long travel distances

— occupants disoriented by unfamiliar layouts

— significant historic fires.

The above key factors indicate the clear benefits of sprinkler protection with the corresponding scope for fire safety engineering.

This group includes shopping malls and complexes for which specific guidance is available[8,25] although designers are not obliged to adopt the principles they contain. Considerable emphasis is now placed on premises management[8]. An approach based on fire dynamics has been produced in the USA by the National Fire Protection Association[26].

The benefits of sprinkler protection have been well demonstrated[27]. In shop design, consideration must be given to the fire characteristics —size, growth rate and the effects of selected sprinkler response — and their implications for active measures, such as smoke management. The provision of sprinklers in high areas (i.e. over 15 m) will be ineffective in controlling fire. However, fire control for these areas is possible by the application of systems designed for atrium base protection, either sidewall- or canopy-mounted. Lateral fire spread can now be controlled by fire resisting curtains and by the combination of window-wetting sprinklers on toughened glazing.

3.5.5 Assembly and recreational buildings

The key factors are:

— potentially high life loss

— significant serious fires

— high occupancy capacity

— designs may call for large volumes and long travel distances

— layouts can lead to disorientation

— some high fire loads

— extensive controls based on investigations of historical fires

— problems with extended height

— increased risk in underground conditions.

Buildings in this group offer scope for fire safety engineering. In the educational sector of this group, extensive fire damage has been caused by arson; there are strong links between security and fire damage. Undivided cavities in system-built, flat-roofed structures have resulted in extensive damage but these are now restricted by the building regulations and associated guidance[2,10,11].

In the fire precautions design of this group, the fire characteristics should be considered, along with their implications for the standard of active measures. Large room volumes should not necessarily imply increased life or property risk because the fire load may be relatively low.

Compartmentation limits can be exceeded without increased risk and extended travel distances should be possible by the provision of compensating features including smoke control and sprinklers. Smoke control provisions could include curtains to limit spread. The maximum population can be determined in occupancies with fixed seating.

The provision of roof-mounted sprinklers in high areas (i.e. over 15 m) will be ineffective in controlling fire. Intelligent side-wall systems can effectively control fire over areas up to 16 m wide.

3.5.6 Industrial buildings

The key factors for industrial buildings are as follows:

— significant historic fires

— high life risk (but often low occupancy with good mobility)

— high fire risks in close proximity

— high fire loads

— hazardous processes requiring special provisions

— firefighting difficulties

— potentially high commercial losses

— potential pollution from smoke and fire products.

Industrial buildings offer scope for fire safety engineering. Special controls and requirements appropriate to industrial processes are available in, for example, BS 5908[28]. The fire characteristics should be considered in the design of buildings in this group, with implications on the standard of active measures. The provision of roof-mounted sprinklers in high areas (over 15 m) will be ineffective in controlling fires but fast response, in-content systems are available. Care should be taken over the differences between approval for shell and core under Building Regulations and when fitting out.

3.5.7 Storage and other non-residential buildings

The key factors are:

— high contents and commercial losses

— high fire loads

— low occupancy

— significant historic fires

— designs may call for large volumes and long travel distances

— underground accommodation may be involved

— firefighting difficulties.

Buildings in this group offer scope for fire safety engineering. Special sprinkler systems are available to cope with densely-stacked goods on high racks. Compartmentation may be disruptive or difficult to provide but is seen as a means of limiting fire damage. In many cases, fire spread may be limited by smoke venting.

In car parks, both above and below ground, a fire safety engineering examination of the actual risks may result in a lowering of the traditionally adopted standards, including the likely omission of sprinklers. Their omission even in underground car parks is permitted under the Approved Document B[2] guidance.

References

1 The Building Regulations 2000 Statutory Instruments 2000 No. 2531 (London: The Stationery Office) (2000)

2 *Fire Safety* The Building Regulations 2000 Approved Document B (London: The Stationery Office) (2000) (amended 2002)

3 BS 5306: *Fire extinguishing installations and equipment on premises*: Part 2: 1990: *Specification for sprinkler systems* (London: British Standards Institution) (1990)

4 The Building Standards (Scotland) Regulations 1990 Statutory Instruments 1990 No. 2179 (S. 187) (as amended) (London: HMSO) (1990 with subsequent amendments)

5 Building Regulations (Northern Ireland) 2000 Statutory Rules of Northern Ireland 2000 No. 389 (London: The Stationery Office) (2000)

6 Williams A W and Hopkinson J S *Important factors in real fires* BRE Information paper IP 20/84 (Garston: Building Research Establishment) (1984)

7   *Access and facilities for disabled people* Building Regulations 1991 Approved Document M (London: The Stationery Office) (1998)

8   BS 5588: *Fire precautions in the design, construction and use of buildings*: Part 0: 1996: *Guide to fire safety codes of practice for particular premises/applications*; Part 1: 1990 *Code of practice for residential buildings*; Part 4: 1998: *Code of practice for smoke control using pressure differentials*; Part 5: 1991: *Code of practice for firefighting stairs and lifts*; Part 6: 1991: *Code of practice for places of assembly*; Part 7: 1997: *Code of practice for the incorporation of atria in buildings*; Part 8: 1999: *Code of practice for means of escape for disabled people*; Part 9: 1999: *Code of practice for ventilation and air conditioning ductwork*; Part 10: 1991: *Code of practice for shopping complexes*; Part 11: 1997: *Code of practice for shops, offices, industrial, storage and other similar buildings* (London: British Standards Institution) (dates as indicated)

9   BS 9999: (draft): Code of practice for fire safety in the design, construction and use of buildings (London: British Standards Institution) (to be published)

10   *Scottish Executive Technical Standards* (6th Amendment) (Edinburgh: Scottish Executive) (2001)

11   *Fire safety* The Building Regulations (Northern Ireland) 1990 Technical Booklet E (London: HMSO) (1994)

12   The Fire Precautions Act 1971 (London: HMSO) (1971)

13   The Fire Precautions (Workplace) Regulations 1997 Statutory Instruments 1997 No. 1840 (London: The Stationery Office) (1997)

14   *Guide to fire precautions in existing places of entertainment and like premises* (London: The Stationery Office) (1990)

15   *Guide to fire precautions in premises used as hotels and boarding houses which require a fire certificate* (London: The Stationery Office) (1991)

16   *Guide to fire precautions in existing places of work that require a fire certificate* (London: The Stationery Office) (1993)

17   *Building Regulations and Fire Safety — Procedural Guidance* (London: The Stationery Office) (2001) (www.safety.odpm.gov.uk/bregs/brpub/firesafety)

18   *Fire Prevention on Construction Sites* (London: Building Employers Confederation/Loss Prevention Council) (1992)

19   *Fire safety in construction work* HSG 168 (London: Health and Safety Executive) (1997)

20   *Standard Fire Precautions for Contractors Engaged on Works for Crown Civil and Defence Estates* (London: HMSO/Standing Committee on Fire Precautions) (1991)

21   *Code of Practice for the Construction of Buildings* (London: Loss Prevention Council) (1992)

22   BS 5839: *Fire detection and alarm systems for buildings*: Part 6: 1995: *Code of practice for the design and installation of fire detection and alarm systems in dwellings* (London: British Standards Institution) (1995)

23   *Houses in multiple occupation — Guidance to local housing authorities on standards of fitness under section 352 of the Housing Act 1985* DoE Circular 12/92 (London: The Stationery Office) (1992)

24   NHS Estates *Firecodes* (various titles) (London: The Stationery Office) (various dates)

25   Morgan H P and Gardner J P Design principles for smoke ventilation in enclosed shopping centres BRE Research Report BR 186 (Garston: Building Research Establishment) (1990)

26   *Smoke management systems in malls, atria and large areas* NFPA 92B (Quincey MA: National Fire Protection Association) (1991)

27   Sprinklers provide the edge in L.A. riot *Record* (Oct/Nov 1992)

28   BS 5908: 1990: *Fire precautions in the chemical and allied industries* (London: British Standards Institution) (1990)

4 Means of escape and human factors

4.1 Introduction

4.1.1 General

This section covers the basic principles of designing for escape by using the established prescriptive design codes or an alternative fire safety engineering approach.

This Guide is not intended to replace existing codes of practice and reference to them will still be necessary. However, it is intended that this section will assist designers in applying best practice to means of escape design and provide an understanding of the underlying principles.

4.1.2 Requirements of UK building regulations

Building regulations within the UK, see section 2, are supported by guidance documents which describe how adequate provision for escape can be achieved. These guidance documents are prescriptive in nature and set limits on maximum travel distances, prescribe exit widths and fire resistance requirements for protected routes, etc.

However, in England and Wales, the regulations allow for other solutions provided that it can be demonstrated that the occupants of a building are ultimately able to reach a place of safety outside of the building. This can be done by means of a fire safety engineering assessment which should be entrusted to suitably qualified and experienced persons. In Scotland the regulations are more prescriptive but proposals are being considered for the introduction of functional requirements and a more flexible approach to design.

4.2 Objectives of escape design

The objectives of any escape design are similar and are typified by the requirements of the Building Regulations for England and Wales[1], that is:

> The building shall be designed and constructed so that there are appropriate provisions for the early warning of fire and appropriate means of escape in case of fire from the building to a place of safety outside the building capable of being safely and effectively used at all material times.

This objective should be achieved without the need for outside assistance except where particular assistance may be necessary, e.g. for people with disabilities. Arrangements should be made for such assistance to be provided without reliance on the fire brigade, whose arrival may be delayed.

4.2.1 Evacuation strategies

The simplest escape strategy is to ensure that as soon as a fire has been confirmed, all of the occupants proceed to leave the building simultaneously. However, some situations require variations from this strategy of simultaneous evacuation, for example:

— the provision of protected refuges where people with disabilities can await assistance in relative safety, i.e. protected from the effects of fire and smoke

— hospitals where escape involves progressive horizontal evacuation from the fire affected area into adjoining fire compartments

— some multi-storey buildings where phased evacuation is adopted and only the fire floor (and usually the one above) is evacuated in the first instance

— some buildings (e.g. very tall multi-storey buildings) where protected refuge levels are provided where people can wait in safety

— facilities where the immediate interruption of some function could cause major problems, (e.g. air traffic control centres or hazardous process plants) and the evacuation of key personnel may be delayed

— prisons where escape may be into adjoining secure areas or into a secure compound.

Basic to the philosophy of means of escape design is that it should be possible to turn one's back on the fire and to move away from it. This is achieved by providing at least two escape routes that are well separated either spatially or by fire resisting construction. Exceptions to this, where only a single direction of escape is available (often referred to as 'dead-ends'), are only acceptable if the distance of travel to an exit is very short (typically not more than 15 to 25 m).

4.3 Prescriptive codes

Prescriptive guidance on means of escape design is given in various documents such as:

— Building Regulations (England and Wales) Approved Document B: *Fire safety*[2] (section B1)

— Technical Standards for compliance with The Building Standards (Scotland) Regulations[3]

— BS 5588: *Fire precautions in the design, construction and use of buildings*[4]

— NFPA 101: *Life safety code*[5].

The British Standard BS 5588 series of codes and the (US) NFPA codes are internationally recognized and are widely used outside of their respective countries of origin. In certain parts of the world designers will have the option of using NFPA, BS or local codes.

4.3.1   Designing for escape

In general terms all of the traditional prescriptive codes adopt a broadly similar approach to escape route design in that they set out recommendations for:

— the design population

— required width of exits to accommodate the anticipated population

— the separation and number of alternative exits

— limitations on the distance of travel before reaching an exit

— degree of fire protection required to escape routes (e.g. enclosure of stairs and certain corridors).

To facilitate the evacuation process other measures may also be required depending upon the size and complexity of the building. These include:

— fire alarm system

— exit and escape route signage

— escape lighting

— automatic fire detection.

These measures are considered in detail in section 6 of this Guide.

The key steps involved in escape design using traditional prescriptive codes are illustrated in Figure 4.1.

4.3.2   Occupant capacity

The occupant capacity of a room, storey or other part of a building is the maximum number of persons that it is designed or expected to hold. In theatres and cinemas where a fixed number of seats are provided the maximum number of occupants can be readily and accurately established. However, in many situations it is necessary to estimate the likely maximum occupancy based on floor space factors.

Floor space factors are given in terms of the likely minimum area occupied by each person (m² per person). The occupant capacity can then be determined by dividing the area of the room or storey by the floor space factor. Some typical floor space factors given in various guidance documents are summarised in Table 4.1.

Where specific data are available to demonstrate the actual maximum occupancies (e.g. a retailer's own trading figures) these may be used instead of the standard floor space factors.

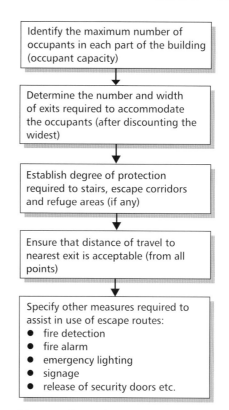

Figure 4.1 Escape design: key steps

The occupancy of a room can be determined as follows:

$$\text{Occupant capacity} = \frac{\text{area of room}}{\text{floor space factor}} \qquad (4.1)$$

In calculating the occupant capacity, toilets, stair shafts and fixed elements of structure (but not counters and display units etc. in retail premises) can be discounted from the floor area calculation.

The floor space factors given in regulatory guidance documents such as Approved Document B[2] and the Scottish Technical Standards[3] will generally provide a worst case assumption. However, if it can be demonstrated that the occupancy will be lower, this should be accepted by the enforcing bodies but may result in some restrictions on future usage. A common example is the acceptance of a floor space factor of 10 m² per person in office buildings where Approved Document B suggests 6 m² per person. However, if the use changes from a traditional office to a call centre with a more densely packed seating arrangement the exit provision may prove to be inadequate.

In some escape designs it may be necessary to hold people in a protected refuge area before they ultimately leave the building. When estimating the holding capacity of a protected refuge area, a figure of 2 persons per m² may be assumed as a reasonable maximum occupant density. (This figure is taken from CIBSE Guide D: *Transportation systems in buildings*[6], which recommends it as appropriate to 'dense' conditions in bulk queues.)

4.3.3   Exit widths

When the occupant capacity has been established the required width of exits can be determined. Subject to a minimum exit width (typically 1100 mm) most guidance

Table 4.1 Floor space factors recommended in UK and US guidance documents

Type of accommodation	Floor space factor / (m² per person)	
	UK (ADB and STS★)	USA (NFPA 101[5])
Bars, standing spectator areas (concentrated use without fixed seating)	0.3	0.65
Amusement arcade, assembly hall, bingo hall (less concentrated use without fixed seating)	0.5	1.4
Exhibition hall	1.5	1.4
Restaurant, committee room, staff room etc.	1.0	1.4
Shop sales area	2.0 to 7.0†	2.8 to 5.6
Office	6.0	9.3
Library	7.0	4.6 to 9.3
Kitchen	7.0	9.3
Art gallery or museum	5.0	—
Industrial production	5.0	9.3
Airport terminals		
Concourse		9.3
Waiting areas		1.4
Baggage claim		1.9
Baggage handling		27.9

★ ADB: Approved Document B[2]; STS: Scottish Technical Standards[3]
† For retail premises the Scottish Technical Standards and BS 5588[4] suggest a floor space factor of 4 m²/person where the actual maximum occupancy is unknown

documents (Approved Document B[2], BS 5588: Part 11[4] and NFPA 101[5]) recommend the provision of 5 mm of clear exit width for each person. However, a figure of 5.3 mm per person has been adopted in the Scottish Technical Standards[3].

The route to any one exit may be blocked by fire and it is therefore usual practice in UK codes to discount the largest exit from the calculations. Therefore, if three equally sized exits are available and these need to accommodate 500 people, the required width would be (500 × 5 mm) = 2500 mm. Since it is necessary to discount one exit, the required width of each of the remaining two exits would be (2500 / 2) = 1250 mm.

An exit less than 1100 mm wide will have a proportionately lower capacity than a larger exit and the exit capacities given in Table 4.2 can be adopted.

Table 4.2 Capacities for narrow exits

Maximum number of persons	Minimum clear width of exit / mm
50	750
110	850
220	1050
>220	5 per person

4.3.4 Stair capacities

4.3.4.1 General

A stair enclosure can be considered as a place of relative safety which provides a refuge space. The capacity of a stair is therefore dependent upon the rate at which people can leave by the final exit and the number of people that can be accommodated in the enclosure.

The capacity of a stair (used for simultaneous evacuation) can be derived from the following equation:

$$P = 200\,w + 50\,(w - 0.3)\,(n - 1) \qquad (4.2)$$

where P is the number of people that can be served by the stair, w is the width of the stair (m) and n is the number of storeys served.

Equation 4.2 can be rewritten to give the required width of the stair, as follows:

$$w = \frac{P + 15\,n - 15}{150 + 50\,n} \qquad (4.3)$$

4.3.4.2 Phased evacuation

In high rise buildings it is common practice to design the stairways on the basis of phased evacuation, i.e. a process in which a number of floors (usually two) are initially evacuated, the remaining floors being evacuated as and when necessary. This requires adequate compartmentation to protect those not evacuated immediately.

Where designed for phased evacuation, the widths of stairways and their final exits are generally calculated on the same basis as for doorway openings, see section 4.3.3. No account is taken of the holding capacity of the stairway, i.e. the design is on the basis that the flow into the stair is equal to the flow out. This exclusion of the holding capacity represents a conservative approach.

To ensure that a phased evacuation may be controlled effectively, additional fire protection measures may be required such as a public address system, fire telephones and an automatic detection system.

Guidance on phased evacuation from office buildings is provided in LDSA Fire Safety Guide No. 3[7].

4.3.5 Alternative exits

A basic principle of designing for escape is that escape routes should be available in at least two directions (unless the distance to be travelled is short and the number of occupants is limited, typically to a maximum of 60 people). A choice of escape routes is of little value if they are all likely to be obstructed by fire at the same time. Alternative escape routes should therefore be provided in directions at least 45° apart or be separated by fire-resisting construction, see Figure 4.2.

Where the maximum occupancy of a room or storey exceeds 600 people at least three adequately separated exits should be provided.

4.3.6 Travel distances

All the traditional prescriptive codes place limitations on the maximum distance that can be travelled to an exit. The travel distances should be measured along the route which will actually be travelled and not the direct (straight line) distance. However, where the final layout of the building is not known the rule of thumb is to assume that the travel distance will be approximately 1.5 times the direct distance.

The recommended maximum travel distances for a selection of different occupancies as given in various prescriptive codes are summarised below in Tables 4.3 and 4.4.

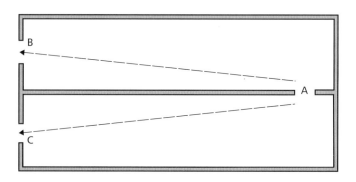

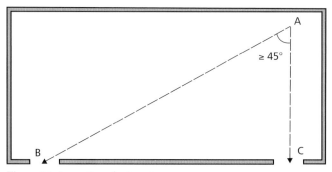

Figure 4.2 Separation of exit routes

Table 4.3 Escape available in at least two directions

Building use	Maximum travel distance (m)		
	ADB* and BS 5588[4]	STS*	NFPA 101[5]†
Office	45	45	60 (91)
Shop and commercial	45	32	30 (60)
Assembly buildings	45	32	45 (60)
Assembly buildings with fixed seating in rows	32	32	45 (60)
Industrial	45	45	60 (75)
Plant rooms (within room)	35	45	60 (75)
High fire hazard	18	32	23 (23)

* ADB: Approved Document B[2]; STS: *Scottish Executive Technical Standards*[3]
† Figures in parentheses indicate the allowable travel distance where sprinklers are installed

Table 4.4 Escape available in one direction only

Building use	Maximum travel distance (m)		
	ADB* and BS 5588[4]	STS*	NFPA 101[5]†
Office	18	18	23 (30)
Shop and commercial	18	15	23 (30)
Assembly buildings	18	15	6.1 (6.1)
Assembly buildings with fixed seating in rows	15	15	6.1 (6.1)
Industrial	25	18	15 (30)
Plant rooms (within room)	9	18	15 (30)
High fire hazard	9	15	0 (0)

* ADB: Approved Document B[2]; STS: *Scottish Executive Technical Standards*[3]
† Figures in parentheses indicate the allowable travel distance where sprinklers are installed

4.3.7 Fire protection to escape routes

Escape stairs and, in certain cases, escape corridors need to be enclosed with fire resisting construction to prevent the ingress of fire and smoke. For escape purposes a minimum fire resistance of 30 minutes is normally recommended, although this may be increased if the stair also acts as a protected shaft providing separation between levels.

It is important to prevent substantial smoke infiltration into protected escape routes and therefore all elements of the enclosing structure should be adequately sealed against smoke ingress; doors should be provided with smoke seals.

4.3.7.1 Protected lobbies

Additional protection against the ingress of smoke into a stairway can be achieved by the provision of a protected lobby (see Figure 4.3).

Protected lobbies to stairs are normally required when:

— only one escape stair is available

— the height of the top storey is greater than 18 m

— the building is designed for phased evacuation

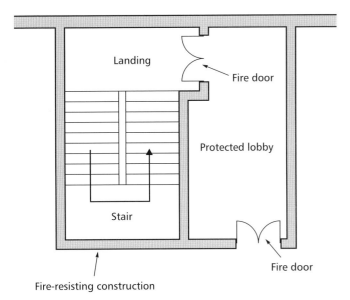

Figure 4.3 Protected lobby to stairway enclosure

— the stair is designated as a firefighting stair (see section 9).

If lobby protection is not provided to all stairs it is normally necessary to discount one whole stair from the exit calculations. However, if lobbies are provided it can be assumed that all protected stairways will be available for escape. (*Note*: it is still necessary to discount one exit on the fire floor.)

4.3.7.2   Protection to corridors

Dead-end corridors should be provided with a 30-minute fire resisting enclosure with smoke-sealed doors (see Figure 4.4). Corridors which provide for escape in two directions do not normally require a fire resisting enclosure (however the specific requirements should be checked against the appropriate code).

4.3.8   Facilities for people with disabilities

To ensure the safe escape of people with disabilities from buildings it is essential to consider both management and design issues.

It should always be remembered that people with disabilities should be fully evacuated from the building during an escape and that suitable plans be provided. It is not appropriate for the designer or management to rely on the fire service to facilitate their escape; the fire service should be considered as a back-up.

Where refuges are provided within a stair or lobby then these should be used in conjunction with a pre-prepared escape plan. Fire marshals should be designated to assist people with disabilities in their descent down the stair. The width of the stair should take account of the possible need to carry down people with certain disabilities. Suitable means of communication should be provided within the stair.

Where a firefighting shaft or evacuation lift is provided it should be equipped with a suitable means of communication and signage for disabled people to ensure that they will be recognized as a method of escape. The area adjacent to the lift should be suitably protected and designated as a safe zone or refuge area. These larger areas can be used as safe areas for a number of disabled people if necessary.

Often the main focus of provision for escape for people with disabilities is towards wheelchair users. However there are many other groups of people that find it difficult to escape and their needs should be considered, both in the design and the management of a building. These groups and their requirements are as follows:

(*a*)   Mobility-impaired people and people able to manage only a few steps in an emergency:

— suitable continuous handrails on steps

— suitable goings and risers of stairs

— suitable places to rest along the escape route

— early warning

— knowledge of the most appropriate direction to travel.

(*b*)   Visually-impaired and blind people:

— suitable continuous handrails on steps

— tactile and visual markings

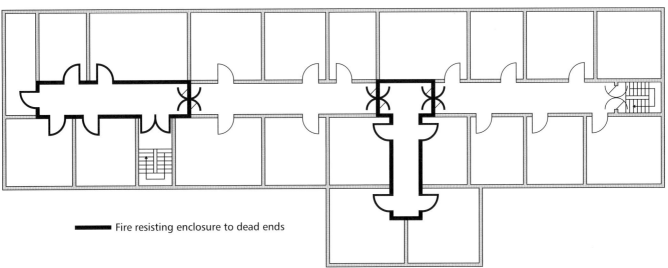

Figure 4.4 Fire protection to dead-end corridor

— clear information

— wide escape routes to facilitate assistance.

(c) Hearing-impaired and deaf people:

— visual indication that there is an emergency

— clear written information.

(d) People with mobility impairments resulting from asthma/heart disease/pregnancy etc:

— smoke free protected routes

— places to rest en-route

— wide escape routes to facilitate assistance

(e) People with learning difficulty and cognitive disabilities:

— identification of escape routes

— clear information.

4.3.9 Lifts

It is common practice to avoid the use of lifts for evacuation purposes unless they are specifically designated as such, and have been designed and constructed for the evacuation of people with disabilities and/or hospital patients. This is because of the potential dangers of smoke ingress into the lift, loss of power and the possibility of discharging at the fire floor.

Whilst it is not recommended in current codes, in certain types of building, particularly high-rise buildings and those with deep basements, it may be advantageous to use suitably designed and constructed lifts in the evacuation of the less physically able members of the population, as well as people with disabilities. BS 5588: Part 8[4] and section 5 of CIBSE Guide D: *Transportation systems in buildings*[6] provide guidance on the design and construction of lifts for the evacuation of people with disabilities. At present there is no authoritative guidance available in the UK on the use and management of lifts for means of escape, other than for their use by people with disabilities. However, guidance on the use of lifts for the evacuation of high-rise buildings is available in NFPA 101[5]. Human factors in the use of lifts for egress are considered in a paper by Pauls et al.[8]

4.3.10 Escalators

For some facilities (e.g. underground stations), escalators provide the primary means of escape and there may be other situations where the use of escalators may be of assistance in the evacuation process. However, it is essential to ensure that escalators (or open stairways) used for means of escape will not discharge people into an area likely to be affected by fire nor that they may be closed off in the early stages of a fire by a shutter operated by a fire alarm or smoke detector.

Current codes do not recognise the use of escalators as part of the means of escape, but if an escalator discharges to an area containing only a very limited fire load (e.g. a well-controlled entrance lobby), then it may be feasible to accept an escalator as an exit route. This is advantageous

as people will, in any case, tend to use routes such as these with which they are familiar. In these circumstances, the escalators leading to the exit could be maintained in operation. When assessing the capacity of an escalator, it should be assumed that, unless a secure power supply is provided, the mechanism is stationary.

The riser and tread dimensions of escalators are not the same as for stairs and movement is not as easy. However, they are often used in the stationery mode and, in these circumstances, the flow capacity may be taken as 56 persons per minute per metre width (measured between innermost part of the handrails). (This figure was obtained from London Underground Ltd.)

4.3.11 Mechanised walkways

Mechanised walkways are generally accepted for means of escape but their capacity is normally assessed on the assumption that they are stationary.

4.3.12 Other measures

When designing for means of escape consideration should be given to the provision of other supporting measures that are described more fully in other sections of the guide.

— fire alarms

— exit and directional signage

— emergency lighting

— automatic fire detection.

These measures are considered in detail in section 6 of this Guide.

4.4 Fire safety engineering design approaches

The recommendations presented in the previous sections reflect the recommendations of prescriptive codes that have historically proved to be effective in ensuring the safety of building occupants. However, many of the prescriptive recommendations do not have a sound scientific basis and do not necessarily provide the optimum solution.

The traditional codes prescribe travel distances and exit widths etc. but make no mention of the time required to escape. However, in reality the escape process is time-related.

For an escape design to be successful the time available before untenable conditions occur must be greater than the time required for escape. This can be written as:

$$\text{ASET} > \text{RSET} \tag{4.4}$$

where ASET is the available safe escape time (i.e. the time from ignition to the onset of untenable conditions) and RSET is the required safe escape time (i.e. the time following ignition after which all the occupants are able to leave the fire affected space and reach a place of safety).

The evaluation of ASET is covered in other sections of this guide (see sections 7 and 10). Some methods for estimating RSET are described below.

The basic equation used to describe the escape from a building or space is as follows:

$$t_{det} + t_a + t_{pre} + t_{trav} = t_{esc} = \text{RSET} \qquad (4.5)$$

where t_{det} is the time from ignition to detection by an automatic system or the first occupant (s), t_a is the time from detection to a general alarm being given (s), t_{pre} is the pre-movement time of the occupants (this may be expressed as a distribution of times for the population or may be represented by a single representative value) (s), t_{trav} is the travel time of the occupants (this may be represented by a distribution of individual times or a single value that is representative of the whole population) (s).

This general approach is illustrated in Figure 4.5. The calculation of t_{det} is described in section 10.6.3 and t_a represents the delay (if any) between activation of a fire detector and the alarm being broadcast. The factors influencing and the methods of determining tenability limits, pre-movement times (t_{pre}) and travel times (t_{trav}) are described below.

4.4.1 Tenability limits for design

Whilst escaping from a fire-affected building, the occupants should not be subjected to undue hazard as a result of smoke or heat. Escape routes can be protected from the effects of fire by passive measures (e.g. enclosure of corridors or stairs with fire resisting construction) or active systems (e.g. smoke control) or a combination of passive and active systems.

The following subsections give suggested design limits for short term exposure (i.e. before the occupants are able to enter a protected route or escape to open air). Conditions within protected routes and refuge areas should not generally approach these values.

4.4.1.1 Smoke

The smoke produced from typical building contents will normally cause loss of adequate visibility before debilitating toxic conditions occur. It is therefore usual to design to ensure adequate visibility is maintained and the toxic impact of smoke can usually be neglected. However, the impact of combustion products from any unusually toxic materials should be checked.

Whilst travelling within a fire affected space and before reaching a protected escape route or other place of relative safety the occupants should not be subject to conditions that will result in a loss of visibility and the following design limits are suggested:

(a) Maintain a layer of air relatively clear of smoke above eye level (typical design values are 2 to 3.5 m above floor level, depending on building geometry and smoke modelling technique), or,

(b) Ensure that the visibility through any smoke will be sufficient for exits to be identified and reached without undue hindrance. (Generally people are reluctant to proceed through smoke if the visibility is less than 8 m[9].

Where there is a clearly defined escape route a visibility of 10 m (equivalent to an optical density per metre of 0.1 dB·m⁻¹) is normally considered reasonable.

In public buildings and large spaces where wayfinding may be difficult, greater visibility distances may be required to ensure that exit routes can be identified, see sections 10.7.5 and 10.7.8.

4.4.1.2 Heat

For the purposes of escape design, the maximum temperature of inhaled air should not exceed 120 °C. Note that under the conditions of high humidity, that may result from firefighting activities (including sprinkler operation), the maximum survivable temperatures will be considerably lower (approximately 60 °C).

Excessive levels of heat radiation can induce severe burns and skin pain. Prolonged exposure to a radiant heat flux

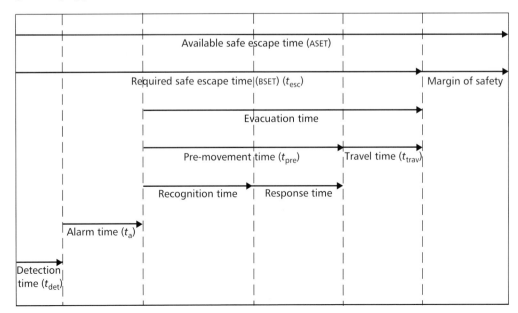

Figure 4.5 Factors involved in assessing the total escape time

exceeding 2.5 kW·m^{-2} can cause severe pain and this figure is the maximum recommended design value for short term exposure[9]. A black body radiator at a temperature of 200 °C will emit a radiant heat flux of approximately 2.5 kW·m^{-2} and therefore people should not be expected to escape below a smoke layer at a temperature greater than this.

4.5　Pre-movement times

4.5.1　Behaviour of people

Studies of behaviour in fires indicate that, generally, people do not panic nor do they act in an irrational way when judged from their perspective of the situation[10]. Their actions are, however, not always what the designer had in mind and this may result in a significant delay (pre-movement time) between an alarm being broadcast and the commencement of movement towards an exit.

Research[11] suggests the following nine principles as a model of people's behaviour:

— Deaths in large scale fires attributed to 'panic' are far more likely to have been caused by delays in people receiving information about a fire.

— Fire alarms cannot always be relied upon to prompt people to move immediately to safety.

— The start-up time (i.e. people's response to an alarm) can be more important than the time it takes to physically reach an exit.

— Much of the movement in the early stages of fires is characterised by activities such as investigation rather than escape.

— As long as an exit is not seriously obstructed, people have a tendency to move in a familiar direction, even if further away, rather than to use an unfamiliar fire escape route.

— Individuals often move towards and with group members and maintain proximity as far as possible with individuals to whom they have emotional ties.

— Fire exit signs are not always noticed (or recalled) and may not overcome difficulties in orientation and wayfinding in a complex architectural layout.

— People are often prepared, if necessary, to try to move through smoke despite the dangers that this may present.

— People's ability to move towards exits may vary considerably (e.g. a young, fit adult as opposed to a person who is elderly or who has a disability).

4.5.2　Occupancy types

The mobility of occupants, their familiarity with their surroundings and the ease of wayfinding posed by the setting can have an effect upon the time required to evacuate a building.

When considering the effect of different types of occupancy, the following characteristics can be significant:

(a) occupants predominantly familiar with the building and awake (e.g. offices, schools and industrial premises etc.)

(b) occupants possibly unfamiliar with the building but awake (e.g. shops, exhibitions, museums, leisure centres, other assembly buildings)

(c) occupants possibly sleeping but predominantly familiar with the building (e.g. dwellings)

(d) occupants possibly sleeping and unfamiliar with the building (hotels etc.)

(e) significant number of occupants requiring assistance (e.g. hospitals, nursing homes)

(f) occupants held in custody (e.g. prisons).

Access to buildings for people with disabilities is now required in most new buildings and increasingly in existing buildings. Therefore when designing for escape an appropriate proportion of people with disabilities should be assumed in all of the above categories. In multiple-use buildings the effect of one use on another must be considered to ensure that means of escape from one use will not be prejudiced by another, e.g. where one use will be closed down outside trading hours, independent means of escape may have to be provided for another, more continuous use. Similarly, where security requirements might compromise the availability of exits, suitable measures must be taken to ensure that exits are available to all occupants under emergency conditions.

4.6　Evaluation of total pre-movement time

Research[10] indicates that the pre-movement time can be as important as the time that it takes to travel to and through an exit.

For each occupant the time taken from the first cue indicating the presence of fire and the start of movement towards an exit represents the total pre-movement time for the occupant and will be influenced by factors such as:

— the spatial location of the occupant

— the location of the fire and the pattern of fire growth

— the visibility of the fire in relation to the spatial location of the occupant (i.e. those nearest to the fire with clear visual access are more likely to respond quickly)

— the type of cue or warning received (voice alarm, bells, smell of smoke etc.).

This pre-movement time can be subdivided into two parts: recognition time and response time (see also Figure 4.5).

4.6.1   Recognition time

The recognition time is the period after an alarm or other cue is evident but before the occupants begin to respond. During the recognition period the occupants continue with their current activities. The length of the recognition period can be extremely variable, depending upon factors such as the type of building, the nature of the occupants, their familiarity with the alarm system and fire safety management procedures.

The recognition time ends when the occupants accept that there is a need to respond and take some action (e.g. putting on a coat before leaving).

4.6.2   Response time

The response time is the period after the occupants recognise the alarms or cues and begin to respond to them, but before they begin to move towards an exit. As with the recognition period the response time may range from a few seconds to many minutes, depending upon the circumstances.

During the response period the occupants cease their normal activities and may engage in a variety of activities in response to the potential emergency.

Examples of activities undertaken during the response period include:

— investigation to determine the source, reality or importance of a fire alarm

— stopping machinery/production

— securing money

— searching for children and other family members

— putting on coats

— collecting belongings

— first aid firefighting etc.

4.6.3   Design approach

It is possible to introduce both recognition and response behaviour into an evacuation model to estimate the total pre-movement time but there is a lack of data and the range of possible behaviours are difficult to quantify.

The most practical approach is therefore is to derive pre-movement time distributions from staged evacuations or the investigation of real incidents.

Pre-movement times may vary considerably for different individuals or groups of individuals both within an enclosure and in different enclosures. An important factor is the degree of visual access afforded . For example, in an open plan setting such as a theatre auditorium, the distribution of pre-movement times is likely to be narrow and everyone will start to move at about the same time. In a multiple enclosure setting, such as a hotel, there is likely to be a wide distribution of pre-movement times characterised by a 'tail' of late starters. Those in the enclosure containing the fire may complete the evacuation process

before those in other enclosures recognise the need for action.

4.6.4   Pre-movement time of the first few occupants

The time at which the first few occupants start to move towards an exit is particularly important because the evacuation process does not begin until this time is reached. The duration of the pre-movement stage will be very dependent upon the occupancy type, the nature of the warning system and the implementation of the emergency management procedures.

In situations where occupants are awake and familiar with a building, and well trained in the emergency procedures (e.g. a well managed office), then the pre-movement time of the first occupants to respond can be very short (less than 20 seconds). In occupancies such as shops or assembly buildings (where the occupants are awake but unfamiliar with their surroundings) this phase of pre-movement time can also be very short, providing that staff are well trained. A voice alarm can significantly reduce the pre-movement time in settings where the occupants are unfamiliar with the emergency procedures.

These very short times to first response are typical of evacuations observed in a range of occupancies in these categories. Where fire safety management is not of a high standard, then the pre-movement time can be much longer and is unpredictable. Good fire safety management is therefore an essential requirement whether the escape provisions have been designed on the basis of prescriptive codes or fire safety engineering principles.

Where occupants may be asleep the pre-movement time is likely to be much longer, irrespective of the warning and fire safety management system used. Even for very well designed and managed hotels pre-movement times for some individuals may extend towards 30 minutes (e.g. staff need to identify the location of guests who may have taken sleeping pills or be under the influence of alcohol.)

4.6.5   Pre-movement time distribution

Once the first few occupants have begun to move, the pre-movement times for the remainder of the occupants in an enclosure tend to follow a logarithmic–normal frequency-time distribution[12].

Figure 4.6 illustrates typical pre-movement time distributions in well managed open plan occupancies.The delay period before the first few occupants move, is typically followed by a rapid increase in the proportion of the population entering their travel phase. There is then typically an extended 'tail', during which the last few occupants begin to travel.

Pre-movement time distributions are likely to be much wider in multiple enclosure buildings than in single enclosures and will be influenced by the type of warning and management system. Generally, short and narrow pre-movement time distributions occur where the occupants are awake and familiar with their surroundings. In well managed single enclosures the pre-movement time should

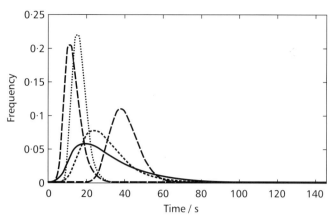

Figure 4.6 Pre-movement distributions from a number of studies[12]

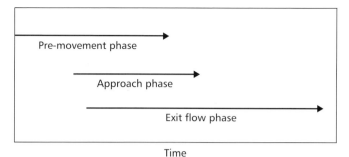

(a) High occupancy (e.g. shop)

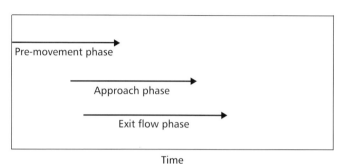

(b) Low occupancy (e.g. warehouse)

Figure 4.7 Overlap between phases of the evacuation process

be less than one minute. In multiple occupancy sleeping scenarios the pre-movement time distribution is likely to be much wider (e.g. 10 to 30 minutes).

It is important to recognize that whilst the total pre-movement time can constitute a large proportion of the total evacuation time it is not appropriate to simply add total pre-movement and total travel times as this will often over-estimate the total evacuation time.

For spaces with a high occupant density the initial period before the first individuals start to move is the important pre-movement factor as after this period the travel time is likely to dominate.

Where occupant densities are low the total evacuation time will be equivalent to the sum of the total pre-movement time and the travel time.

This overlap between pre-movement and travel times is illustrated by the timelines in Figure 4.7.

Table 4.5 provides guide values for pre-movement times where a good standard of fire safety management is implemented.

4.7   Travel time

The travel time is the time required to reach and pass through an exit into a place of safety.

Once the population of a space have begun to move towards the exits the travel time can be estimated, taking account of the following parameters:

—   number and distribution of occupants

—   speed of travel towards exit

—   rate of flow through restrictions (doorways, stairs etc.).

An analysis of these factors can provide an indication of the minimum time in which a room, floor or building could be evacuated if the occupants were to react immediately and appropriately in response to a warning of fire.

Calculations will indicate whether it is the distance to be travelled or the width of the escape route that is the limiting factor in determining the travel time. The

Table 4.5 Suggested guide values of pre-movement times (well-managed environment)

Occupancy type	Pre-movement time / min
Residential:	
— hotel bedrooms	30
— university hall of residence	20
— residential college	20
Institutional and health:	
— day centre, surgery, clinic, health centre	3
Education:	
— school	3
— nursery school	3
— university/college	3
— adult training centre	3
Offices:	
— office	1
— bank, building society, post office	2
Shops:	
— small shop	2
— department store	3
— supermarket	2
— shopping complex	5

number and distribution of occupants will usually be evaluated in a similar manner whether adopting the prescriptive or fire safety engineering approach to escape route design.

4.7.1   Time of travel to an exit

The speed of travel and the crowd density are related; at high crowd densities the ability to walk freely is restricted and hence the speed of travel will be reduced. At densities of approximately 4 person·m^{-2}, movement can become very slow and lead to anxiety and discomfort. Where occupant density is relatively low (i.e. 2 m^2 per person or more), 1.2 m·s⁻¹ can be taken as an average walking speed for design purposes.

When descending stairways the typical free movement speed is reduced to 1.1 m·s⁻¹ giving a vertical component of velocity of the order of 0.75 m·s⁻¹.

On the flat, provided adequate space and accessible doors are provided, wheelchair users can evacuate quickly without causing obstruction[13]. However, persons using walking aids require much more time. This varies widely but for design purposes it may be assumed that they can move at about half the speed of the average person, say 0.6 m·s⁻¹.

Once people start to evacuate, the time taken for them to reach a place of safety will usually be dominated by the time taken to pass through restrictions such as doorways, which are traditionally designed to accommodate all of the occupants in a nominal period of 2½ minutes. As it will rarely take as much as 2½ minutes to travel to an exit, the rate of arrival is likely to be greater than the doorway can accommodate and a queue will form. This is implicit in the established prescriptive codes.

In most buildings with a high occupant density the occupants will be distributed throughout the accommodation and those people located nearest to an exit will have a very short travel time of only a few seconds. Individuals who are located some distance from an exit will clearly take longer. However, unless the time taken to move to the exit exceeds the notional evacuation time (typically 2½ minutes in prescriptive codes), it is likely that the individuals will still have to queue on arrival at the exit doorway. Therefore, in many cases unless the distance to be travelled exceeds 150 m it is unlikely to have a significant effect on the overall evacuation time, i.e. 150 m can be travelled in about two minutes at a speed of 1.2 m·s⁻¹.

However, it may be desirable to restrict distances so that the location of exits can be readily identified and so that those who are only able to walk slowly are not put at risk.

In the case of buildings over a certain height and floor area, provision for access and facilities for firefighting may dictate the maximum distance between stairs. This is considered in section 9.

In large open areas travel distances substantially in excess of the 45 m, as typically specified in prescriptive codes, should be acceptable provided that the exits are clearly visible and accessible.

In areas where the route to an exit is unavoidably tortuous, a good wayfinding system should be provided and it may be necessary to provide exits more frequently than in large open areas to ensure that the occupants can readily locate the exit route. The use of wayfinding systems incorporating illuminated floor tracks may be of considerable assistance in guiding people to the nearest exit (see section 4.8.10).

Where stairs must be negotiated prior to reaching a storey exit, allowance should be made for the slightly slower speed of travel on stairs (see earlier in this section and the effect on any people with disabilities, e.g. wheelchair users.

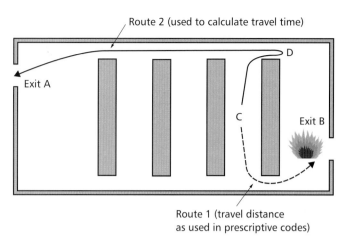

Figure 4.8 Measurement of travel distances

A fire could occur adjacent to an exit so, when estimating the time required to reach a storey exit, one of the exit routes should be assumed to be unavailable. This results in the need for distances to be travelled (and hence estimates of travel times) to be measured in a different way to that used in prescriptive codes which always measure travel distance to the nearest exit. Figure 4.8 illustrates the measurement of travel distances.

Figure 4.8 illustrates the traditional method of measuring travel distances (route 1) and the method that should be used in a fire engineering assessment of travel time (route 2). When designing in accordance with the traditional prescriptive codes, the travel distance is measured along the the shortest route of travel to the nearest exit (taking account of any obstructions). From point C, the shortest route to exit B is route 1. With the exception of hospitals, there is usually no limit placed on the distance of travel to an alternative exit (exit A in this instance).

When carrying out a fire safety engineering assessment, it is necessary to establish the time required to travel to an exit. In a sparsely occupied office space where the fire location is obscured (e.g. by high racking or shelving), some of the occupants may move towards the nearest exit, which may be blocked by the fire. In these circumstances the calculation of travel time should take account of the actual route that may be taken before the fire becomes visible. Route 2 illustrates this concept, where an occupant initially moves towards the nearest exit (exit B) but only on reaching point D realises that the exit is blocked by fire. It is then necessary to retrace part of the route and leave through exit A.

The measurement of travel distances or calculation of travel times should either be on the basis of the worst case condition or take account of all the possible occupant locations.

4.7.2   Exit widths

4.7.2.1   General

Traditional prescriptive codes set exit width requirements based upon the anticipated population. The time required to pass through the exits is not explicitly stated but is normally based upon a notional evacuation time.

This notional time does not take account of the delays that are likely to occur before people respond to an alarm. The notional time implicit in most guidance is 2½ minutes although this may be extended to up to 8 minutes in open air sports stadia.

Whilst prescriptive guidance on exit widths has historically proved to be adequate there is no scientific basis for the original choice of 2½ minutes.

In many cases where smoke filling times are prolonged (due to a high ceiling or the provision of smoke ventilation etc.) exit widths based on longer evacuation times may be acceptable. For example, the maximum notional exit time implicit in BS 5588: Part 10[4] (which deals with fire safety in shopping centres) is 5 minutes. This can be justified in terms of the smoke control and sprinkler protection provided in large centres. However, it is essential to realise that, due to the characteristic delay before people start to move and deviations in movement from the optimum escape route, the notional travel time can be much less than the actual time required to evacuate a space.

4.7.2.2 Exit flows

Once evacuation has started towards the exits the main physical constraint on the time taken to evacuate will usually be the width of doorway openings, corridors and stairs. For design purposes it may be assumed that the maximum flow rate of persons through a doorway or level corridor is given by the equation 4.6 below.

For openings and corridors of width 1.1 m and greater:

$$F_p = 1.333\,w \qquad (4.6)$$

where F_p is the number of persons passing through the opening in one second (person·s^{-1}), w is the width of the opening or corridor (m) after allowing for any obstructions.

Assuming a notional exit time of 2½ minutes, equation 4.6 is equivalent to the method of determining exit widths given in standard UK guidance, i.e. that the capacity of an exit (at least 1.1 m wide) is 1 person per 5 mm of exit width.

It should be noted that the flow rate through an exit may be reduced if there is downstream congestion (i.e. if the occupant density significantly exceeds 2 person·m^{-2}).

4.7.2.3 Stairway capacity

It is generally assumed that a protected stair provides a place of relative safety where people may remain for the duration of the evacuation process. However in very tall buildings it may take up to an hour to descend the stairway and reach open air.

Despite the considerable time that the complete evacuation may take, a stair must have sufficient capacity to enable all of the occupants of a fire affected floor to enter within a short period of time.

The maximum number of people that can be physically accommodated by an escape stair in a given time depends on three main factors:

(a)   the width of the storey exits at each level

(b)   the width of the final exit

(c)   the number of persons that may be accommodated within the stair enclosure.

The doors opening into the stair (see (a) above) should be sized to accommodate the anticipated number of people at each level. However, if the stair is congested with large numbers of people descending from the floors above, it may not be possible to enter the stair, even if the individual storey exits are of adequate width.

During the evacuation process people will be entering the stair at a number of levels and some will be leaving through the final exit. Therefore the stair must have sufficient floor space to accommodate those persons remaining within the stair enclosure (i.e. the difference between the number who have entered and the number who have left the stair).

The maximum number of people that can be accommodated within a stairway at any one time is given by:

$$N_{c(max)} = p\,A\,S \qquad (4.7)$$

where $N_{c(max)}$ is the maximum number of people that can be accommodated within a stairway at any one time, p is the maximum occupant density of the stair (person·m^{-2}), A is the horizontal area of stair and landings per storey (m^2) and S is the number of storeys.

The maximum density of people who can be accommodated on stairs and landings without suffering extreme discomfort[4] is approximately 3.5 person·m^{-2}. The number of persons leaving the stair is limited primarily by the width of the final exit and can be obtained using the calculation described in section 4.6.2.2.

The exit capacity of a stairway can therefore be estimated as follows:

$$N_{in(max)} = 1.333\,W_s\,t + 3.5\,A\,(S-1) \qquad (4.8)$$

where $N_{in(max)}$ is the maximum number of people able to enter the stair within a specified period, W_s is width of stair (m), t is the time available for escape (s), A is the horizontal area of stair and landings per storey (m^2) and S is the number of storeys served.

Equation 4.8 gives similar (but not necessarily identical) results to those given in tables in BS 5588[4] and Approved Document B[2]. These documents give stairway capacities which are based upon the same general principle but using a simplified calculation procedure see section 4.3.4.

The *SFPE Handbook*[9] indicates that the stairway provisions presented in BS 5588[4] are not adequate to provide for escape within the notional period of 2½ minutes. However, there is no evidence to suggest that stairway widths designed on this basis are inadequate when used in conjunction with the population densities and fire protection standards given in these codes.

For the purposes of a fire engineering design, when it is important to have an accurate assessment of the total number of persons that a stairway is able to accommodate in a specified period, it is recommended that an approach similar to that described in the *SFPE Handbook*[9] be adopted and that the following conditions are assumed:

— an occupant density (p) in the stair of 2 person·m^{-2}

— a flow of 1.2 person·s^{-1}·m^{-1} of effective stair width, where the effective stair width, W_e, is as shown in Figure 4.9.

The acceptance of the stair is then given by the following equation:

$$N_{in(max)} = 1.2\, t\, W_e + p\, A\, (S - 1) \qquad (4.9)$$

where A is the horizontal area of stair and landings per storey (m^2), S is the number of storeys served, t is the available exiting time (s) and W_e is the effective stairway width (m).

Note that equation 4.9 gives the maximum acceptance of the stair. The actual flow into the stair may be constrained if the storey exits are too narrow.

Note: stairs which extend vertically more than 30 m should not exceed a width of 1.4 m unless they are provided with a central handrail in which case they should be at least 1.8 m wide. This is because in very tall buildings people prefer to stay within reach of a handrail when making prolonged descent, hence the centre part of a wide stair is little used and could be hazardous.

4.7.3 Evacuation simulation models

There are a number of computer software packages available which enable the psychological response and movement of people under emergency conditions to be explored. Features of some of these models include the ability to accept computer-aided design (CAD) generated files for building designs, the evaluation of travel distances, population density calculations, and real-time animation of people movement. Such models are becoming increasingly sophisticated in their ability to represent different aspects of evacuation movement such as the physical parameters of individual motion and the effects of fire and smoke on the occupants. However they are still very dependent for their accuracy on the assumptions made regarding human behaviour and people flow characteristics. There is a lack of research data regarding the behaviour of merging flows of people and the accuracy of such models is severely limited by this lack of data.

The sophistication of the graphical output of some of these models often exceeds the underlying physical model and the user should be aware of the intrinsic assumptions made within the software and these should be presented along with the results of the simulation.

4.7.4 Design safety margin

Calculation procedures and design assumptions should be chosen on a conservative basis (worst credible case) and, if this is done, an additional safety margin should not be necessary.

4.8 Information and wayfinding systems

4.8.1 General

It is important to emphasise the role played by effective information, warning and wayfinding systems, including the architectural design of a setting, in achieving an adequate level of life safety.

4.8.2 Informative fire warning systems

Informative fire warning (IFW) systems have electronic visual displays to supplement other forms of alarm and such systems can significantly reduce pre-movement time (see section 4.5). A BRE report[15] provides an assessment of their effectiveness.

4.8.3 Signs

Prescriptive codes recommend that exits are marked with pictographic exit signs depicting a running man. These signs should be located so that they are not obscured by the building contents. BS 5499[16] deals with the design and construction of fire safety signs.

In certain circumstances, e.g. where direct line of sight of an exit is not possible and doubt may exist as to its position, a direction sign (or series of signs) should be provided. There are also requirements for other notices, e.g. 'FIRE DOOR — KEEP SHUT' on doors.

Where escape lighting is required all exit and exit routes signs should be illuminated in the event of failure of the

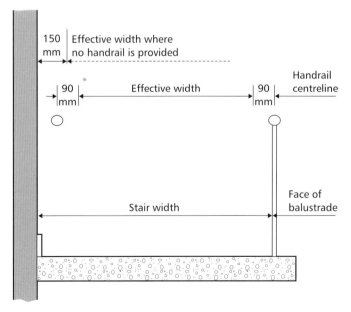

Effective width based on SFPE Handbook[9]

Figure 4.9 Measurement of the effective width of an escape stair (fire engineering analysis only)

normal lighting. This may be achieved by one of the following:

— externally illuminated signs

— internally illuminated signs

— self-luminous signs.

See section 6.10.4 for illumination of exit signs.

4.8.4   Wayfinding systems

In situations where wayfinding could be difficult, serious consideration should be given to the advantages offered by continuous luminous wayfinding systems and directional markers over conventional high-level emergency lighting[17,18].

References

1   The Building Regulations 2000 Statutory Instrument 2000 No. 2531 (London: The Stationery Office) (2000)

2   *Fire safety* Building Regulations 2000 Approved Document B (London: The Stationery Office) (2000) (ISBN 1 85112 351 2)

3   *Scottish Executive Technical Standards* (6th Amendment) (Edinburgh: Scottish Executive) (2001)

4   BS 5588: *Fire precautions in the design, construction and use of buildings*: Part 11: 1997: *Code of practice for shops, offices, industrial, storage and other similar buildings* (London: British Standards Institution) (dates as indicated)

5   *Code for safety to life from fire in buildings and structures* NFPA 101 (Quincey MA: National Fire Protection Association) (2000)

6   *Transportation systems in buildings* CIBSE Guide D (London: Chartered Institution of Building Services Engineers) (2000)

7   *Phased evacuation from office buildings* LDSA Fire Safety Guide No. 3 (Bromley: London District Surveyors Association) (1990)

8   Pauls J, Gatfield A and Juillet E Elevator use for egress: the human-factors problems and prospects *Proc. Symp. Elevators and Fire, New York, February 1991* (1991) (reprinted in *Elevator World* 60–68 (1992))

9   *SFPE Handbook of Fire Protection Engineering* (third edition) (Bethesda, MD: Society of Fire Protection Engineers) (2002)

10   Sime J D *Escape behaviour in fires and evacuations* in Stollard P and Johnson L (eds.) *Design against fire — an introduction to fire safety engineering design* (London: Chapman and Hall) (1994)

11   Sime J D *Human Behaviour in Fires Summary — Report Central Fire Brigades Advisory Council* Joint Committee on Fire Research Report No. 45 (London: HMSO) (1992)

12   Purser D A and Bensilum M *Quantification of escape behaviour during experimental evacuations* (Garston: Building Research Establishment) (1999)

13   Shields T J *Fire and disabled people in buildings* BRE Report BR 231 (Garston: Building Research Establishment) (1993)

14   BS 7974: 2001: *Application of fire safety engineering principles to the design of buildings. Code of practice* (London: British Standards Institution) (2001)

15   Wishart J and Canter D *Assessment of informative fire warning systems — a simulation study* BRE Report (Garston: Building Research Establishment) (1985)

16   BS 5499: *Fire safety signs, notice and graphic symbols*: Part 1: 2002: *Specification for geometric shapes, colours and layout*; Part 2: 1986: *Specification for self-luminous fire safety signs*; Part 3: 1990: *Specification for internally-illuminated fire safety signs*; Part 4: 2000: *Code of practice for escape route signing*; Part 5: 2002: *Signs with specific safety meanings*; Part 11: 2002: *Water safety signs* (London: British Standards Institution) (dates as indicated)

17   Webber G M B and Aizelwood C E *Emergency wayfinding lighting systems* BRE Information Paper IP 1/93 (Garston: Building Research Establishment) (1993)

18   Webber G M B and Aizelwood C E *Emergency lighting systems in smoke* BRE Information Paper IP 17/94 (Garston: Building Research Establishment) (1994)

5 Compartmentation and spread of flame

5.1 Introduction

A fire will progress through various stages from ignition to fully developed unless action is taken to extinguish it. The development of a fire is represented graphically in Figure 5.1.

A key aspect of the development of a fire is 'flashover'. As a fire starts to grow, flames will reach the ceiling of the room or space and then spread laterally under the ceiling. These flames will radiate heat down onto the contents of the space, heating them to a temperature at which they will start to undergo thermal degradation accompanied by the evolution of flammable decomposition products. Subject to sufficient oxygen being available these decomposition products will ignite such that the whole space is then filled by burning gas at which stage flashover is said to occur. Prior to flashover, a fire can be related to individual items contained within the space but after flashover the whole space will be involved in the fire.

Where there is insufficient oxygen in a space for flashover to occur there will be a build-up of hot flammable gases. If air is admitted to a space under these conditions by, for example, a window breaking or a door being opened, then an immediate flashover can occur.

Conditions for flashover are considered in section 10.5.4. Flashover can be very dangerous since it can occur with explosive force.

Up to flashover it is possible to restrict the rate of growth of a fire by controlling flame spread, heat release and ease of ignition but once flashover has occurred it is necessary to restrict the spread of fire by containment. This containment of fire is known as compartmentation.

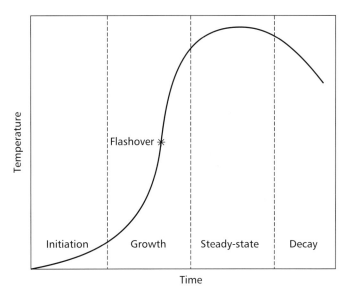

Figure 5.1 Stages of development of a fire

In certain circumstances, with low fire loads, flashover will not occur. Fire resistance is normally relevant to post-flashover fires only.

Traditionally, compartmentation is a significant aspect of the fire safety arrangements required in a building. In principle it is the sub-division of a building into a series of fire-tight cells. These cells are generally constructed to resist complete burn-out of the contents of the cell.

5.2 Compartmentation and statutory controls

5.2.1 Post War Building Studies

Standards for compartmentation have been specified in a wide range of guidance documents in support of legislation. Much of this guidance has been based on the recommendations of the report on fire grading of buildings originally published in 1946 as part of the Post War Building Studies[1]. This study considered both the extent to which buildings need to be compartmented and the standard to which the compartments need to be enclosed.

In this study buildings were classified as 'high', 'moderate' or 'low' fire loads based on the heat content per unit floor area and 'normal' or 'abnormal' risk according to the likelihood of fire occurring. Recommendations for limits on compartment sizes for the different classifications were then developed. The recommended sizes of compartments could be doubled for buildings protected by sprinkler systems.

The classification of buildings into high, medium and low fire loads was also used to identify the standards required for the walls, floors etc. forming the compartment boundaries and to prevent structural collapse under fire conditions. This was defined in terms of 'fire resistance' which was measured in a standard test whereby a representative element of a building structure was exposed to standard heating conditions in a furnace.

The relationship between fire resistance and fire load was based on work carried out in the USA in the 1920s. This work involved burning a range of fire loads in a purpose-built structure, measuring the temperature in the structure and comparing the areas under the time–temperature curves with those for the standard test furnace.

5.2.2 Building Regulations

When the Building Regulations[2] were introduced in 1965 the standards adopted for compartmentation were essentially those recommended in the Post War Building

Studies[1]. However the Building Regulations were concerned only with the safety of people whereas the Post War Building Studies were also concerned with damage to property. This meant that the standards required by the Building Regulations were in many instances difficult to justify in respect of the purpose of the Regulations.

When the Building Regulations 1985[3] were introduced the prescriptive standards required by the earlier Regulations were incorporated, largely unchanged, into Approved Document B[4]. The recommendations of Approved Document B were reviewed as part of the process leading to the introduction of the Building Regulations 1991[5] and a revised edition of Approved Document B[6]. This review included bringing the recommendations for compartmentation more into line with the stated objectives of the Regulations, i.e. the health and safety of people in and around the building. This resulted in compartment sizes being defined much more in terms of floor area only, greater scope being given for increased compartment sizes where sprinklers are to be used and reduced standards of fire resistance.

Compartmentation is generally required by regulations in order to:

— reduce the chance of fires becoming large, on the basis that large fires are more dangerous, not only to occupants and fire service personnel, but to people in the vicinity of the building

— reduce the number of occupants immediately threatened by a fire

— protect those occupants required to remain in a building while a fire is in progress (e.g. blocks of flats, buildings using concepts of zoned or phased or horizontal evacuation)

— reduce the risk of fire spread to adjacent buildings by restricting the area of unprotected openings which can radiate heat onto an adjacent building.

Approved Document B was further revised in 2000[7].

5.2.3   British Standards

There are a number of British Standards which give recommendations related to compartmentation. The most important of these is the BS 5588 series[8]. The various parts of this standard do not in general give recommendations for fire resistance periods for different types of buildings but refer instead to Approved Document B[7]. They provide a substantial amount of guidance on the technical issues related to compartmentation such as need for dampers, fire rated ductwork, firestopping etc.

However, it is intended to replace the existing BS 5588 series with a new set of standards, BS 9999[9]. Unlike the BS 5588 series, the new standards are likely to contain extensive recommendations for fire resistance periods for buildings. This is discussed in more detail below.

5.3   Property protection

Apart from the safety of people, compartmentation plays an important role in reducing damage to property in the event of a fire. Standards for property protection have historically been similar to those required to meet the Building Regulations.

However, as the recommendations contained in Approved Document B[7] have become more directly concerned with the objectives of the Building Regulations, i.e. life safety rather than property protection, the Loss Prevention Council has produced separate guidance on behalf of the insurance industry[10]. That publication recommends, in a number of instances, standards much higher than those contained in Approved Document B.

5.4   Compartment boundaries

5.4.1   General

For compartmentation to be effective the enclosing boundaries such as walls and floors must be able to resist the spread of fire. This requires that:

— all enclosing surfaces must have an appropriate standard of fire resistance

— all junctions of constructional elements are effectively sealed

— all holes are fire-stopped

— ducts penetrating boundary elements are provided with fire dampers or are also fire resisting

— openings are protected by self-closing fire doors or fire resisting shutters.

Guidance on fire-stopping, fire resisting walls and floors and the protection of services passing through compartment boundaries is contained in Approved Document B[7] and BS 5588[8].

Fire dampers and fire resisting shutters are usually actuated by fusible links. It should be noted that this method of actuation is effective at controlling fire spread only and not the spread of smoke. Large quantities of smoke can pass through an opening protected by a fire damper or shutter during the early stages of a fire before a fusible link-actuated mechanism will operate.

5.4.2   Measurement of fire resistance

The enclosing boundaries to a compartment are usually required to meet a specified period of fire resistance. Fire resistance is a property of each element of the building construction and is measured in accordance with the procedures given in a British Standard test. The test methodology has been developed over a number of years and is currently specified in BS 476: Part 20[11].

It should be noted that there is no direct correlation between exposure times in fire resistance tests and exposure times in real fires because the rates of heat release and mechanisms of heat transfer are different between test fires in furnaces and actual fires.

The test essentially involves placing an element of the building structure in a furnace and exposing it to the heating curve shown in Figure 5.2.

Depending on the nature of the element of construction under test, it is given a rating in minutes depending on its ability to fulfil the following criteria:

— *loadbearing capacity*: a measure of a loadbearing elements ability to support its design load under test conditions

— *integrity*: a measure of the ability of a separating element not to develop holes etc. through which flame or hot gases can pass

— *insulation*: a measure of the ability to resist heat transmission through a separating element so as to limit temperature rise on the unexposed side such that combustible materials in contact with the unexposed side will not be ignited.

There is a wide range of published guidance on the fire resistance of different types of elements of building construction, both loadbearing and non-loadbearing[12,13].

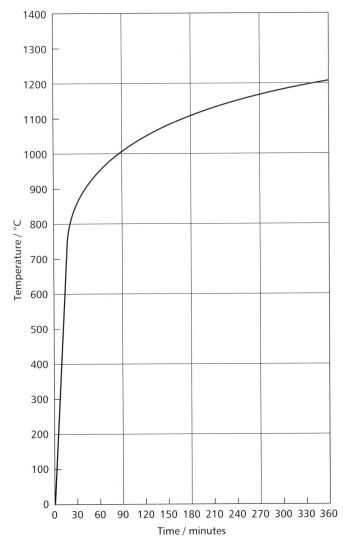

Figure 5.2 Heating conditions specified in BS 476: Part 20[11] fire resistance test (reproduced by permission of the British Standards Institution; copies of this Standard may be obtained from BSI Customer Services, 389 Chiswick High Road, London W4 4AL)

5.5 Compartmentation and modern building design

5.5.1 General

Recent developments in building design, e.g. shopping malls, sports stadia, airport terminal buildings etc. and, most notably, atrium buildings, have caused the traditional need for compartmentation of buildings to be questioned. A fundamental concept of the design of such buildings is to provide large open spaces, often much larger than the conventional limits on compartment sizes for these types of building.

In such buildings the need for compartmentation must be seen within the context of an overall fire safety strategy for the building. The role and purpose of compartmentation needs to be clearly defined and understood within this strategy. In these circumstances, it is often acceptable to develop a package of fire safety arrangements which will preclude the need for conventional standards of compartmentation. This is dependent on having a clear understanding of the objectives of the fire safety strategy for the building and how they will be achieved.

5.5.2 Compartmentation and sprinklers

The ability of fire sprinklers to control fires means that they have often been used to justify increasing the size of a compartment and/or reducing the standard of fire resistance of the enclosing boundaries.

Traditionally, compartment sizes have been allowed to be doubled where sprinklers are provided. This relationship was originally proposed in the Post War Building Studies[1]. The same recommendation was incorporated into the Building Regulations 1965[2], although its application was limited to shops. Similar increases are now allowed in other types of buildings within the provisions of Approved Document B[7].

There is no evidence to suggest that the traditional doubling of compartment size where sprinklers are provided leads to problems in practice. However, it can be unduly restrictive to have a single correlation between sprinklers and compartment size when, in practice, there are many different reasons for providing compartmentation and the possible consequences of failure can be significantly different.

The relationship between compartmentation and sprinklers should be developed as part of a fire safety strategy rather than as ad-hoc justification for one aspect of fire safety in isolation.

5.6 Structural fire protection

Structural fire protection is outside of the scope of this publication and is covered by British Standards and various publications from the Institution of Structural Engineers. However, the recommendations for structural fire protection of buildings have largely followed the same pattern as the recommendations for compartmentation and generally the same standards of fire resistance have been specified for structural fire protection as for compartmentation.

In recent years there has been a substantial body of research work carried out on structural fire protection for buildings, which also has implications for the accurate assessment of fire resistance requirements for compartmentation. This is discussed more fully in the following section.

5.7 Fire engineering approach to compartmentation

5.7.1 General

A fire engineering approach to compartmentation needs to address three questions:

— Does the building need to be compartmented?

— How big can a compartment be?

— To what standard does the compartment need to be enclosed?

The answers to the first two of these questions will be determined by the fire safety strategy for the building. Where this strategy includes compartmentation (which is not always essential) the size of the compartments will be determined by the fire safety strategy rather than by adherence to conventional prescriptive requirements, although these may provide useful guidance.

Conventionally, the standard to which the compartment is enclosed is based on the premise that the severity of a fire is determined solely by the fire load density. It has been

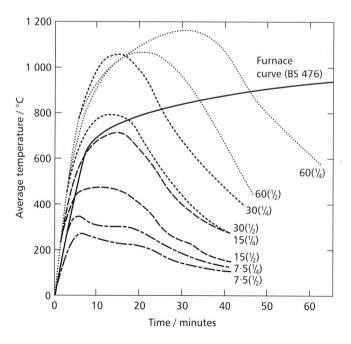

(*Note*: 60(½) means fire load 60 kg·m⁻² of floor area and ventilation 50% of one wall)

Figure 5.3 Variation of fire severity with fire load and ventilation conditions[15]

widely recognised for many years that, in many instances, the severity of a fire in an enclosed space is principally determined by the ventilation conditions (i.e. the size, number and locations of openings through which air can enter the space) as much as by the fire load density. The fire load density is more important in determining the duration of a fire once the rate of burning has been established. Some examples showing how the temperature conditions in a compartment can vary with ventilation conditions and fire load[14] are given in Figure 5.3[15].

There has been considerable research into the severity of fires in enclosed spaces and this work has been incorporated into a CIB Design Guide[16,17]. This design guide enables the standard of enclosure to be based either on a prediction of the actual severity of a fire in the space or on the concept of an 'equivalent fire resistance period'. In addition, a Eurocode has been published[18] which gives recommendations for using similar methods to assess the structural fire protection requirements in a building.

5.7.2 Severity of fires in enclosed spaces

The actual severity of a fire in a space is a complex balance of heat and mass flows into and out of a compartment, both through the openings into the compartment and through the enclosing walls and floors. Table 5.1 gives an example of how the heat produced by a fire is dissipated[17].

It can be seen from Table 5.1 that only a small proportion of the heat produced by a fire is likely to be lost through the enclosing surfaces of a room or compartment. Most of the heat is lost through the windows or other openings in the enclosing surfaces.

Computer predictions of likely fire severity have been made and temperature–time curves for a range of ventilation conditions and fire loads have been defined, see section 10.10.5. These predicted temperature–time curves can be used to assess the standard required for enclosing walls and floors. This approach is, however, likely to be impractical for most applications because of the difficulty in relating existing information on wall and floor constructions under standard test conditions to fire severity curves for individual spaces.

5.7.3 Equivalent fire resistance period

A more practical approach is that of 'equivalent fire resistance'. This is based on an empirical relationship between the likely fire severity in a space and the exposure conditions in a standard fire resistance test.

There are a number of publications available which deal with the concept of equivalent fire resistance. The concept was first codified in the CIB Design Guide[16,17]. More recently, a Eurocode[18] has been produced which contains detailed guidance on the calculation of equivalent fire resistance. The proposed British Standard BS 9999[9] also uses the equivalent fire resistance concept.

Table 5.1 Heat balance for a room fire

Fire load / kg·m²	Ventilation	Heat release rate	Percentage of heat dissipated			
			Through windows / %	Through openings in surfaces / %	As fuel / %	By radiation / %
877	11.2	1900	65	15	11	9
	5.6	1900	52	26	11	11
1744	11.2	3200	61	15	11	13
	5.6	2300	53	26	11	9
	2.6	1600	47	30	11	7

5.7.3.1 CIB Design Guide

The CIB Design Guide defined the equivalent fire resistance period by means of the following equation:

$$T_e = c\, w_v\, q \tag{5.1}$$

where T_e is the equivalent fire resistance period (minutes), c is a constant dependent on the thermal properties of the enclosing walls, w_v is the ventilation factor and q is the fire load density (MJ·m⁻²).

The ventilation factor, w_v, is defined by the following equation:

$$w_v = \left(\frac{A_f}{A_t\sqrt{h_o}}\right)^{1/2}\left(\frac{A_f}{A_o}\right)^{1/2} \tag{5.2}$$

where A_f is the floor area of the compartment (m²), A_t is the total interior surface of compartment including openings (m²), h_o is the average height of openings (m) and A_o is the total area of door and window openings (m²).

The equivalent fire resistance period is therefore a function of both the openings into the space and the total area of the enclosing surfaces, as well as the fire load density. From these equations a more precise assessment of the required standard of enclosure to a compartment can be obtained.

Care needs to be taken when using this approach since it assumes that a fire in a space will be controlled by ventilation and this will not always be the case. Guidance on ventilation-controlled fires is given in section 10.5.4.2. In addition, some concern has been expressed that the validation of these equations has largely been restricted to relatively small compartments and therefore may not be wholly applicable to large compartments.

5.7.3.2 Eurocode 1: Part 2.2

More substantive recommendations for the calculation of equivalent fire resistance are contained in Eurocode 1: Part 2.2. This is a draft publication, which contains a 'National Application Document' that will provide guidance on the application of the Eurocode in the UK.

The calculation of equivalent fire resistances as given in the Eurocode uses the following equation, which is very similar to equation 5.1:

$$t_e = q_{f,d}\, k_b\, W_f \tag{5.3}$$

where t_e is the equivalent fire severity (minutes), $q_{f,d}$ is the fire load per unit area (MJ·m²), k_b is the conversion factor dependent on the thermal properties of the enclosing surfaces and W_f is the ventilation factor.

The ventilation factor W_f is calculated from the following equation:

$$W_f = \left(\frac{6}{h}\right)^{0.3}\left(0.62 + \frac{90(0.4-\alpha_v)^4}{(1+b_v\,\alpha_h)}\right) \tag{5.4}$$

where α_v is the ratio of the area of vertical openings in the façade (A_v) to the floor area of the compartment (A_f), α_h is the ratio of the area of horizontal openings in the roof (A_h) to the floor area of the compartment (A_f), b_v is a numerical factor related to α_v (see equation 5.5) and h is the height of the fire compartment (m).

The factor b_v is given by:

$$b_v = 12.5(1 + 10\,\alpha_v - \alpha_v^2) \ge 10 \tag{5.5}$$

Note: for most applications there are no horizontal vents in the compartment ceiling, therefore $\alpha_h = 0$.

Fire load per unit area

The National Application Document (NAD) for the Eurocode gives a specific calculation procedure for the fire load per unit area that should be used in the analysis. This procedure applies safety factors to the fire load dependent on the risk of fire and the consequences of failure of the structure. Tall buildings have more serious consequences if they collapse than do low rise buildings, so the safety factor is higher for the former.

The design fire load (q_d) for use in the calculations is given by:

$$q_d = \gamma_q\,\gamma_n\,q_k \tag{5.6}$$

where q_d is the design fire load (MJ·m⁻²), γ_q is the safety factor depending on the consequences of failure and frequency of fires, γ_n is a factor accounting for active fire protection measures and q_k is the fire load (MJ·m⁻²).

Safety factor γ_q is given by:

$$\gamma_q = \gamma_{q1}\,\gamma_{q2} \tag{5.7}$$

Table 5.2 Values of γ_{q1} for office buildings

Height of top floor of building/ m	Value for γ_{q1}
≤ 5	0.8
≤ 20	1.1
≤ 30	1.6
>30	2.2

Table 5.3 Values of γ_n

Sprinklers	Value for γ_n for stated value of γ_{q1}	
	$\gamma_{q1} \leq 1.6$	$\gamma_{q1} > 1.6$
Approved system	0.6	0.75
Other (non-approved)	1.0	1.0

Values of γ_{q1} for office buildings are given in the Table 5.2. The safety factor γ_{q2} depends on the type of occupancy, as follows:

— offices or residential buildings: $\gamma_{q2} = 1.2$

— shops and assembly buildings: $\gamma_{q2} = 0.8$

— car parks: $\gamma_{q2} = 0.4$

The value of the active protection factor γ_n depends on the provision or otherwise of a sprinkler system and also on the value of γ_{q1}, see Table 5.3.

If active fire suppression (i.e. sprinklers) is provided and gq is greater than 1.6, γ_n takes a value of 0.75

Ventilation factor

The Eurocode model is valid for ventilation factors α_v between 0.025 and 0.25. For extensively glazed buildings, the ventilation factor is likely to fall outside these limits of applicability. For such buildings the fire severity is likely to reduce when the limits of applicability are exceeded. However, it is important to assess the significance of any application where the ventilation factor is outside the specified range of applicability.

Conversion factor

The conversion factor is dependent on the thermal properties of the enclosing surfaces to the compartment. The Eurocode specifies values which vary from 0.04 to 0.07.

Use of equivalent fire resistance

Equivalent fire resistance is being increasingly used to provide an alternative means of identifying the fire resistance standard required for buildings, rather than the prescriptive recommendations of Approved Document B[7]. This is applicable to both compartmentation and structural fire protection.

When using the equivalent fire resistance concept it is important to note that it is an empirical method that retains the benefits of being based on the traditional fire resistance test whilst introducing additional factors which determine fire severity in a building. Any analysis must be the subject of a sensitivity study as extreme conditions may not produce the most severe fire conditions in a building. The most severe conditions may arise from a fire in a compartment of limited area and ventilation conditions, rather than a fire in a large open-plan area.

The use of equivalent fire resistance has been the subject of a 'determination' under the Building Regulations for a large high rise office building. This determination has highlighted the following:

— the fire load should be based on the 80% fractile and not the 50% fractile as used in the Eurocode and its associated National Application Document, and

— the importance of the conversion factor (k) in the analysis and the need to consider how linings may change as a result of the fitout of the building or other changes to the building during its lifetime.

The use of equivalent fire resistance has the advantage that it is much more flexible and reflects flexible and reflects the circumstances of each individual building. It is also more cost effective as it helps to ensure that fire resistance periods are not unnecessarily onerous and can give greater design freedom.

It is also has a number of disadvantages which need to be considered. If not careful it can lead to loss of flexibility in the building as fire resistance requirements will have been assessed against a particular set of conditions. There will be more complexity as buildings become more 'individual' and this will have implications for future building owners/occupiers. The design of the building may also more become more critical in respects which would not arise with the traditional conservative approach based on Post War Building Studies[1].

British Standard BS 9999

The British Standards Institution has also been considering the use of equivalent fire resistance for inclusion in the proposed BS 9999[9]. The draft standard uses equivalent fire resistance in conjunction with a concept of 'occupancy risk category' (ORC) to provide a wide range of recommendations for compartmentation.

The ORC is used to identify different types of buildings according to the nature of the building occupants rather than the use of the building.

The recommendations are presented in tabular form so that from the ORC, together with other key building parameters such as height, it is possible to read-off from the tables a fire resistance period which is derived from equivalent fire resistance.

The recommendations in BS 9999[9] are derived using a slightly different method of calculating equivalent fire resistance. This uses the same basic equation as given above for the CIB and Eurocode methods (e.g. equation 5.3) but simplified as follows:

$$t_e = (k_b \, q_{f,d} \, A_f) / (A_t \, A_v \, \sqrt{h})^{0.5} \qquad (5.8)$$

where t_e is the equivalent fire severity (minutes), k_b is a conversion factor dependent on the thermal properties of the surroundings, $q_{f,d}$ is the fire load per unit area (MJ·m²), A_f is the floor area of the compartment (m²), A_t is the area of compartment surfaces including areas of openings (m²),

A_v is the area of vertical openings (m^2) and h is the height of the vertical openings (m).

The factors of safety for the probability of fire, consequences of fire and the effect of sprinklers are then applied to the equivalent fire resistance, rather than to the fire load as in the Eurocode method. The conversion factor (k_b) is taken as 0.07.

Other methods

Other methods are available for assessing standards of compartmentation based on a prediction of real fire severity and heat flow analysis techniques for predicting heat flow though separating elements. However, for most typical separating elements, there is not likely to be sufficient data for carrying out this type of analysis.

5.8 Control of fires during growth stage

During its early stages, the rate of growth of a fire is largely determined by the nature of the contents of the space and by the exposed surfaces. The latter are usually controlled by placing restrictions on the combustibility, flame spread characteristics and heat release characteristics of the exposed surfaces.

These characteristics are usually measured by laboratory tests of the type specified in Parts 4, 6, 7 and 11 of BS 476[11]. These tests are empirical in nature and have been subject to extensive criticism because of their lack of scientific credibility and their inability to provide worthwhile data for fire engineering purposes. More scientifically-based tests have been proposed in recent years, such as the cone calorimeter which can provide more fundamental information on, for example, rates of heat release. However, more recent European equivalent tests, introduced as part of European harmonization, have included tests which do provide useful data.

The spread of flame over a surface is a function of the nature of the surface and the transfer of heat from a flame to the surface ahead of the flame. In the case of flame spread in an upwards direction, the principle means of heat transfer is by convection and, to a lesser extent, radiation from the flame. Flame spread in this direction can be very rapid because of the close contact between the flame and the surface. Horizontal flame spread is mainly caused by convective heat transfer from the edge of the flame and, to a lesser extent, by conduction through the solid surface material.

In principle the rate of flame spread can be predicted from heat transfer equations and is inversely proportional to the product of the density, thermal conductivity and thermal capacity of the lining. However, in practice the calculation of flame spread is usually impracticable due to the wide variations in wall linings. Commercially available wall linings are often laminates or composite materials of varying composition and the behaviour of surfaces can be very complex, involving the de-bonding or de-lamination of layers, melting, blistering etc.

In addition, other phenomena related to the geometry of the surfaces and air movement over the surfaces may be significant such as the rapid spread of flames up wooden escalators which took place during the fire in Kings Cross Underground station in 1988[19]. Such phenomena are very difficult to predict.

Therefore, except in very exceptional circumstances, it is not usually practical or possible to make accurate predictions of flame spread. Detailed discussions of the calculation of flame spread are published elsewhere[14].

In many instances the growth of fires during their early stages can be usefully represented by fire growth equations, see section 10.5.

More general guidance on the control of flame spread over surfaces, including those related to building services, is given in Approved Document B[7].

References

1   *Fire Grading of Buildings — Part 1: General Principles and Structural Precautions* Post War Building Studies No 20 (London: Her Majesty's Stationery Office)) (1946)

2   The Building Regulations 1965 Statutory Instrument 1965 No. 1373 (London: Her Majesty's Stationery Office) (1965) (withdrawn — superseded by reference 3)

3   The Building Regulations 1985 Statutory Instrument 1985 No. 1065 (London: Her Majesty's Stationery Office) (1985) (withdrawn — superseded by reference 5)

4   *Fire spread* Approved Document B2/3/4 (London: Her Majesty's Stationery Office) (1985) (withdrawn — superseded by reference 6)

5   The Building Regulations 1991 Statutory Instrument 1991 No. 2768 (London: Her Majesty's Stationery Office) (1991)

6   *Fire safety* Approved Document B (London: Her Majesty's Stationery Office) (1991) (withdrawn — superseded by reference 7)

7   *Fire safety* Approved Document B (London: The Stationery Office) (2000)

8   BS 5588: *Fire precautions in the design, construction and use of buildings*: Part 9: 1999: *Code of practice for ventilation and air conditioning ductwork* (London: British Standards Institution) (1999)

9   BS 9999: (draft): *Code of practice for fire safety in the design, construction and use of buildings* (London: British Standards Institution) (to be published)

10 *Code of Practice for the Construction of Buildings — Insurers' Rules for the Fire Protection of Industrial and Commercial Buildings* (London: Loss Prevention Council) (1992)

11 BS 476: *Fire tests on building materials and structures*: Part 4: 1970 (1984): *Non-combustibility tests for materials*; Part 6: 1989: *Method of test for fire propagation for products*; Part 7: 1997: *Method of test to determine the classification of the surface spread of flame of products*; Part 11: 1982 (1988): *Method for assessing the heat emission from building materials*; Part 20: 1987: *Method for determination of the fire resistance of elements of construction (general principles)* (London: British Standards Institution) (dates as indicated)

12 *Guidelines for the construction of fire resisting structural elements* BRE Report BR 128 (Garston: Building Research Establishment) (1988)

13   BS 5268: *Structural use of timber*: Part 4: *Fire resistance of timber structures*: Section 4.1: 1978: *Recommendations for calculating fire resistance of timber members*; Section 4.2: 1989: *Recommendations for calculating fire resistance of timber stud walls and joisted floor constructions* (London: British Standards Institution) (dates as given)

14   Drysdale D D *An introduction to fire dynamics* (Chichester: Wiley) (1987)

15   Butcher E G and Parnell A C *Designing for fire safety* (Chichester: Wiley) (1983)

16   CIB Report W14: A conceptual approach towards a probability-based design guide on structural fire safety *Fire Safety* **6** 1-79 (1983)

17   *Natural fires in large scale compartments* (Rotherham: British Steel Technical) (1994)

18   *Eurocode 1: Actions on structures. General actions: Part 1.2: Actions on structures exposed to fire* (London: British Standards Institution) (2003)

19   Fennel D *Investigation into the Kings Cross Underground fire* (London: HMSO) (1988)

6 Alarm, detection and emergency lighting

6.1 Introduction

Part B of the Building Regulations[1] requires that a system be put in place within all new commercial buildings to notify occupants of a fire. This requirement can be satisfied in small premises simply by someone shouting 'Fire!' or, in larger buildings, by a sophisticated analogue addressable fire alarm system.

In order that an adequate and appropriate system is considered from a project's inception, some initial considerations must be made.

6.1.1 Initial considerations

First, it is necessary to determine if a fire alarm system is required at all. This will depend upon the size, complexity, and use of the building.

If, for example, the building under consideration were to be a single storey workshop with a handful of rooms and no public access, then it may be appropriate to dismiss the need for a fire alarm system.

It must be borne in mind however that other parties need to be consulted in this decision and these are discussed below.

Should it be decided that a fire alarm system is required, then the following types need to be considered:

— manual fire systems

— automatic fire detection systems.

Manual alarm systems, which consist of breakglass units and alarm sounders connected to a control panel, can only be operated and the alarm raised when activated by an individual having detected a fire incident. Automatic systems, which consist of smoke and heat detectors, in addition to breakglass units and alarm sounders connected to a control panel, are designed to raise the alarm whether or not personnel are present at the time, thus giving early warning of a fire incident.

BS 5839[2] identifies automatic fire alarm systems as being either 'P' systems, which are designed to protect property, or 'L' systems which are primarily designed for the protection of life. A P-type system may be used where a building has valuable contents but is seldom occupied by people. An L-type system may be used in a highly populated building such as a hotel.

Further sub-division is identified in BS 5839 by classifying type P and L systems as either P1 or P2 (see section 6.2.2) and L1, 2, 3, 4 or 5 (see section 6.2.3), respectively.

It is essential that the type of system required be identified at the outset. The building user and, particularly, its insurer should be consulted as to the classification of any automatic system.

It should be noted that, for a complex building, there is likely to be a significant difference in cost between a P1/L1 system and a P2/L3 system.

Codes of practice for fire alarm and detection systems for buildings are given in BS 5839[2]. Part 1 deals with system design, installation and servicing and Part 4 provides a specification for control and indicating equipment. Part 6 provides a code of practice for detection and alarm systems in domestic buildings. BS EN 54[3] covers the design of control and indicating equipment, detection devices, sounders, and power supplies.

The principal documents covering the need for fire protection in various types of premises are as follows:

— The Fire Precautions Act 1971[4] and its associated Designating Orders, i.e. Statutory Instruments 1972 No. 238[5] and Statutory Instruments 1972 No. 238 (S26) Scotland[6]

— The Health and Safety at Work etc. Act 1974[7]

— The Fire Certificates (Special Premises) Regulations 1976[8]

— The Factories Act 1971[9]

— The Offices, Shops and Railway Premises Act 1963 (Commencement No. 3) Order 1989[10]

— BS 5588: *Fire precautions in the design, consideration and use of buildings*[11]

— Building Regulations Approved Document B: *Fire Safety*[12] (or the equivalent guidance for Scotland and Northern Ireland, see section 2.3.1).

This section of Guide E gives the basic requirements for the design, installation and application of fire systems and equipment and it is not intended as an alternative to BS 5839: Part 1[2].

6.1.2 Premises requiring alarm systems

As mentioned above the decision as to the need for a fire alarm system should be made at the project inception. Relevant considerations include the following:

— What will the building be used for?

— Is the protection for life or property?

— Are members of the general public likely to be present?

— Are any unusual hazards present?

6.2 Specification of alarm systems

6.2.1 Need for consultation

A large proportion of the various types of buildings and their requirements are covered by national and local legislation. It is always advisable to consult the local fire prevention officer regarding the legislation covering particular premises and for guidance on the type of system that may be required.

In the initial stages of the design of a fire alarm system it is important to consult with all interested parties, i.e:

— building user

— building control authority

— local fire authorities

— architectural and engineering consultants

— system installers

— Health and Safety Executive

— building insurers

— English Heritage (for buildings under conservation order).

6.2.2 Systems for property protection

Fire alarm systems intended for the protection of property (P-type systems) will automatically detect a fire at an early stage, indicate its location and raise an effective alarm in time to summon the firefighting forces (i.e. both the 'in-house' firefighting team and the fire brigade).

P-type systems are subdivided as follows:

— *P1 systems*: all areas should be covered by detectors except:

  (*a*) voids less than 800 mm in height (unless the spread of fire between rooms can take place through such voids)

  (*b*) lavatories and water closets.

— *P2 systems*: for defined areas in buildings which have a high fire risk, e.g. areas containing the presence of ignition sources and easily ignitable materials. Areas without detection should be separated by a fire resisting construction.

— *P3 systems*: there is no P3 standard as the requirement to protect property depends on a fire being detected in vulnerable areas. Any reduction in the level of detection provided in a P2 type of system would therefore be ineffective in protection of property.

6.2.3 Systems for life protection

Fire alarm systems for the protection of life (L-type systems) can be relied upon to sound a fire alarm while sufficient time remains for the occupants to escape.

L-type systems are sub-divided as follows:

— *L1 systems*: as for P1 systems, see above.

— *L2 systems*: for specified areas where a fire could lead to a high risk to life safety, such as: sleeping areas without supervision; areas having high probability of ignition which would spread to affect building occupants, e.g. day accommodation, store rooms, kitchen and plant rooms; where the occupants are especially vulnerable owing to age, illness or may be unfamiliar with the building. Areas covered by L2 systems should always include those appropriate to L3.

— *L3 systems*: for protection of escape routes, e.g: corridors, passageways and circulation areas; in rooms opening onto escape routes; at tops of stair(s)/stairway(s); on landing ceilings at vertical intervals not exceeding 10.5 m below the top of any staircase; at tops of vertical risers such as lift shafts; at each level within 1.5 m of access to lift shafts or other vertical risers. Areas covered by L3 systems should always include those appropriate to L4.

— *L4 systems*: for protection of escape routes including corridors and stairwells. This level of cover may be appropriate where corridor lengths are short and are unlikely to become smoke logged before adequate warning is given. Heat detectors should not be used in L4 systems.

— *L5 systems*: for protection of selected rooms only. Where it can be identified that only certain areas of a building present an unacceptable risk from fire, then it may be appropriate to install automatic detection in these rooms only.

BS 5839: Part 1[2] gives further details on the system categories.

6.2.4 Manual fire alarm systems

Manual fire alarm systems are designated M-type systems. Such systems provide a manual alarm only. Type M systems have no further subdivisions.

6.3 Types of fire detection systems

All fire detection systems use the same principals to detect a fire situation; i.e. by means of a device, either smoke or heat activated, causing a disturbance in the steady-state current flowing through a detection system. The differences in types of system are limited to the way that the 'disturbance' signal is processed by the fire alarm control panel.

Most fire detection systems fall into one of two main categories:

— conventional monitored systems

— addressable systems (including analogue addressable).

6.3.1 Conventional monitored systems

Conventional monitored systems use a basic method of detecting a fire. The detection points (either smoke or heat) are wired in radial circuits from the control panel. At the end of each circuit, a resistor is used to create a known resistance across the circuit and hence provide a steady-state reference. Because the circuits are constantly monitored, wiring does not need to be fire rated as a circuit break will immediately be notified to the panel as a change in the steady-state. If a detector is activated by a fire, then its operation will also alter the steady-state resistance of the circuit to which it is connected and the fire alarm panel will raise the alarm. Since each radial circuit from the control panel will have a number of detectors connected to it, identification of the location of a fire is limited to the knowledge of the affected circuit. It is common practice to allocate one radial circuit to one fire zone and therefore activation of a detector will be registered at the control panel as being within the zone covered by that circuit. See Figure 6.1 for a diagram of this type of system

Following activation of a device, the zone in which the device is located must be searched to identify the precise location of the alarm. No other information about the zone can be obtained at the control panel.

Sounders on this type of system are wired on separate circuits in fire resisting cable as they are not monitored and must continue to operate in the event of a fire.

6.3.2 Addressable systems (including analogue addressable)

Whilst detectors connected to addressable systems operate in the same basic way as for conventional monitored systems, they are connected to 'loops' rather than radial circuits. Each detector is allocated a unique identification or 'address' during the commissioning process. This allows the control panel to recognise the change in the stead-state of individual detectors as opposed to changes in circuit steady-state with conventional monitored systems. The benefit of connecting to loop rather than radial circuits is that damage to part of the circuit can be isolated and allow the system to continue in operation. In order to achieve this, zone isolator units are placed in the loop between zones.

Analogue addressable systems are the most common type of system being installed at present. They use detectors which constantly relay information on their operating condition to the control panel. This type of information will allow the control panel to determine if a particular detector is being subjected to an abnormally high ambient level of smoke in normal use, and hence compensation can be made. In addition, the control panel can monitor the contamination levels on each of the systems detectors and report when maintenance is required.

In some buildings it may be desirable for the detectors to be less sensitive during the daytime, when the building is occupied, than at night when the building is unoccupied. Analogue addressable systems can be programmed to operate in this way.

Zones of conventional detectors and call points may be connected to an analogue system by means of suitable interfacing devices.

6.4 Zoning

6.4.1 General

To ensure rapid and unambiguous identification of the fire source, the protected area should be divided into zones. When determining the area to be covered by a zone, consideration should be given to accessibility, size, the fire routine determined for the premises and, particularly in occupied premises, that each zone is accessible from the main circulation routes leading from where the control panel is situated.

Addressable systems are able to give far more accurate information on the location of a fire source, and therefore (whilst still required), make the zoning of such systems somewhat superfluous.

In general, the following guidelines for the size of a zone should be observed:

(a) If the total floor area (i.e. the total of the floor areas for each storey) of the building is not greater than 300 m^2 then the building may be treated as a single zone, no matter how many storeys it may have.

(b) The total floor area for a zone should not exceed 2 000 m^2.

(c) The search distance (i.e. the distance that has to be travelled by a searcher inside a zone to determine visually the position of a fire) should not exceed 30 m. The use of remote indicator lamps outside doors may reduce the number of zones required.

(d) Where stairwells or similar structures extend beyond one floor but are in one fire compartment, this should be treated as a separate fire zone.

(e) If the zone covers more than one fire compartment, then the zone boundaries should follow compartment boundaries.

(f) If the building is split into several occupancies, no zone should be split between two occupancies.

When planning zones, the following points should also be considered:

— A fire compartment is an area bordered by a fire-resisting structure which usually has at least 30 minutes resistance.

— Zone limits can be relaxed only for certain M-type systems.

— Following a fire incident, a person escaping from the source of the fire may activate a breakglass on the escape route but in a different zone to that in which the fire is located; therefore it may be an advantage to have manual call points on separate zones to those of the detectors. This will avoid misleading information regarding the position of fire, particularly on staircase landings.

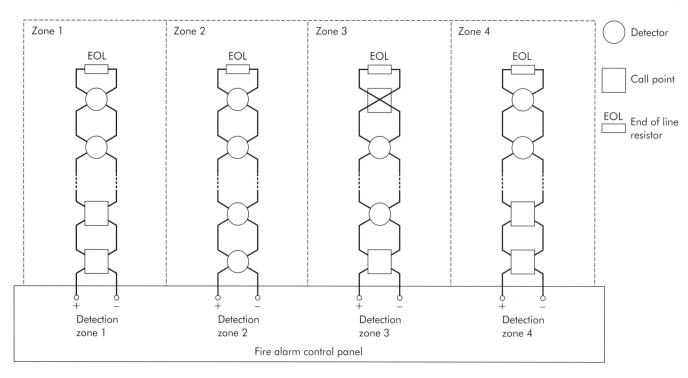

Note: a wiring fault in one detection zone will not cause a fault in another detection zone

Figure 6.1 Wiring of detectors and call points within a detection zone

— BS 5839: Part 1[2] requires that the wiring of the detectors should be arranged such that a fault on one detection zone does not prevent the operation of detectors in another zone; for compliance, detectors are normally wired on a conventional panel as shown in Figure 6.1.

6.4.2   Zoning with addressable/analogue addressable systems

With addressable/analogue addressable systems, each device, e.g. detector or call point, is given a numerical address code. Devices are wired in a loop arrangement. The manufacturer should be consulted on the maximum number of devices, and length of one loop. One loop can cover several detection zones.

For compliance with BS 5839: Part 1[2], short-circuit isolators are placed between each zone as shown in Figure 6.2, so that a fault on one zone does not affect devices in another zone. With addressable systems devices can be assigned into separate zones by programming of the panel software.

The maximum area covered by one loop should not exceed 10 000 m². With addressable/analogue addressable systems the detector or manual call point in alarm can be shown by the use of an alpha numeric display; this on its own will not be acceptable and the zone in which the detector/manual call point has operated must also be displayed, e.g. by means of an LED indicator.

The zonal identification diagram or chart may be mounted adjacent to the control panel and, since BS 5839: Part 1 also requires a plan of the building to be displayed,

the use of a mimic diagram provides a suitable means for zone identification.

BS 5839: Part 1 recognises that in small systems, where the location of an incident by an individual device will not cause confusion, the zonal information is not required.

6.5   Breakglass and manual call points

The breakglass call point is a device to enable personnel to raise the alarm, in the event of a fire, by simply breaking a frangible element and thus activating the alarm system.

The following notes provide guidance for the correct siting and positioning of breakglass call points:

— Breakglass call points should be located on exit routes and, in particular, on the floor landings or staircases and at all exits to the open air.

— Breakglass call points should be located so that no person need travel more than 30 m from any position within the premises in order to operate one.

— Generally, call points should be located at a height of 1.4 m above the floor at easily accessible, well illuminated and conspicuous positions, free from obstructions.

— The method of operation of all call points in an installation should be identical unless there is a particular reason for differentiation.

— Manual and automatic devices may be installed on the same system; however, it may be advisable to install the manual call points on separate zones for speed of identification, see section 6.4.1.

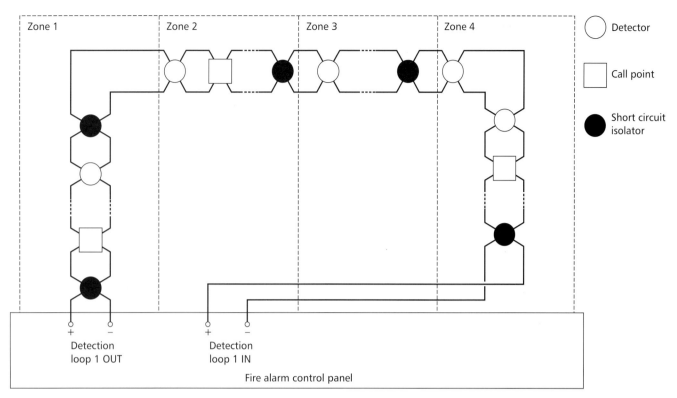

Note 1: short-circuit isolators are fitted between each zone so that a wiring fault in one detection zone will not cause a fault in another detection zone.

Note 2: short-circuit isolators are also fitted between LOOP OUT and the first detection device, and LOOP IN and the last detection device; in many cases these are built into the control panel circuitry.

Figure 6.2 Wiring of detectors and call points on a detection loop

6.6 Types of fire detection devices

6.6.1 General

There are several types of smoke detector including point ionisation smoke detectors, point optical smoke detectors, optical beam detectors and aspirating systems. Types of heat detector include point fixed heat detectors, point rate of heat rise detectors, combined detectors and beam-type heat detectors. Flame detectors may be used in applications where both smoke and heat detectors are unsuitable. Types of flame detector include ultraviolet flame detectors and infrared flame detectors. Each of these types is considered below.

When choosing the type of detector to be used in a particular area it is important to remember that the detector must be able to discriminate between fire and the normal environment within the building, e.g. smoking in hotel bedrooms, fumes from forklift trucks in warehouses, steam from bathrooms or kitchens etc.

6.6.2 Point-type smoke detectors

The type of detector chosen will usually depend on the smoke particles and the nature of the risk.

There are two principal types of smoke detectors:

— ionisation chamber detectors

— optical scatter chamber detectors.

Both types have a sufficient range of sensitivity to be used for general fire risks but careful consideration must be given to any specific risks which may occur.

6.6.3 Ionisation chamber detectors

In ionisation chamber detectors an electrical current flows between two electrodes. The current is reduced by the presence of smoke. Ionisation detectors are particularly sensitive to small particle smoke, such as that produced by rapidly burning fires, but are relatively insensitive to large smoke particles such as those produced by overheated PVC or smouldering polyurethane foam. They are responsible for a higher level of false alarms than optical types.

6.6.4 Optical chamber detectors

In optical chamber detectors, light is scattered or, in some cases, absorbed by smoke particles. They are sensitive to large particles found in optically dense smoke but are less sensitive to smaller smoke particles. Optical detectors are the most common type in use due to their better performance in terms of false alarms.

6.6.5 Combined heat and smoke detectors

In combined detectors, the benefits of both heat and smoke detection are gained. This type of detector generally uses the optical method of smoke detection along with a flat response heat detector.

6.6.6 Point-type heat detectors

Point-type heat detectors respond to temperatures surrounding a particular spot.

All point-type heat detectors should include a fixed temperature element operating at a pre-determined temperature. Some may also include a rate of rise element designed to operate in response to a rapid rise in temperature.

In general, heat detectors are less sensitive than other types of detector and therefore should be used where background smoke or steam would render smoke detectors unsuitable.

6.6.7 Line-type heat detectors

A line-type detector consists of a special cable which is able to detect changes in temperature along its length.

6.6.8 Beam detectors

In many installations point-type heat detectors and smoke detectors will be satisfactory. However, in buildings with very high ceilings these types of detectors are ineffective and detection may not occur until the fire is well established. In these situations dedicated optical beam detectors are more suitable.

Figure 6.3 shows the general arrangement of a beam detector. During a fire condition any smoke present reduces the amount of infrared radiation detected by the receiver.

The transmitter propagates an infrared beam which travels across the protected area to the receiver. In the event of a fire, the amount of infrared light that will be received by the receiver is reduced due to the presence of smoke. Excess heat also affects the signal received and the receiver will indicate whether an excess of smoke or heat has been detected.

Beam detectors are normally sited just below the ceiling, and can be used in areas with high ceilings, areas where the installation of point detectors may prove difficult to install and/or maintain (such as in warehouses), too expensive or may interfere with the decor of the building. They are particularly suited to warehouses, aircraft hangers, historic buildings, art galleries and loft spaces.

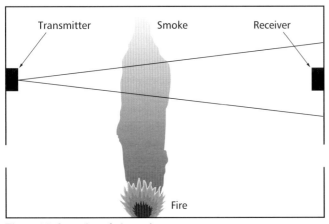

Figure 6.3 Operation of a beam detector

However, care must be taken to ensure that any possible flexing of the building is taken into account when choosing the locations of the units.

6.6.9 Aspirating systems

In some premises where expensive equipment is housed, such as computer rooms and telephone exchanges, it is important to detect smoke *before* the outbreak of flaming combustion. In such situations an aspirating system should be used.

Aspirating systems generally consist of the following:

— an extremely sensitive detector (approximately 10–200 times more sensitive than a typical point detector) housed in a control unit

— one or more pipes, drilled at regular intervals, installed throughout the area to be protected and connected to the detector (the holes serve as individual smoke detectors)

— a pump which draws air through the pipes to the detector where it is analysed for the presence of smoke

— an optional filter to remove dust particles etc. which may have been drawn into the pipes

— appropriate electronic equipment to indicate the presence of smoke and control the operation of output relays etc.

Aspirating systems have an advantage over other types of fire detection systems in that the pipework can be hidden in the ceiling or behind walls. In addition, they are unaffected by high air flows. Unlike point detectors, which wait for smoke to reach them, air is drawn to the detector, therefore they can be used in areas where smoke detection would otherwise prove difficult such as in atria, stadia, gymnasia and large function rooms with high ceilings. They are also suitable for use in dusty environments.

Detection equipment of this type may be more costly than a conventional fire detection system and control system.

Normally, the control panels can be configured to give three levels of response, for example:

— *level 1*: notify responsible personnel that smoke has been detected

— *level 2*: switch off air vents and/or switch off power supplies to certain areas to prevent the fire from igniting

— *level 3*: indicate a general fire alarm condition and signal that a fire has been detected to other systems and communication centres.

Requirements for the design and installation of aspirating systems are given in BS 5839: Part 1[2].

6.6.10 Flame detectors

Flame detectors can be used in areas that contain materials that are likely to produce rapidly spreading flaming fires, such as flammable liquids.

There are two main types of flame detector:

— ultraviolet flame detectors that detect the ultraviolet radiation within a flame

— infrared detectors that respond to the flickering component of the infrared radiation from a fire.

Flame detectors are unable to detect smoke from smouldering fires and are therefore used in specialised applications or to supplement heat or smoke detectors. They are not used as general purpose detectors.

6.6.11   Gas combustion detectors

This type of device is capable of detecting some of the gaseous products of combustion rather than the smoke or heat that is generated. They are more commercially known as carbon monoxide detectors and are particularly good at detecting a fire where the oxygen supply to that fire is restricted. This makes them very effective at detecting smouldering fires where the supply of oxygen is insufficient to allow the fire to progress quickly.

It also makes them suitable for use in residential properties as monitoring devices where gas fired heating equipment is present and there is a risk of the air supply to that equipment being restricted or the flue being blocked.

Although carbon monoxide detectors have advantages over other types, there are some disadvantages which should be borne in mind. These include the following:

— Carbon monoxide will diffuse within the atmosphere and contained within a building can travel a significant distance from the source of the fire. This means that a detector responding to the gas may not be the nearest to the source of the fire and may not even be in the same zone or floor level.

— Because they are designed to detect gases rather than particles of smoke or rises in temperature, carbon monoxide detectors may not respond to a fire which generates a high level of smoke and has a good oxygen supply.

— The sensing element within carbon monoxide detectors has a finite life and replacement must become part of the maintenance regime for the system in which they are installed.

Careful thought should be given to the placing and spacing of these detectors, and their use alongside smoke and heat detectors rather than instead of them.

6.7   Siting and spacing of detectors

6.7.1   Heat and smoke detectors

In a building, the greatest concentration of smoke and heat will generally occur at the highest parts of enclosed areas, see section 10.8, and therefore detectors should normally be sited at these locations.

Heat detectors should be sited so that the heat sensitive element is not less than 25 mm nor more than 150 mm below the ceiling or roof. If a protected space has a pitched or north-light roof, smoke detectors should be installed in each apex.

The maximum horizontal distance between any point in the area and the nearest detector is as follows for line and beam detectors (the horizontal distance should be taken to the nearest point on the line/beam; coverage can be taken as extending to that distance on both sides of the line/beam):

— Under flat horizontal ceilings and in corridors more than 5 m wide (Figure 6.4(a)): 5.3 m (maximum area 50 m^2) for point-type heat detectors; 7.5 m (maximum area 100 m^2) for point-type smoke detectors.

— For square-type arrays (Figure 6.4(b): maximum spacing between smoke detectors is 10 m; for heat detectors the maximum distance is 7 m.

— In corridors less than 5 m wide, add to the maximum horizontal distance 50% of the difference between 5 m and the actual width of the corridor; e.g. for a 3 m wide corridor, difference in width is 2 m, hence maximum distance of travel for a point-type smoke detector is (7.5 + 1) m = 8.5 m.

— In the apex of a pitched or northlight roof, add to the maximum horizontal distance 1% for each degree of slope to a maximum increase of 25% (Figure 6.4(c)); e.g. for a point smoke detector at the apex of a 20° slope, 20% of 7.5 m = 1.5 m, therefore maximum distance of travel is 9 m; the maximum area of coverage may also be increased proportionally.

Where the passage of smoke or hot gases towards a detector is likely to be disturbed by a ceiling obstruction (such as a beam), further allowances must be made, as follows:

— For an obstruction having a depth greater than 150 mm but less than 10% of the height of the ceiling, the horizontal distance should be decreased by twice the depth of the obstruction; e.g. for a point-type smoke detector obstructed by a beam of 200 mm depth, the maximum distance of travel must be reduced by (2 × 0.2 m) = 0.4 m, giving a maximum travel distance of (7.5 − 0.4) = 7.1 m.

— For an obstruction having a depth greater than 10% of the height of the ceiling, the areas either side of the obstruction should be considered as separate rooms.

— Ceiling obstructions having depths less than 150 mm can be ignored.

6.7.1.1   Ceiling height limits

The operation of detectors may be delayed if they are mounted on ceilings with heights which exceed the general limits given in Table 6.1. If small areas of a ceiling (i.e. not exceeding a total of 10% of the ceiling area) exceed the general limit, these areas may be protected by point-type heat detectors, provided that the ceiling height in the higher areas does not exceed 10.5 m, or by point-type smoke detectors provided that the ceiling height in the higher areas does not exceed 12.5 m.

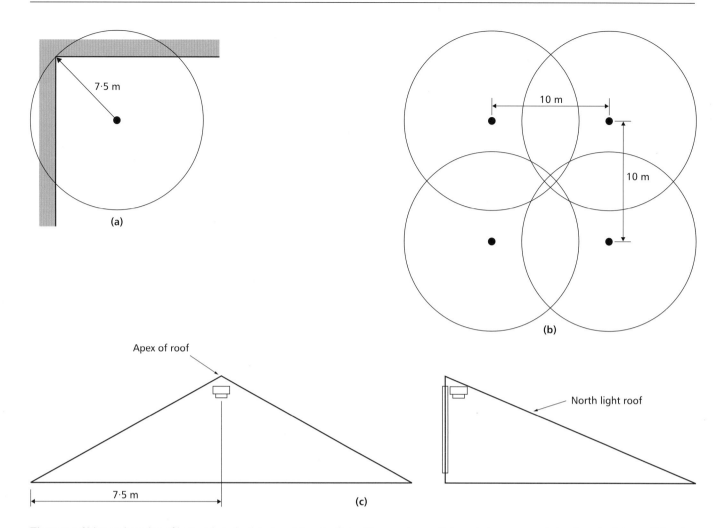

Figure 6.4 Siting and spacing of heat and smoke detectors; (a) under flat ceiling, maximum distance between any point and smoke detector (5.3 m for heat detector), (b) maximum spacing for smoke detectors in square array (7 m for heat detectors), (c) under apex or north-light roof

6.7.1.2 Ceiling height limits with rapid attendance

The delay in operation caused by increased ceiling heights may be acceptable if the delay between detection and the start of firefighting is small.

If the detection system is connected to the fire brigade, either directly or via a central (fire alarm) station, and the usual attendance time of the fire brigade is not more than five minutes, the 'rapid attendance' limits to ceiling height given in Table 6.1 may be applied. If small areas of a ceiling (not exceeding a total of 10% of the ceiling area) exceed the 'rapid attendance' height limits, these higher areas may be protected by point-type heat detectors if their height does not exceed 15 m, or by point-type smoke detectors if their height does not exceed 18 m.

6.7.2 Beam detectors

The area protected by a single optical beam detector should not exceed 100 m in length.

Generally the beam should not pass closer than 500 mm to a wall or partition. However, up to 3 m of beam length may pass closer than this limit.

If there is a probability of people walking in the area of the beam then the beam detector should be installed between 2 and 7 m above the floor.

Table 6.1 Ceiling height limits

Detector type	Limiting ceiling height (m)	
	General	Rapid attendance
Heat detectors (BS 5445[12]: Part 5):		
— Grade 1	9.0	13.5
— Grade 2	7.5	12.0
— Grade 3	6.0	10.5
High temperature heat detectors (BS 5445[12]: Part 8)	6.0	10.5
Smoke detectors (BS 5839[1]: Part 1: Section 11.3)	10.5	15.0
Optical beam smoke detectors (BS 5839[1]: Part 5)	25.0	40.0

6.7.3 Flame detectors

Flame detectors operate by monitoring the frequency of light in the protected area. Types are available to monitor infra-red and ultra-violet light. If a flame detector 'sees' the particular frequencies of light which correspond to a fire, then the alarm is raised. Flame detectors do not depend on smoke or heat being transported to them, therefore they do not need to be ceiling-mounted. They should be installed strictly in accordance with the manufacturer's recommendations. More than one flame detector can be used to cover the same area to ensure that the flame is detected in the shortest possible time.

6.8   Control equipment

6.8.1   Siting of control panel

The control and indicating panel which identifies the location of a fire, indicates faults and controls the operation of alarm sounders and other signalling devices, should comply with the requirements of BS 5839: Part 4[2].

In deciding where the control panel is to be sited two factors should be considered:

— Availability to staff: in residential premises the control panel needs to be located in a position where staff on duty can easily see the indications being given by the panel.

— Accessibility by the fire brigade: the control panel should be located preferably on the ground floor and in the immediate vicinity of the entrance to the building likely to be used by the fire brigade. Adjacent to the control unit should be a zone designation chart or, better still, a diagrammatic plan showing zone locations.

6.8.2   Alarm sounders

An important component of any fire alarm system is the alarm sounder, normally a bell or electronic sounder, which must be audible throughout the building in order to alert the occupants of the building, see section 4.6.2.

The following notes provide guidance on the correct use of alarm sounders:

— A sounder should produce a minimum sound level of either 65 dBA or 5 dBA above any background noise likely to persist for a period longer than 30 seconds, whichever is greater, at any occupiable point in the building. Note that most single doors will reduce the sound level by 20 dBA or 30 dBA in the case of fire doors. During commissioning of the system it is common to find areas of the building in which the sound level falls slightly below 65 dBA due to the furnishings and fit-out items absorbing and attenuating the sound. This generally results in the subsequent installation of additional sounders where, if the area in question is a small confined area or small room, then a measured level 2 or 3 dBA below that set out in BS 5839[2] may be acceptable as this difference would be imperceptible to the human ear.

— If the alarm system is to be used in premises such as hotels, boarding houses, etc. where it is required to wake sleeping persons then the sound level should be 75 dBA minimum at the bedhead; this may require the installation of a sounder in the bedroom.

— If the alarm system is used in premises such as a nightclub where the background sound can be at such a high level as to limit the effectiveness of the sounders, provision should be made to disconnect the music equipment on activation of the fire alarm system.

— In cases where one or more of the occupants are deaf there are a number of ways of alerting the person(s) of a fire. In many instances there will be enough people about to ensure that any deaf occupants are made aware of the fire alarms sounding. In situations where a deaf occupant is working alone or undertakes an activity which results in their location being difficult to pin-point, then radio paging may be an option to consider.

— In cases where persons who need to be alerted of a fire alarm include people who are deaf, then flashing beacons can be wired into the sounder circuits. In situations such as nursing homes a vibrating disc may be used, placed under a mattress or pillow.

— All audible warning devices used in the same system should have a similar sound and should be distinct from any alarm sounder which is used for other purposes. Ideally, the frequency should lie in the range 500–1000 Hz for fire alarm sounders. Modern electronic sounders offer a choice of sound tones (fluctuating or constant) and whilst the sound power level (SPL) will not change within a particular sounder, experimentation with different tones can result in a more distinctive sound against the background noise.

— A large number of quieter sounders rather than a small number of very loud sounders may be preferable to prevent noise levels in some areas from becoming too loud.

— At least one sounder per fire compartment will be necessary; it is unlikely that sounder noise levels in a room will be satisfactory if more than one dividing wall or door separates it from the nearest sounder.

— The level of sound provided should not be so high as to cause permanent damage to hearing.

— The number of fire alarm sounders used inside a building should be sufficient to produce the sound level recommended, but should in any case be at least two.

— For P-type systems an external sounder is required, coloured red and marked 'FIRE ALARM'.

— Where mains powered sounders are used to supplement 24 V DC sounders, the 240 V AC supply should be monitored.

— In cases where public address systems are used to alert occupants of fire, the public address system would need to comply with requirements of BS EN 60849[13].

6.8.3   Activating other safety measures

In addition to controlling alarm sounders, fire alarm panels may also be used to activate other safety measures. These include disabling lifts, activating sprinklers, activating extinguishing systems, activating public address announcements, closing smoke and fire doors, shutting down plant, etc.

In some circumstances, it may prove economical to have more than one fire alarm panel in a building to avoid having to bring the cabling required for smoke detectors, call-points, sounders etc. back to one central point. In such cases it may be necessary for one fire alarm panel to send signals to other alarm panels. Fire alarm panels may also be used to send signals to building management systems, radio paging systems, communications monitoring systems or to an off-site monitoring station.

Many systems have the capability to communicate with computer systems whereby graphical and textual information may be displayed on a computer screen. Events such as device activations, silencing of alarm sounders etc., may be stored by the computer and in the control panels event log and a print-out obtained.

6.8.4   Cables

The type of cable used in fire alarm systems can be divided into two main types: those which need to continue to function during a fire condition and those which can fail, having first served their purpose.

Cables which need to continue operating during a fire condition include power supply cables and links to sounders and remote communication centres. Those which do not need to continue to operate, having served their purpose, include cables to detectors and fail-safe cables to auxiliary devices such as door release devices.

In general, cables which function after the outbreak of fire will be expected to resist fire for at least half an hour. Suitable cables include mineral insulated copper sheathed cable (MICC) complying with BS 6207[15] and 'soft skin' types complying with BS 7629[14] with respect to their construction. However, the performance of the latter types when subjected to fire should be verified with the cable manufacturer prior to their use.

Other types of cable can be used and the standards to which they should comply are given in section 26 of BS 5839: Part 1[2].

Fire alarm cables should be segregated from cables used for other systems unless insulated in accordance with BS 7671[16] and complying with the requirements on electrical interference detailed in BS EN 50081[17] and BS EN 50082[18].

6.8.5   Radio-based systems

Fire alarm systems are available in which communication between the detectors and the control panel is made by means of radio signals. The advantages and disadvantages which need to be considered before designing a radio-based system are listed below.

The advantages are as follows:

— In general, the absence of wiring between system components, e.g. detectors and control panel, means that radio-based systems are generally cheaper and quicker to install than hard-wired systems. Disruption is kept to a minimum since installation can normally take place while the building is occupied. Systems can extend beyond a single building without the need for inter-building wiring.

— Since only a minimal amount of wiring is involved during installation, damage to existing surfaces is kept to a minimum.

— Individual detectors can be identified.

— Radio-based systems can continue to operate during a fire condition. Hence the need for fire resistant cable is reduced.

— Temporary fire cover for special risks, e.g. a marquee or an exhibition, can be easily arranged.

The disadvantages of radio-based systems include the following:

— Each detector, call point or other device which is not wired to the control panel will require a local power source.

— There is a possibility that the receiver may be affected by interference signals from other sources or that the transmission path could be temporarily or permanently blocked.

— There are limitations on the allowed frequency spectrum which could lead to interference between simultaneous signals, therefore it is considered unwise to send monitoring signals at frequent intervals. Hence for some (but not all) faults there may be a significant delay (possibly hours) before the occurrence of a fault is registered on the control panel.

The installation of a radio-based system must, as with other fire alarms systems, comply with the requirements of BS 5839: Part 1[2], section 18 of which deals with radio-based systems.

6.8.6   Power supplies

In general, the fire alarm control panel and associated devices operate extra low voltage (ELV), typically 24 V DC, and receive this supply either from a built-in charger/rectifier circuit (powered from the 230 volts AC supply) or from a dedicated ELV DC power supply. In the event of failure of the 230 volt mains supply, a standby ELV DC supply is automatically provided by batteries.

The power supply to fire alarm equipment should be used for the fire alarm only.

Connection to the mains 230 V supply should be from a dedicated circuit which derives its supply from a point as close as possible to the origin of the supply within a building. This will typically be a spare fuse-way in a main switch panel rather than a downstream distribution board. The advantage being a reduction in the risk of loss of supply due to circuit failure. The protective device, be it fuse, MCB, or MCCB should be clearly marked in red, carry some means of preventing accidental operation, and bear a notice stating 'FIRE ALARM — DO NOT SWITCH OFF'.

Care should be taken in the design of the power supply to ensure that the transition from mains to standby batteries does not cause momentary interruptions in the supply to the equipment. Operation of a single protective device should not interrupt supplies or cause the system to fail. The construction of the power supply must comply with the requirements of BS 5839: Part 4[2].

The duration and power required for the standby power supply will depend on the purpose of the system.

For L-type and M-type systems, if a mains failure will be recognised within 12 hours, then a standby duration of 24 hours is required. If the premises are likely to be unoccupied and not supervised so as to meet this requirement, then the duration is required to be 24 hours after the detection of the fault.

For P-type systems, if the fault will be recognised immediately on occurrence, either in the building or over a remote link, then a standby duration of 24 hours is required. If the building has no remote link, and may be unattended at times, then the required duration is 24 hours longer than the period for which the building may remain unoccupied. For example, for a building with a P-type system and no remote link which is likely to remain unoccupied from 1700 hours on Friday to 0900 hours on the following Monday, the standby period required would be 88 hours.

The British Fire Protection Systems Association has published a formula[19] that can be used to calculate the battery size required, however fire alarm equipment manufacturers will ensure that batteries supplied with their equipment are adequate for the standby period required by the design. Once again, early consultation is essential to ensure the requirements of the system are fully understood by all parties.

6.9 Hazardous areas

There are potentially explosive areas in which fire detection equipment needs to be installed. Such premises are protected in one of the following ways.

6.9.1 Flameproof equipment

Detection equipment is housed within a flameproof enclosure. If a fault should occur which produces an electrical spark, the spark is contained within the housing and not released into the potentially explosive environment.

6.9.2 Intrinsically safe equipment

Detection equipment installed in the potentially explosive area is fed through suitable barriers or isolators which limit the amount of electrical energy entering into the hazardous area, see Figure 6.5. If a fault occurs on electrical equipment installed within the hazardous area, causing a spark to be produced, the amount of energy released will be insufficient to cause an explosion.

The zener barrier is an electronic device which limits the current which may enter the hazardous area. The end-of-line resistor is used to monitor the supply from the control panel to the detection devices.

6.10 Emergency lighting

6.10.1 General

Emergency lighting (sometimes referred to a 'escape route' lighting) is provided to ensure that during failure of a building's main lighting system, there remains a level of artificial illumination which will allow safe and unambiguous egress from the building.

Emergency lighting must be viewed in a different way to fire alarm systems. Whereas, for many types of building, the Building Regulations do not specifically require that a fire alarm system be installed, a different view is taken on the need for emergency lighting. In commercial properties, all areas over 60 m^2 must be provided with emergency lighting, along with other specific requirements. This different approach is taken for a very good reason. Whilst a fire alarm system provides early notification of a potentially catastrophic event, the building owner/occupier will be happy if the system is never called into action. However, loss of power to the workplace is not uncommon. It is, in fact, common enough for the building occupants to view it with bemusement rather than panic. The sudden loss of lighting can put people in grave danger, however, should they attempt to move about. Therefore, the need for emergency lighting is very important as it is more likely to be put to use during its lifetime than is a fire alarm system.

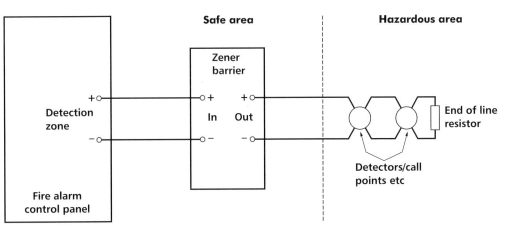

Figure 6.5 Wiring of detectors within a hazardous area

Note 1: the control panel and zener barrier are wired in the safe area.

Note 2: current entering the hazardous (i.e. potentially explosive) area is limited by the use of a zener barrier

It is sometimes desirable to link operation of the fire alarm system with the emergency lighting system. Whilst this can be beneficial if the main power source is lost in a fire, self contained types will automatically perform this function should the circuit be disrupted.

The following provides guidance on emergency lighting with regard to fire engineering. More detailed guidance on the general principles of emergency lighting are given in the CIBSE *Code for lighting*[20] and CIBSE *LG12: Emergency lighting*[21].

A glossary of terms relevant to emergency lighting is provided at the end of this section as Appendix 6.A1.

6.10.2   Legislation and standards

A considerable body of legislation and associated standards exist, covering various types of premises in which it may be necessary to incorporate emergency lighting. The relevant statutory documents include the following:

—   Building Regulations Approved Document B[12]

—   Cinemas Act 1985[22]

—   Theatres Act 1968[23]

—   Fire Precautions Act 1971[4] and its associated Designating Order SI 1972 No. 238[5]

—   Health and Safety at Work etc. Act 1974[7]

The main British Standards are:

—   BS 5266: *Emergency lighting*: Part 1: 1988: *Code of practice for the emergency lighting of premises other than cinemas and certain other specified premises used for entertainment*[24]

—   BS 4533: *Luminaires*: Section 102.22: 1990: *Specification for luminaires for emergency lighting*[25]

—   BS 5499: *Fire safety signs, notices and graphic symbols*: Part 1: 1990: *Specification for fire safety signs*; Part 3: 1990: *Specification for self-luminous fire safety signs*[26]

—   The Health and Safety (Safety Signs and Signals) Regulations 1996[27].

The relevant European Directives are:

—   The Workplace Directive (89(654)EEC)[28]

—   The Construction Products Directive (89(106) EEC)[29]

—   The Safety Signs Directive (90(664)EEC)[30].

6.10.3   Siting of essential escape lighting

6.10.3.1   Initial design

It is important to identify specific escape routes before commencing on the design of an emergency lighting system. This should be done in consultation with the architect (if appointed), building owner, Fire Officer and Building Control Officer. At this stage it would also be advisable to identify any specific requirements that the buildings insurers may wish to impose. Following consul-

tation with these parties, the initial design is conducted by siting luminaires to cover specific hazards and to highlight safety equipment and safety signs. Locations where such lights should be sited are listed in section 6.7 of BS 5266: Part 1[24]. These are shown in Figure 6.6 and include the following:

—   at each exit door

—   near intersections of corridors

—   near each staircase so that each flight of stairs receives direct light

—   near each change in direction (other than on a staircase)

—   near any change in floor level

—   near firefighting equipment

—   near each fire alarm call point

—   near first aid equipment

—   to illuminate exit and safety signs as required by the enforcing authority.

In the above list 'near' is taken to be within 2 m, measured horizontally.

6.10.3.2   Additional escape lighting

After siting luminaires at the locations listed in 6.10.3.1, consideration should be given to installing luminaires at other locations including the following:

—   lift cars; although not considered as part of the escape route emergency lighting is required since failure of the normal lighting could result in persons being confined in a small dark space for an indefinite period

—   moving stairs and walkways

—   toilets with areas exceeding 8 m²

—   external areas in the immediate vicinity of exits.

6.10.3.3   High-risk task areas

In addition to the above, emergency lighting should also be provided for areas in which high-risk tasks are undertaken. These include areas such as plant rooms, lift motor rooms, electrical switch rooms, and any area where a safety hazard is present and may become a danger to people moving about in darkness. Whilst BS 5266[24] does not specify minimum illumination levels for these areas, European standards suggest that a minimum of 10% of the normal illumination level, or 15 lux be provided in an emergency, whichever is the higher.

6.10.4   Illumination of exit signs

Exit signs can be either illuminated internally or externally from a remote source. The graphic requirements for exit signs are given in the Health and Safety (Safety Signs and Signals) Regulations 1996[27].

All emergency exit signs within a particular building should be uniform in colour and format.

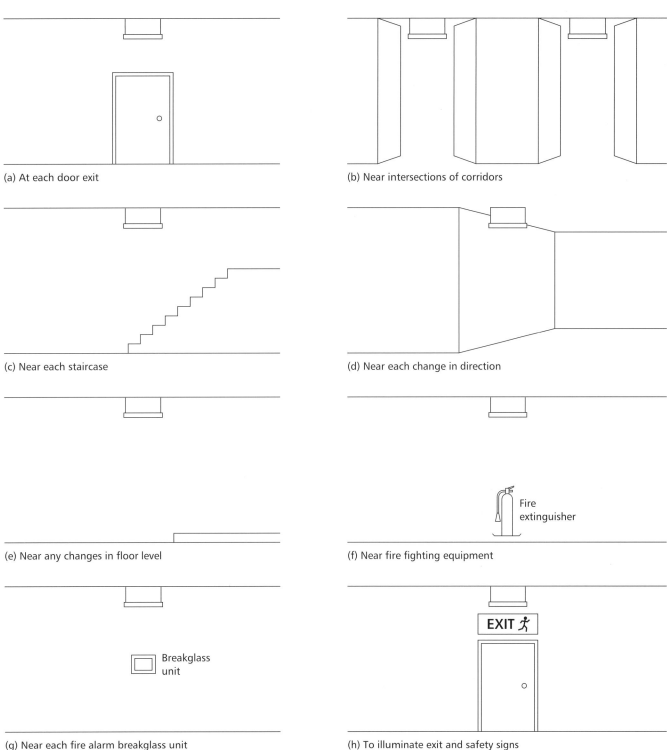

(a) At each door exit

(b) Near intersections of corridors

(c) Near each staircase

(d) Near each change in direction

(e) Near any changes in floor level

(f) Near fire fighting equipment

(g) Near each fire alarm breakglass unit

(h) To illuminate exit and safety signs

Figure 6.6 Locations where emergency luminaires must be sited

Signs complying with BS 2560[31] are no longer allowed and should have been replaced.

Signs complying with BS 5499: Part 1[2] may still be used if they are to be installed in a building which currently has this type of sign.

Self-luminous signs may also be used as exit signs. If used, however, these must also comply with the Safety Signs and Signals Regulations 1996.

6.10.5   Lighting levels for escape routes

Escape routes have specific requirements in terms of minimum illumination. It is essential that a minimum level of illumination is maintained along escape routes during a main lighting failure, see Figure 6.7. BS 5266[24] incorporates the requirements of European Standard EN 1838[32] which states a minimum of 1 lux on the centre line of escape routes.

The UK has obtained a deviation from the European standard, however, for unobstructed escape routes. Where a guarantee of clear unobstructed access can be given, then a minimum of 0.2 lux on the centre line of escape routes can be applied. It should be noted however that such a guarantee is difficult to uphold over the lifetime of a building and designers would be wise to consider designing systems to meet the higher requirement of 1 lux in all situations.

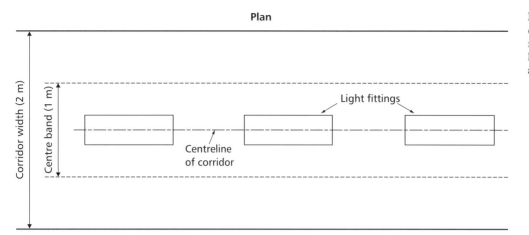

Plan

Figure 6.7 Lighting levels for defined escape routes; the minimum lighting level should be 0.2 lux along centre line and 0.1 lux across the 1 m wide centre band

In terms of design for emergency lighting in corridors, points such as changes of direction, changes in level, fire extinguisher locations and exit doors will require dedicated emergency lighting as well as that for general egress.

In order to calculate the number of luminaire required to illuminate an escape route, a certain amount of information must be obtained. The length, width and height of the area will be known. However, further information will be required, as follows:

— Average illumination level required (E): if the escape route is unrestricted, then 0.2 lux will suffice but, as suggested above, it would be prudent to use the higher level of 1 lux as it is difficult to ensure that escape routes will remain unrestricted. If the area is undefined (open areas, see 6.10.6) then 0.5 lux may be used.

— Utilisation factor (U_f): this factor represents the efficiency of the luminaire being used and can be obtained from the luminaire manufacturer once the room index has been calculated.

— Room index (RI): the room index is calculated from the dimensions of the escape route using the following equation:

$$\text{RI} = \frac{L \times W}{h_m (L + W)} \qquad (6.1)$$

where RI is the room index, L is the length of the room (m), W is the width of the room (m) and h_m is the height of the luminaires above the working plane (taken as the floor for emergency lighting) (m).

— Maintenance factor (MF): the maintenance factor represents the effect that cleanliness of the environment will have on the luminaires. If the environment is particularly dirty, then the maintenance factor will be lower than if the environment had been clean.

— Emergency lamp design luminous flux (ELDL): the ELDL is obtained from the luminaire manufacturer for the particular lamps being used.

— K-factor (K): this is used to allow for the reduction in light output at the end of discharge, or five seconds after mains failure, whichever is the lower. The factor can be obtained from the luminaire manufacturer.

Once this information has been assembled, then the following formula should be used to determine the number of luminaires required:

$$N = \frac{E \times L \times W}{\text{UF}_0 \times \text{SF} \times \text{ELDL} \times K} \qquad (6.2)$$

where N is the number of light fittings required, E is the average illuminance required (lux), L is the length of the room (m), W is the width of the room (m), UF_0 is the utilisation factor at zero reflectance, MF is the maintenance factor, ELDL is the emergency lamp design luminous flux (lumens) and K is the K-factor.

Further information on how to establish the various elements of this formula is provided in CIBSE *Code for lighting*[20].

6.10.6 Open (anti-panic) areas

Areas over 60 m² are required to be provided with emergency lighting by the Building Regulations[1]. Due to the size and nature of such large spaces, they will also include areas previously referred to as undefined escape routes. In such situations, occupants of a space may take several different routes to the nearest exit. Examples include common rooms in schools and colleges as well as canteen dining rooms. The furniture in such areas would represent a safety hazard to persons trying to leave the area in total darkness.

This type of area should be provided with a minimum illumination level of 0.5 lux in the core area. However a perimeter border of 0.5 metres is excluded.

Whilst this requirement is a minimum level, designers are advised to assess the dangers from loss of main lighting on an individual project basis dependant on the hazards present.

6.10.7 Types of system and modes of operation

Emergency lighting systems fall into two categories, each with their advantages and disadvantages. Regardless of the type of system used, the following functions must be available:

— sub-circuit monitoring: the system should be capable of identifying a partial failure of a building's lighting system and activate the emergency lighting in that particular area

— a test facility

— a visual means of identifying the charging system for the batteries is functioning.

6.10.7.1   Self-contained systems

Self-contained emergency lighting systems are so named because they utilise luminaires which contain both the emergency lamp and a battery. Each unit works independently of others in the system and is therefore unaffected by a failure in any other part of the system. Self-contained emergency luminaires require a permanent electrical supply in order to maintain the charge level in their batteries. This is obtained from the lighting circuit local to the individual luminaire and therefore the unit benefits from sub-circuit monitoring. A local switch is provided for isolation of the battery charger supply. This usually takes the form of a key-operated switch (to avoid the risk of accidental operation) which acts as a means of isolation for maintenance and a test facility.

Self-contained systems can utilise up to three types of luminaire:

— *Non-maintained*: this type of luminaire is designed to illuminate its lamp(s) only in the event of a failure in the main lighting system local to its position. At all other times its lamp(s) will remain switched off. It is 'non-maintaining', therefore, in that it does not maintain operation of the main lighting system during a power failure.

— *Maintained*: maintained emergency lumnaires contain the same lamp(s) as non-maintained types, however the unit's lamp(s) is/are utilised to provide illumination which is required during the buildings normal operation. Power for this normal operation is derived from the main electrical supply. In the event of a mains failure, the unit powers the lamp from its internal batteries and is therefore said to 'maintain' the normal lighting. An example is a cinema auditorium where the exit signage must be illuminated at all times of occupation.

— *Sustained*: This is used in the same situation as a 'maintained' type; however in a 'sustained' luminaire, there are different lamps for normal and emergency operation. The luminaire is therefore said to sustain the lighting, rather than maintain it, as illumination is being provided by a different source within the luminaire.

The advantages of self-contained systems are as follows:

— installation is simple and economic compared to that for a central battery system

— the system can be extended as required

— each unit works independently

— protected wiring is not required.

The disadvantages include the following:

— limited battery life requires that batteries be replaced between every 5 to 8 years

— ambient temperature range is restricted to 0–25 °C.

6.10.7.2   Central battery systems

In medium to large buildings, where a large number of emergency light fittings are required, a central battery system may be considered as an alternative to the installation of a large number of self-contained luminaires.

A central battery system consists of an emergency power source (with its own battery charger) and switchover device located centrally and slave luminaires installed where required throughout the building. This enables a system to be controlled and maintained from a central location. The slave luminaires are wired to the central battery unit by means of protected cabling.

The advantages of central battery systems are as follows:

— higher light output per luminaire

— battery may be selected to provide an appropriate life span of between 5 and 25 years.

The disadvantages include the following:

— battery failure disables the whole system

— comparatively high installation costs

— cables must be carefully selected to minimise voltage drop

— cables must be fire-resistant

— a separate monitoring system must be installed to detect local mains failure and ensure sub circuit monitoring.

Central battery systems are also available the three types of operation as for self contained systems, that is:

— *Non-maintained*: all emergency luminaires are normally off, failure of any circuit will energise the entire emergency lighting system.

— *Maintained*: in the event of failure of any lighting sub-circuit, the luminaires will be supplied by power from the central battery unit.

— *Sustained*: in the event of failure of any lighting sub-circuit, the luminaires will be supplied by power from the central battery unit.

6.10.8   Duration of operation

In an emergency, time is needed to evacuate the building. The time required for such evacuation may be increased due to the fact that some escape routes may be unavailable or persons within the premises may have been injured and in need of medical attention before evacuation. Time may also be required to allow the building to be searched to ensure that evacuation is complete.

Taking these factors into account, the minimum design period of an emergency lighting system should be one hour for most applications and a duration of 1–3 hours should meet normal requirements.

6.10.9 Cables

Cables which connect the standby power supply to the emergency lighting luminaires should have a high resistance to physical damage and attack by fire.

Where possible cables should be routed through low risk fire areas. If this is achieved it may be possible to reduce the fire protection standard of the cables.

Suitable cables include mineral-insulated copper sheathed cable in accordance with BS 6701: Part 1[33] and cable in accordance with BS 6387[34]. Cables should meet category 'B' requirements at minimum.

Details of wiring systems requiring additional fire protection can be found in section 8 of BS 5266: Part 1[24]. In selecting suitable cables it must be noted that to comply with BS 5266: Part 1 the voltage drop for the central battery power supply to each slave luminaire should not exceed 10% of the system nominal voltage at the maximum rated current and at the highest working temperature.

6.10.10 System testing and maintenance

The system should include facilities for regular testing and recording the system condition, appropriate to the specific site.

Regular servicing of the system is essential to ensure that the system remains at full operational status. This will normally be performed as part of the system testing routine but in the case of consumable items, such as lamps, spares should be provided for immediate use.

References

1   The Building Regulations 2000 Statutory Instruments 2000 No. 2531 (London: The Stationery Office) (2000)

2   BS 5839: *Fire detection and alarm systems for buildings*: Part 1: 2002: *Code of practice for system design, installation, commissioning and maintenance*; Part 2: 1983: *Specification for manual call points*; Part 3: 1988: *Specification for automatic release mechanisms for certain fire protection equipment*; Part 4: 1988: *Specification for control and indicating equipment*; Part 5: 1988: *Specification for optical beam smoke detectors*; Part 6: 1995: *Code of practice for the design and installation of fire detection and alarm systems in dwellings*; Part 8: 1998: *Code of practice for the design, installation and servicing of voice alarm systems* (London: British Standards Institution) (dates as indicated)

3   BS EN 54: *Fire detection and fire alarm systems* Part 1:1996: *Introduction*; Part 2: 1998: *Control and indicating equipment*: Part 3: 2001: *Fire alarm devices. Sounders*; Part 4: 1998: *Power supply equipment*; Part 5: 2001: *Heat detectors. Point detectors*; Part 7: 2001: *Smoke detectors. Point detectors using scattered light, transmitted light or ionization*; Part 10: 2002: *Flame detectors. Point detectors*; Part 11: 2001: *Manual call points* (London: British Standards Institution) (dates as indicated)

4   Fire Precautions Act 1971 (London: HMSO) (1971)

5   Fire Precautions (Hotels and Boarding Houses) Order 1972 Statutory Instruments 1972 No. 238 (London: HMSO) (1972)

6   Fire Precautions Order 1972 Statutory Instruments 1972 No. 238 (S26) Scotland (London: HMSO) (1972)

7   Heath and Safety at Work etc. Act 1974 (London: HMSO) (1974)

8   Fire Certificates (Special Premises) Regulations 1976 Statutory Instruments 1976 No. 2003 (London: HMSO) (1976)

9   The Factories Act 1961 (London: HMSO) (1961)

10   The Offices, Shops and Railway Premises Act 1963 (London: HMSO) (1963)

11   BS 5588: *Fire precautions in the design, construction and use of buildings*: Part 0: 1996: *Guide to fire safety codes of practice for particular premises/applications*; Part 1: 1990: *Code of practice for residential buildings*; Part 4: 1998: *Code of practice for smoke control in protected escape routes using pressurization*; Part 5: 1991: *Code of practice for firefighting stairs and lifts*; Part 6: 1991: *Code of practice for places of assembly*; Part 7: 1997: *Code of practice for the incorporation of atria in buildings*; Part 8: 1999: *Code of practice for means of escape for disabled people*; Part 9: 1999: *Code of practice for ventilation and air conditioning ductwork*; Part 10: 1991: *Code of practice for shopping complexes*; Part 11: 1997: *Code of practice for shops, offices, industrial, storage and other similar buildings* (London: British Standards Institution) (dates as indicated)

12   *Fire Safety* Building Regulations 2000 Approved Document B (London: The Stationery Office) (2000) (amended 2002)

13   BS EN 60849 (IEC 60849): 1998: *Sound systems for emergency purposes* (London: British Standards Institution) (1998)

14   BS 7629: *Specification for 300/500 V fire resistant electric cables having low emission of smoke and corrosive gases when affected by fire*; Part 1: 1997: *Multicore cables*; Part 2: 1997: *Multipair cables* (London: British Standards Institution) (dates as indicated)

15   BS 6207:*Mineral insulated cables with a rated voltage not exceeding 750 V*: Part 3: 2001: *Guide to use* (London: British Standards Institution) (2001)

16   BS 7671: 2001: *Requirements for electrical installations. IEE Wiring Regulations. Sixteenth edition* (London: British Standards Institution) (2001)

17   BS EN 50081: *Electromagnetic compatibility. Generic emission standard*; Part 1: 1992: *Residential, commercial and light industry*; Part 2: 1994: *Industrial environment* (London: British Standards Institution) (dates as indicated)

18   BS EN 50082: *Electromagnetic compatibility. Generic immunity standard*: Part 1: 1992/1998: *Residential, commercial and light industry*; Part 2: 1995: *Industrial environment* (London: British Standards Institution) (dates as indicated)

19   *Guidance for power supplies for use in fire alarm systems* (Kingston-upon-Thames: British Fire Protection Systems Association) (1995)

20   *Code for lighting* (London: Chartered Institution of Building Services Engineers) (2002)

21   Emergency lighting CIBSE LG12 (London: Chartered Institution of Building Services Engineers) (in preparation)

22   Cinemas Act 1985 (London: HMSO) (1985)

23   Theatres Act 1968 (London: HMSO) (1968)

24   BS 5266: *Emergency lighting*: Part 1: 1999: *Code of practice for emergency lighting of premises other than cinemas and certain other specified premises used for entertainment* (London: British Standards Institution) (1999)

25   BS 4533: *Luminaires*: Section 102.22 (EN 60598-2-22): 1990: *Specification for luminaires for emergency lighting* (London: British Standards Institution) (1990)

26   BS 5499: *Graphical symbols and signs. Safety signs, including fire safety signs*: Part 1: 2002: *Specification for geometric shapes, colours and layout*; Part 2: 1986: *Fire safety signs, notices and graphic symbols. Specification for self-luminous fire safety signs*; Part 3: 1990: *Specification for internally-illuminated fire safety signs*; Part 4: 2000: *Code of practice for escape route signing*; Part 5: 2002:

Signs with specific safety meanings; Part 6: 2002: *Creation and design of graphical symbols for use in safety signs. Requirements* (London: British Standards Institution) (dates as indicated)

27   The Health and Safety (Safety Signs and Signals) Regulations 1996 Statutory Instruments 1996 No. 341 (London: HMSO) (1996)

28   Directive Concerning the Minimum Safety and Health Requirements for the Workplace 89(654)EEC (Brussels: Commission for the European Community) (1989)

29   The Construction Products Directive 89(106)EEC (Brussels: Commission for the European Community) (1989)

30   The Safety Signs Directive 92(58)EEC (Brussels: Commission for the European Community) (1992)

31   BS 2560: 1978: *Specification for exit signs (internally illuminated)* (London: British Standards Institution) (1987) (withdrawn)

32   BS EN 1838: 1999 and BS 5622: Part 7: 1999: *Lighting applications. Emergency lighting* (London: British Standards Institution) (1999)

33   BS 6701: 1994: *Code of practice for installation of apparatus intended for connection to certain telecommunication systems* (London: British Standards Institution) (1994)

34   BS 6387: 1994: *Specification for performance requirements for cables required to maintain circuit integrity under fire conditions* (London: British Standards Institution) (1994)

Appendix 6.A1: Emergency lighting definitions

Anti-panic (open) lighting

That part of emergency escape lighting provided to avoid panic and provide illumination allowing people to reach a place where an escape route can be identified.

Central battery system

A system in which the batteries for a number of luminaires are housed in one location, usually for all the emergency luminaires in a complete building.

Emergency exit

An exit which is intended to be used only during an emergency.

Emergency escape lighting

That part of emergency lighting which is provided to ensure that all means of escape can be safely and effectively used at all material times.

Escape route

A route forming part of the means of escape from a point in a building to a final exit.

Exit

A way out which is intended to be used at any time whilst the premises are occupied.

Final exit

The terminal point of an escape route, beyond which persons are no longer in danger from fire or any other hazard requiring evacuation of the building.

High-risk task area lighting

That part of emergency escape lighting provided to ensure the safety of people involved in a potentially dangerous process or situation and to enable proper shutdown procedures for the safety of the operator and other occupants of the premises.

ICEL 1001 certification

The industry standard for the approval of photometric performance and claimed data of emergency lighting equipment which is tested by the British Standards Institution.

Luminaire

Apparatus which distributes, filters and transforms the light produced by a lamp or lamps and which includes all the items necessary for fixing and protecting the lamps and for connecting them to the supply circuit. Internally illuminated signs are a special type of luminaire.

Maintained emergency luminaire

A luminaire containing one or more lamps all of which operate from the normal supply or from the emergency supply at all material times.

Mounting height

The vertical distance between the luminaire and the working plane. For emergency lighting the working plane is taken to be the floor.

Non-maintained emergency luminaire

A luminaire containing one or more lamps which operate from the emergency supply only upon failure of the normal mains supply.

Normal lighting

All permanently installed electric lighting, operating from the supply in normal use, which, in the absence of adequate daylight, is intended for use during the whole time that the premises are occupied.

Rated duration

The manufacturer's declared duration for a battery operated after mains failure. This may be for any reasonable period but is normally one to three hours (when fully charged).

Self-contained emergency luminaire

A luminaire or sign providing maintained or non-maintained emergency lighting in which all the elements such as battery, the lamp and the control unit are contained within the housing or within 1 m of the housing.

Slave or centrally supplied luminaire

That part of an emergency luminaire without its own batteries that is designed to work in conjunction with a central battery system.

Standby lighting

Emergency lighting which may be provided to enable normal activities to continue in the event of a mains supply failure.

Sustained emergency luminaire

A luminaire containing two or more lamps at least one of which is energised from the emergency supply and the remainder from the normal supply. (Since the emergency lamp is illuminated only during a mains failure condition such luminaires are regarded as non-maintained for the purposes of fire authority approval.)

7 Fire and smoke ventilation

7.1 Introduction

7.1.1 General

There are a wide range of smoke control methods available which can be used to improve life safety, property protection or aid firefighting. They generally form part of a package of fire protection measures which may include heat or smoke detection, smoke barriers, fire-resisting construction and other measures to suit particular circumstances. However it is essential to ensure that the detail and the objectives of the smoke control system are consistent with the planning of the spaces within the building and the means of escape from it.

The system should be as simple and reliable as possible consistent with the objectives of the design. The provision of an overly complex design can lead to a lower level of reliability.

At the outset of the design it should be clear why a smoke control system is required. Some simple examples are as follows:

— to improve visibility on a long-distance escape route

— to improve tenability during escape from a large enclosure

— to improve visibility and tenability for fire fighting access

— to limit smoke spread during phased evacuation

— to limit smoke damage to equipment and furnishings.

It is likely that part of a smoke control system will be designed by others (usually building services engineers or architects). Therefore particular care should be taken to agree and define the respective responsibilities at an early stage in the design process.

7.1.2 Objectives of a smoke control system

Smoke control systems have one or both of the following objectives:

— to protect the area of the building where the fire starts

— to protect areas of the building remote from the fire.

Where it is required to meet both objectives, the systems installed must be compatible.

7.1.3 Systems intended to protect the area where the fire starts

Systems of this type can be based on the following objectives:

(a) Maintaining a smoke free layer on escape routes: systems designed in this way are often used in shopping malls. The relevant relationships for the design of such systems are given in section 10: *Fire dynamics*.

(b) Diluting the smoke within the space with fresh air, in order to maintain tenability and improve visibility: this will assist means of escape where the fire sizes are relatively small and spaces are large. This approach is particularly useful in circumstances where the normal internal conditions or wind pressures adversely affect the formation of a stable smoke layer.

Systems designed to meet objective (b) are employed as a means of smoke control for less critical applications such as the removal of cold smoke from a space after a fire has been extinguished or cross-ventilation of a space as an aid to firefighting. However, where the fire sizes are relatively small and spaces are large this approach may offer a viable option to assist means of escape.

7.1.4 Systems intended to protect areas beyond the fire area

Systems of this type can be based on:

(a) enclosing a space with barriers to contain smoke, e.g. fire walls and smoke curtains

(b) pressurisation or depressurisation

(c) slit extract at the edge of a smoke reservoir to prevent smoke leakage of cooled smoke

(d) maintaining a smoke free layer on the pedestrian routes

(e) opposed airflow: designed to prevent smoke spread through large openings using opposing air flow.

7.2   Design of systems to protect area where fire starts

7.2.1   Design of systems to maintain a smoke-free layer

The base of the smoke layer is usually set above head height i.e. at a minimum of 2 m above the floor. It may need to be higher than this, because the downward intensity of radiation should not exceed 2.5 kW·m^{-2}. On a conservative assumption this corresponds to a limiting smoke layer temperature of 185°C. It can be assumed that the smoke layer will not reach 185 °C if the fire is sprinkler-controlled.

To determine the actual clear layer adequate for means of escape the temperature of the smoke and the extent of the smoke layer needs to be taken into account and a limit of 2.5 kW·m^{-2} set on the radiation (see section 10).

7.2.1.1   Area of reservoir

Historically, an area of 2000–3000 m^2 has been adopted as the maximum reservoir size to prevent excessive cooling and downward mixing of smoke. This area limit is based upon the size of the test rig used in the experiment.

However, recent work on large enclosures shows that this downward mixing is unlikely to occur until the fire has decayed. Where necessary the dynamics of smoke in a very large volume can be assessed with a validated time related computational fluid dynamics CFD model.

7.2.1.2   Reservoir screens and curtains

The screens or curtains enclosing the edges of a reservoir must be constructed from materials which can withstand the calculated smoke temperature for the required period. These screens should be impermeable but some leakage, e.g. at the junction of screens, is not likely to be critical for most applications. The depth or drop of the screens or curtains should be the same as the calculated depth of the smoke layer. It is not considered to be necessary to add a margin of safety into the depth of the screen, i.e. the actual depth can be equal to the calculated depth.

7.2.1.3   Replacement air

For any smoke removal system to work effectively it requires a source of replacement air. The replacement air can be supplied either by natural means or mechanically.

The velocity of the incoming air should be limited; 5 m·s^{-1} is commonly used in buildings but 11 m·s^{-1} is set as the upper limit for passengers in tunnel ventilation systems in NFPA 130[1].

Note: in practice, replacement air will come via the flowpaths of least resistance which may not be the inlets assumed in the design and façade leakage rates may be added to the design.

When designing mechanical smoke removal systems the replacement air requirement should be based on volume balance, not mass balance. When designing natural smoke removal systems, replacement air should be based on mass balance. However, a powered inlet should not be used with a powered exhaust since this will lead to the creation of a pressure 'balance point' which will change as the fire size changes. This could have a serious effect on the forces acting on the fire escape doors.

7.2.1.4   Number of extract points

For a smoke removal system to work effectively there must be sufficient extract points to prevent air below the smoke layer being drawn up into the smoke layer, see section 10: *Fire dynamics*. The required number of extract points should be distributed across the reservoir to prevent stagnation and possible cooling, which could result in the clear layer becoming progressively smoke-logged.

7.2.1.5   Plenum extract systems

In some cases smoke may be extracted via a plenum. Smoke extract plenums should not contain cavity barriers or combustible materials. Sprinklers should be provided over the fire risk, not in the plenum.

7.2.1.6   Suspended ceilings

Where suspended ceilings are provided below the level of smoke extract points they should be at least 25% open, uniformly distributed[2].

7.2.2   Design of systems to dilute the smoke to a tenable condition

A smoke control system can be based on diluting the smoke within a space such that the design criteria within that space, e.g. tenability limits, are not exceeded, see sections 10.7.3, 10.7.4 and 10.7.5. This can be based on simple dilution either with or without the removal of smoke from the space, see section 10.

Except in relatively large spaces, such as atria, with relatively small fires it is unlikely that sufficient dilution can be obtained to maintain tenable conditions for a substantial period.

Dilution as a means of smoke clearance is often used for removal of cold smoke from a large space after the fire has been extinguished. An extract rate of six air changes per hour has been widely adopted for this purpose. The time to improve the visibility within a space to a predetermined level can be calculated from the following equation[3]:

$$m_s / m_{so} = \exp\left(-n_v\, t_d\right) \tag{7.1}$$

where m_s is the concentration at time t_d, m_{so} is the initial concentration, n_v is the air changes per hour (h^{-1}) and t_d is the dilution time (h).

Removal of smoke to delay the drop of the smoke layer base would normally be by mechanical means but can be achieved by natural venting utilising the stack effect and internal environmental flows.

The effect of wind on natural vents can be obtained from wind tunnel test or CFD modelling.

The number of air changes produced can be calculated using conventional calculation techniques[4]. Since there is no need to maintain a clear layer, replacement air for dilution systems may be from both high and low levels.

Cross ventilation has been widely used as a means of smoke dilution and/or dispersal, particularly for firefighting operations. This has traditionally been based on providing vent areas of 2.5% or 5% of the floor area of the building, equally distributed on two sides of a space. No theoretical justification has been given for this arrangement although it is reasonable to suppose that the relatively large vent area which result in large spaces are such that, in most instances, they would provide an effective means of removal of heat and smoke. A properly designed smoke control system could provide an alternative approach.

7.2.3 Fire venting for protection of structure

The performance of structures in fires can be assessed against a predicted time–temperature profile, rather than the standard time–temperature criterion given in BS 476: Part 20[5].

By venting the heat of the fire, either with an active fire venting system or by the provision of non-fire-resisting construction which will automatically vent the fire at higher temperatures, it is possible to demonstrate that a structural system may perform better than would have been the case had the design been carried out in accordance with the prescriptive approach.

7.2.4 Car park ventilation

Where natural ventilation cannot be provided to an underground car park it is normal to provide a mechanical smoke extraction system that operates at 10 air changes per hour. This type of system uses temperature rated ducts to dilute smoke and heat in an enclosed space. An alternative to using a ducted system is to use a jet fan system that does not require ducts to be provided. Jet fan

systems will significantly reduce temperatures in the fire compartment in addition to providing smoke free zones within the car park. A jet fan system is therefore superior to a normal ducted system both for prevention of fire spread and firefighting.

Jet fan technology has also been used for structures other than car parks, e.g. road tunnels and retail malls.

7.3 Design of systems to protect escape routes and firefighting shafts

7.3.1 Provision of an enclosure to contain smoke

The use of passive fire protection measures to contain smoke is the most widely used method of controlling smoke movement and has been based on requiring the structure surrounding a space to be fire resisting or smoke resisting. As there is no standard for smoke resistance the temperature of the smoke must be assessed against the material used in the smoke barrier.

7.3.2 Opposed air flow

This method of smoke control has been widely used in the USA and detailed recommendations have been published in NFPA 92B[6] and the *SFPE Handbook*[3]. It is based on inducing an air flow towards the area of the building containing the fire such that the air velocity is sufficient to prevent the outflow of smoke, see Figure 7.1.

The required airflow rate for an opening can be calculated from the following equation[6]:

$$u = 0.64 \, (g \, h_o \, (T_s - T_o) / T_s)^{1/2} \qquad (7.2)$$

For a corridor[3]:

$$u = 0.292 \, (Q_{pc} / w_c)^{1/3} \qquad (7.3)$$

where u is the air velocity (m·s^{-1}), g is the acceleration due to gravity (m·s^{-2}), h_o is the height of the opening (m), w_c is

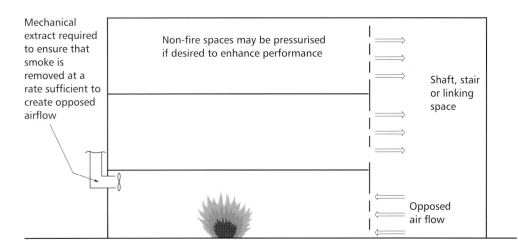

Mechanical extract required to ensure that smoke is removed at a rate sufficient to create opposed airflow

Non-fire spaces may be pressurised if desired to enhance performance

Shaft, stair or linking space

Opposed air flow

Figure 7.1 Opposed airflow/depressurisation

the corridor width (m) and Q_{pc} is the convective portion of heat release rate into corridor (kW).

For large openings the volumes of air required are substantial except where the smoke temperature is relatively low. Therefore this method is suitable only for large openings where, for example, the fuel load is low or the fire is sprinkler-controlled.

7.3.3   Depressurisation

This method of smoke control is based on the extraction of air and/or smoke from the fire-affected part of the building to reduce the pressure in the space to less than that in the adjacent parts of the building. The induced pressure differential then inhibits the spread of smoke. This approach can be assisted by pressurising the space not affected by fire. This is a popular system in the USA and Australia.

The method is fully described[3,6–8] for situations where, for example, the fire-affected part of the building is an occupied floor adjacent to a large space and depressurisation can be effectively carried out using the normal air handling systems provided in building. In general, the air handling systems operate in extract mode on the fire-affected floor and supply mode on other floors. For this method to prevent the spread of smoke the areas available for leakage must be relatively small.

Fire-rated fans and fire resisting ductwork may be required although this will depend on fire size, heat losses and dilution of the smoke within the duct system itself. High temperature fans are not necessarily required. The temperature rating of the fan should be greater than the calculated design smoke temperature for the required period. The performance characteristics of smoke and heat exhaust fans are given in BS 7346: Part 2[9].

7.3.4   Slit extract

A slit extract system may be employed across the flow to supplement an exhaust system and remove the need for a downstand. Similarly, a slit extract system can be used across the openings in a room to prevent any outflow of smoke.

Such a system is likely to work best with further extraction distributed within the fire room, which for a sprinklered room may possibly be provided by the normal extract ventilation system. While the system is designed to prevent smoke entering the atrium void, it will not necessarily maintain a clear layer within the room itself. The extraction should be provided very close to the opening from a continuous slit, which may be situated in the plane of the false ceiling.

It has been shown[10] that powered exhaust from a slit at right angles to a layer flow can completely prevent smoke passing that slit, provided that the extraction rate at the slit is at least $5/3$ times the flow in the horizontal layer flowing towards the slit. This allows a useful general method for sizing such extracts.

7.3.5   Pressurisation

This method of smoke control is based upon the principal of raising the protected area to a higher pressure to that of the surrounding spaces see Figure 7.2. The movement of air will be from the protected enclosure into the surrounding area. This will keep the escape routes clear of smoke. The design process is laid out in BS 5588: Part 4[11].

The system places reliance upon routes being maintained so that air can be vented from the fire area to the outside.

As outlined in BS 5588, air is injected into the protected areas and allowed to escape through the unpressurised area to the outside by automatic means.

One of the problems associated with this technique when applied to an office development is that when a floor is leased to a tenant, the lessor loses control of the space. For example, partitions may be installed that block the leakage paths; automatic openings may be disconnected following a number of false alarms; maintenance may be inadequate due to restricted access.

In the case of residential developments, the trend is to pressurise the stair and corridor eliminating the need for the 1.5 m^2 vent. Some designers provide leakage from the flats which prevents the smoke entering the corridor. However the opening is uncontrollable once a flat is sold. Other designers provide pressure relief from the corridor. Practical commissioning indicates that when the door of the fire flat is open the flat will quickly reach equal pressure before the smoke flows into the corridor. As the adjacent flats are at a lower pressure to that of the corridor, smoke could be forced into adjacent flats.

The fans and power supplies are similar to the depressurisation system, see section 7.3.3, apart from the temperature rating of the fans, which can be ambient.

Careful consideration on the use of the building needs to be given before designing a pressurisation system.

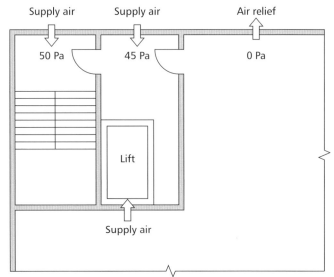

Figure 7.2 Pressurisation of protected area

7.3.6 Natural ventilation systems

Systems of this type differ slightly to the above in that smoke is allowed to flow into part of the protected escape route with passive protection providing the final level of protection. There are three forms of natural ventilation in use:

— natural venting of a common corridor in a residential single stair building, see Figure 7.3

— natural venting of a firefighting shaft, see Figure 7.4

— natural venting using 3 m² shaft[12].

In the case of residential buildings, Building Regulations Approved Document B[13] recommends that a 1.5 m² vertical vent be provided from the lobby directly to the outside on every floor. The vent should open automatically on the fire floor. The vent is mainly intended to prevent smoke entering the stair. Research tends to indicate that the methods of natural venting currently proposed by BS 5588: Part 5[14] are not efficient in maintaining the stair clear of smoke if the door between the stair and lobby is open.

In the case of firefighting shafts, BS 5588: Part 5[14] outlines the area of vent required in the stair and fire lobbies which is opened manually by the fire service. The principle is to allow the smoke into the fire lobby, where it can then be vented into a large vertical shaft. It is assumed the door between the lobby and stair is closed.

In the 3 m² shaft method, it is assumed that the door between the lobby and the stair is open.

The traditional approach of the fire service is to set up the bridgehead on the floor below the fire floor. In doing so, the fire hose will prop open the door between the lobby and the stair. In doing so, smoke could flow into the stair, thereby contravening the principles of BS 5588 Part 5[14].

7.3.7 Fan assisted shaft

These systems have come about as part of fire-engineered solutions incorporating the above objectives and practical measures. Both full size and scale model tests have been carried out which have shown excellent results.

As with natural ventilation, the system can be used in common corridors in single stair residential buildings, see Figure 7.5, or in firefighting shafts, see Figure 7.6.

In the residential case, a vertical shaft is provided up to the full height of the building. This is connected to the lobby by an automatic opening, which will open on the fire floor only. Using computational fluid dynamics (CFD), the fan at the top of the shaft is sized by the leakage through a flat door. Replacement air needs to be provided

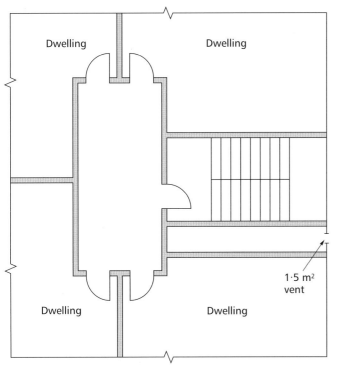

Figure 7.3 Natural ventilation of a common corridor in a residential single stair building

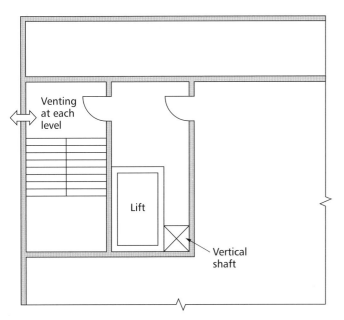

Figure 7.4 Natural ventilation of a of a firefighting shaft

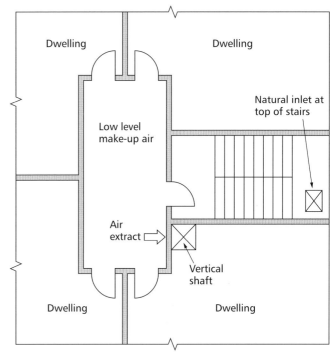

Figure 7.5 Fan assisted ventilation for a residential building

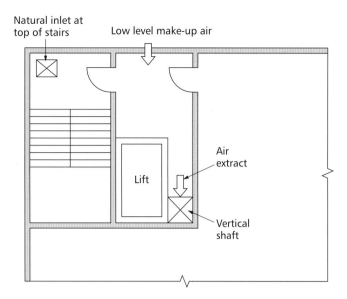

Natural inlet at top of stairs

Low level make-up air

Air extract

Lift

Vertical shaft

Figure 7.6 Fan assisted ventilation for a firefighting shaft in a commercial building

at each level. In calculating the fan and replacement air requirements, caution should be exercised to prevent smoke being drawn from the fire into the lobby.

These systems allow stair cores to be in the middle of the building will little loss of floor space.

Despite the different operational practices employed by firefighters in different parts of the country, this system will satisfy all requirements.

In commercial buildings a vertical shaft is provided to the full height of the building, which is connected to each lobby by means of an automatic opening vent which will open on the fire floor. In designing the system the following need to be considered:

— 	smoke flowing into the lobby

— 	lobby size

— 	fire protection measures provided in the building

— 	fire service response time.

Fan assisted systems rely on passive measures to prevent smoke entering the stairs. Clean replacement air must be introduced to the lobby at low level to prevent smoke being drawn from the fire floor. The fans and ducting will need to be temperature rated to match the design fire temperatures.

The fans and power supplies are similar to those for a depressurisation system, see 7.3.3.

Benefits of fan assisted systems are that all the plant and components are under the control of the lessor and that the system is compatible with any firefighting operations.

Detailed performance criteria should be agreed with the regulating authority but the primary aim is to ensure that the stairs remain tenable.

7.4 Design of systems to aid firefighting

7.4.1 General

The smoke control systems described in sections 7.2 and 7.3 for means of escape and protection of property are likely also to benefit firefighting operations.

7.4.2 Smoke clearance

After a fire has been controlled or extinguished, the removal of smoke from the affected spaces can be achieved by either natural or mechanical smoke control systems. In the latter case, it is important that override controls be provided for the use of firefighters.

Smoke clearance can also be achieved by the use of portable smoke control equipment deployed by the fire service (e.g. positive pressure fans) or by the partial demolition of the building. These two eventualities are not sufficiently predictable to be taken into account in the design procedures for smoke control systems.

7.4.3 Fire venting

Firefighting in basements and other spaces with few openings to fresh air may be severely hampered by high temperatures. In these circumstances, pavement lights or mechanical ventilation offer alternatives to conventional roof vents.

The principal benefits of such a system is not the control of smoke but the removal of heat and flames and the subsequent reduction of the internal temperatures, and to improve visibility so that firefighters can find the source of the fire.

7.5 Choice of system

7.5.1 Co-ordination with other design disciplines

The process of developing and understanding the reasons and logic for providing a smoke control system requires careful co-ordination with the other design disciplines. An appreciation of client requirements and some knowledge of the relative costs of alternative approaches is essential. Factors affecting the choice of system can include, amongst others, the architectural design objectives, the fire safety management requirements, the building services design and the construction process itself. Therefore, detail design should not begin until a concept scheme has been developed that identifies the type of system that will be simple and reliable in practice. This may require a flexible approach from suppliers, clients and other designers to establish the most cost-effective scheme. The following sections consider the situations than most commonly arise.

There are likely to be a number of ways of achieving a given design objective. To establish the most suitable option it is necessary to review the objectives of the smoke control system and the alternative means for achieving those objectives. Reference should be made to established authoritative design methods where these are available[10,15–18].

7.5.2   Limiting temperature criteria

If the objective of a smoke control system is to limit the maximum temperature of the smoke and there are no requirements for means of escape, there is correspondingly no requirement for dilution to a tenable level or the maintenance of a clear layer. Natural or mechanical smoke extraction could be specified for such cases, with aesthetics, cost and reliability being the major considerations. The efficiency of a natural vent is not very sensitive to the size of the fire and it is for this reason that a natural system is often favoured over a mechanical one. Natural ventilation systems should normally be designed and maintained so that they fail safe in the open position. Mechanical systems also need to be maintained and standby power may be required for extra reliability, where this is justified by the design. However, if a natural system is not an option, it is often possible to design a mechanical system to meet these requirements.

It is essential that those responsible for detail design and the supply of equipment and maintenance are fully aware of the performance and reliability requirements. In the case of the limiting temperature criterion, it is unlikely that adverse wind effects will be relevant since, at the high temperatures envisaged, the natural buoyancy of the smoke will be sufficient to overcome those of wind pressure. Mechanical systems are more likely to be appropriate in situations where an air conditioning or mechanical ventilation installation can be adapted or boosted to provide the required capacity.

7.5.3   Maintenance of a clear layer below the smoke

In this approach, a clear layer is maintained below the smoke to protect the means of escape in the compartment of origin.

Where the quantities of smoke are large, the smoke is still sufficiently buoyant and there are no adverse wind effects, a natural smoke control system is likely to be the most viable and cost-effective solution. Conversely, if it is not possible to design to overcome adverse positive wind pressures, or a cooler non-buoyant smoke condition is critical, a mechanical system may be more appropriate.

The very high rates of air entrainment into spill plumes entering a mall or atrium space create large increases in mass flow as the plume height increases. This tends to suggest that there may be some cut-off point above which a smoke control system becomes economically impracticable. Experience suggest that this may be for flows larger than 150–200 kg·s^{-1}.

When fire sizes are relatively small compared to the size of the space, the time taken to fill the space with smoke may be long compared to the times required for escape and firefighting and therefore a smoke extract system may not be required. Such an approach is economic and can be particularly useful where there are adverse wind overpressures or it is difficult to incorporate vents or equipment into existing buildings such as historic buildings. In addition consideration should be given to a dilution type system.

Table 7.1 shows typical applications for various approaches to fire and smoke ventilation. For temperatures, layer heights and dilution criteria suitable for a range of applications, see section 10: *Fire dynamics*.

Table 7.1 Typical applications for fire and smoke ventilation

System type	Typical applications
Temperature controlled	Maintain smoke temperature below that required to cause fracture of glazing in an atrium or to prevent 'flashover'
Clear layer	To extend travel distances or to reduce exit capacity for means of escape
Dilution	To extend travel distances in situations where the space is large compared to the size of the fire, e.g. a tall atrium

7.5.4   Dilution systems

Dilution systems are most beneficial for the case of relatively small fires in large spaces or as means of demonstrating that the initial, smaller and cooler fire does not represent a more hazardous case than the hotter, more buoyant smoke condition which occurs as the fire grows. If a dilution system is designed in combination with a natural smoke control system, wind overpressures are not an issue as long as air change rates are sufficient to ensure adequate dilution.

7.5.5   Wind overpressures

Where natural ventilators are used for smoke extraction, it is important that they be positioned where they will not be adversely affected by external wind conditions. A positive wind pressure can be much greater than the pressures developed by a cooler smoke layer. If this occurs at a smoke exhaust opening the ventilator may act as an inlet rather than an extract. However, if the ventilator is sited in an area of negative wind pressure, the resulting suction force may assist smoke extraction.

The effects of wind pressures on a ventilation system are not isolated to localised wind pressure effects. The wind pressures around the entire building envelope (i.e. global pressures) will dictate the smoke flow patterns within the building and the effectiveness of the ventilation system design. Tall buildings, or taller areas of the same building (such as roof-top plant rooms) can create a positive wind pressure on the upstream section of the lower roof area, see Figure 7.7. On larger roofs there may be sufficiently large variations in the wind pressures to result in adverse inflows even where pressures are negative. Also, large negative pressures at dominant low-level openings can cause a resultant inflow through roof vents even though there may be suction at that roof location. Reference

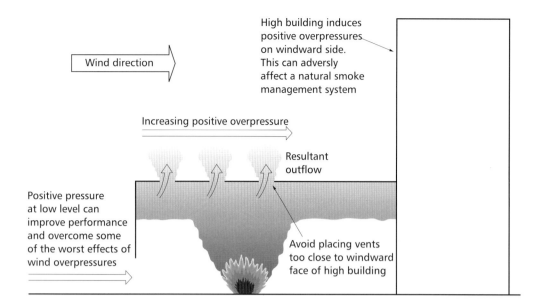

High building induces positive overpressures on windward side. This can adversly affect a natural smoke management system

Figure 7.7 Adverse wind overpressure

Wind direction

Increasing positive overpressure

Resultant outflow

Positive pressure at low level can improve performance and overcome some of the worst effects of wind overpressures

Avoid placing vents too close to windward face of high building

should be made to BS CP3: Chapter V: Part 2[19] to carry out a wind analysis and determine the external pressures at high-level vents and low-level openings, and also to estimate the internal pressure. The commonly quoted acceptance criterion of a roof slope of 30 degrees or less is very simplistic and can only be used as a general guide for simple roof profiles when the internal pressure is zero or positive. A wind analysis should be carried out where there are tall buildings close to natural roof vents.

Ventilators positioned in the vertical façade should be of the casement type to prevent the wind from blowing the smoke back into the smoke reservoir.

In some instances adverse effects may be overcome by positioning the ventilators in regions of the roof which are sheltered from wind action or will always produce suction. In other cases the positioning of suitably designed wind baffles can overcome wind interference or even convert a positive pressure into suction. Locating the low-level openings in regions of positive pressure can also help improve venting. There is a further possibility, whereby vents can be opened selectively in response to signals from a wind direction indicator to ensure that the wind flows are beneficial. For complex building structures, or buildings which may be significantly influenced by the topography of surrounding structures (e.g. those in city centres), it may be desirable to carry out a wind pressure study by one or a combination of the following:

—   consult a wind specialist to carry out a desk study

—   commission a wind tunnel test in conjunction with the structural engineers' wind tunnel tests

—   carry out a computational fluid dynamics (CFD) analysis.

Where adverse wind pressures cannot be overcome, and hence natural ventilators cannot be used, the smoke control designer should employ a mechanical exhaust system.

7.6   Design, reliability and performance

7.6.1   General

The fire engineering design is the first part of a process required to achieve an adequate standard of safety in the building. It is essential to involve the whole design team, the client and the building users. The building services systems required to achieve the performance defined in the fire strategy are a very important component. Particular issues to be addressed include the following:

—   Effective communication of concepts and ideas between design team members is essential.

—   A fault analysis of the engineering system should be carried out at early stage to determine the impact of failure of a component on the performance of the complete system. If the system fails to operate due to the failure of a single component then that component needs to be particularly reliable and therefore may require a particular maintenance regime and, possibly, the provision of back-up arrangements. Careful choice of fail-safe modes and the introduction of sufficient diversity to ensure that single component failure does not cause failure of the system can be advantageous, giving greater flexibility and lower or no safety margins. Fault analysis can take the form of a simple qualitative assessment for straightforward situations with analytical techniques such as 'fault tree' analysis for more complex arrangements.

—   An aspect which is closely allied to the fault analysis is the reliability of the components and the functional dependency of one component on another. The long-term reliability during normal operating conditions and during a fire must be appraised and supported by recognised standard tests and a maintenance programme.

—   The use of a dedicated or non-dedicated system for smoke control systems should be reviewed and assessed in combination with the fault analysis and component failure.

— Effective co-ordination of the normal building services design with the fire engineering requirements at an early stage is likely to give the most cost-effective solution.

The most difficult part of the process is to determine reasonably and economically the engineering system that meets the requirements of the fire strategy. The effects of a fire cannot be predicted precisely and, similarly, the engineering systems cannot be designed to ensure 100% safety. Considerable care, judgement and analysis are required to ensure that an adequate level of safety is reached at a reasonable cost. The following should be considered:

— It is important to know if the fire and smoke predictions are the best estimate and do not include an unknown element of redundancy so that a judgement can be made on the margin of safety, and the extent of any system diversity and reliability required by the design.

— Little or no margin of safety will be necessary if a system design is non-sensitive and the fail-safe modes are clearly defined and advantageous. A requirement of this strategy is that relatively large changes of fire size or hazard result in relatively small changes in the system design. For example, where the objective is to keep the temperature of the smoke below a particular target level, natural smoke ventilation is far less sensitive to changes in fire size than ventilation by mechanical systems. Conversely, a mechanical system is likely to be a more reliable means of maintaining a clear layer in the case of relatively non-buoyant smoke. However, while the above examples are typical, such judgements vary according to the particular design and the criteria which apply to it. The important issue is that the sensitivity of the output to changes in the input must be understood and fully taken into account.

— The method of activation of a smoke control system needs careful thought to ensure correct operation without undue delay (accounting for transport time, dilution and thermal lag) as appropriate to the particular design.

— Many notable fire disasters have involved the failure of control as well as the building performance. Clearly, the designers cannot directly influence building management. However the designer can provide a building that is capable of being managed to achieve a good standard. This requires an understanding of the management requirements and effective communication of the design and maintenance requirements to the client.

With the above background of reliability and performance the fire safety designer should communicate the relevant performance requirements to enable the building services engineer to design the system and specify the appropriate equipment.

7.6.2 Hot smoke tests

Hot smoke tests are commonly performed in Australia but there is no requirement for such testing in the UK.

It is clear that there is a need to demonstrate the functionality of smoke control systems. Many international codes and papers have addressed the issue of hot smoke tests. The only hot smoke test standard identified is Australian Standard AS 4391: 1999: *Smoke management systems — Hot smoke test*[20]. This standard states that the intention is to verify the correct performance of a smoke management system. It makes the point that the test is not intended for all systems. Rather, it provides a tool to resolve uncertainties in some smoke management systems. It also states that the test fire size shall be limited to maximum safe ceiling temperatures. It is accepted that for all other types of fire systems, testing using a real fire source is not required nor desirable. This is because the design calculations used have been based upon tests and incorporates conservative assumptions. The equations used for smoke control systems are also based upon well-established equations that incorporate conservative assumptions. It is therefore recommended that hot smoke tests are not undertaken in non-test house locations in order to validate professionally accepted equations.

As a hot smoke test is used to demonstrate the operation of the smoke control systems, the whole system must be installed and finally commissioned before the test is carried out. In addition, since smoke control relies on certain parts of the air conditioning system being operational to provide make-up air, then the air conditioning system must also be installed and commissioned. Finally, since internal and external doors, windows, walls and other barriers affect the performance of a smoke control system, these must all be in place at the time of the test.

If hot smoke tests are to be carried out, the test fire used should be the minimum required to overcome stratification. In no circumstances should the predicted temperature at the ceiling or on adjacent non-protected surfaces exceed 80 °C. For each test, a test method statement should be produced in advance that includes a theoretical analysis of temperatures in the plume. It is essential that the smoke control systems are complete and commissioned. The test fire must be safely contained and the tracer smoke must be non-toxic.

In order to protect the building's fittings and finishes the fire and type of fuel chosen should be clean burning, producing very little smoke of its own. To visualise the behaviour of smoke under real conditions, the hot plume rising from the fire will have to be doped with a material to make it visible. However, the level of doping cannot be controlled to simulate real conditions of visibility and the exercise cannot be used to assess whether or not tenable conditions would exist on escape routes.

7.6.3 Interaction between sprinklers and smoke vents

There has been much debate over whether sprinklers affect smoke ventilation, or vice versa. Experiments[21] have demonstrated that there are no engineering issues raised where both systems are used in the same building.

7.7 Components of smoke management systems

7.7.1 Ductwork

Smoke extract ducts should be designed to withstand the temperature of the smoke being carried. Where a smoke extract duct passes through another fire compartment it needs to be fire resistant, as it is not acceptable to provide a fire damper. For most buildings, one-hour fire resistance is adequate. For other buildings, e.g. high-rise or retail malls, a higher resistance period may be required.

If a smoke extract system is installed within a single compartment, e.g. car park extract, then the systems does not need to be fire rated. It should comply with Building Regulations Approved Document B[13] and be constructed of material with a melting point above 800 °C. An example of an appropriate specification is HVCA DW144[22].

Some systems of smoke management may not require ductwork to transport smoke to an extract point, e.g. a system using jet fans. Such systems are commonly used in car parks and have been used in retail malls.

7.7.2 Smoke extract fans

Smoke extract fans must be selected to ensure reliability at the design temperature and length of exposure as predicted by the fire engineering calculations. Car park systems for example are commonly specified at 300 °C for one hour.

7.7.3 Dual power supply of standby generator

Smoke extract systems need to function in case of fire. In many cases it is unreasonable to provide a dual power supply or standby generator where local power supplies are of a high quality and are reliable. The likelihood of a power outage affecting the site at the same time as a fire occurring should be assessed. It may not be safe to operate a modern building without normal power and the building may need to be closed until power is returned.

References

1 *Standard for fixed guideway transit and passenger rail systems* NFPA 130 (Quincey, MA: National Fire Protection Association) (2000)

2 Marshall N R, Feng Q S and Morgan H P The influence of a perforated false ceiling on the performance of smoke ventilation systems *Fire Safety J.* **8** (3) 227–237 (1985)

3 *SFPE Handbook of Fire Protection Engineering* (Boston MA: Society of Fire Protection Engineers/Quincey MA: National Fire Protection Association) (2002)

4 *Air infiltration and natural ventilation* Section 4 in CIBSE Guide A: *Environmental design* (London: Chartered Institution of Building Services Engineers) (1999)

5 BS 476: *Fire tests on building materials and structures*: Part 20: 1987: *Method for determination of the fire resistance of elements of construction (general principles)* (London: British Standards Institution) (1987)

6 *Smoke management systems in malls, atria and large areas* NFPA 92B (Quincey, MA USA: National Fire Protection Association) (2000)

7 Klote J H and Milke J A *Design of smoke management systems* (Atlanta GA: American Society of Heating, Refrigerating and Air-Conditioning Engineers) (1992)

8 Barnett C et al. *Fire safety in tall buildings* (New York: Council on Tall Buildings and Urban Habitat/McGraw Hill) (1992)

9 BS 7346: *Components for smoke and heat control systems*: Part 2: *Specification for powered smoke and heat exhaust ventilators* (London: British Standards Institution) (1990)

10 Hansell G O and Morgan H P *Design approaches for smoke control in atrium buildings* BRE Report BR 258 (Garston: Building Research Establishment) (1994)

11 BS 5588: *Fire precautions in the design, construction and use of buildings*: Part 4: 1978: *Code of practice for smoke control using pressure differentials* (London: British Standards Institution) (1998)

12 Harrison R and Miles S *Smoke shafts protecting firefighting shafts: their performand and design* BRE project report 79204 (Garston: BRE FRS) (2002)

13 *Fire safety* The Building Regulations 2000 Approved Document B (London: The Stationery Office) (2003)

14 BS 5588: *Fire precautions in the design, construction and use of buildings*: Part 5: 1991: *Code of practice for firefighting stairs and lifts* (London: British Standards Institution) (1991)

15 Morgan H P and Gardner J P *Design principles for smoke ventilation in enclosed shopping centres* BRE Report BR186 (Garston: Building Research Establishment) (1990)

16 Thomas P H and Hinkley P L *Design of roof venting systems for single storey buildings* Fire Research Technical Paper No. 10 (London: HMSO) (1964)

17 Langdon-Thomas G J and Hinkley P L *Fire venting in single storey buildings* Fire Offices Joint Fire Research Organisation Fire Note 5 (London: HMSO/Ministry of Technology) (1965)

18 *Guidance for the design of smoke ventilation systems for single storey industrial buildings, including those with mezzanine floors, and high racked storage warehouses* Issue 3 (Bourne End: Smoke Ventilation Association/Federation of Environmental Trade Associations) (1994)

19 CP3: *Code of basic data for the design of buildings*: Chapter V: *Loading*: Part 2: 1972: *Wind loads* (London: British Standards Institution) (1972)

20 AS 4391: 1999: *Smoke management systems — Hot smoke test* (Sydney NSW: Standards Australia) (1999)

21 McGrattan, K B, Hamins A and Stroup D W *Sprinkler, smoke and heat vent. Draft curtain interaction: large scale experiments and model development. International fire sprinkler—smoke and heat vent—draft curtain fire test project* NISTIR 6196-1 (Gaithersberg MD: National Institute of Standards and Technology) (1998)

22 *Specification for sheet metal ductwork* HVCA DW 144 (London: Heating and Ventilating Contractors Association) (1998)

8 Fire suppression

8.1 Sprinkler protection

8.1.1 General

The use of a fixed system of water sprayers to fight fire in buildings can be traced back to the 19th century. The earliest systems consisted of simple, manually controlled arrangements of sparge pipes in vital areas but these soon led to individually operated devices attached to a pressurised pipework system. The earliest fixed system in this country is believed to have been installed in the Drury Lane Theatre in 1812.

Other than the refinements in terms of aesthetics and thermal response brought about by improvements in engineering techniques and materials, little has changed in the design principles of sprinkler heads. The original idea of sealing a waterway in a valve with an element which responds to local thermal conditions is both simple and reliable. Unnecessary complexity must be avoided and the introduction of any additional steps between fire detection and the discharge of water must be carefully considered to ensure that real benefits are not outweighed by reduced reliability.

In simple terms a conventional automatic sprinkler system consists of pipes and heat sensitive valves (sprinkler heads) connected to a water supply. Fire is detected by individual sprinkler heads which open to release water, in the form of spray, to the seat of the fire. The alarm is raised at the same time and the fire is kept under control until the arrival of the fire brigade. The principal objective is to control the fire for subsequent extinguishment by the fire brigade but often the sprinklers will have accomplished extinguishment prior to their arrival.

Common factors in large fires are delays in the discovery of the outbreak and a subsequent delay in the commencement of firefighting operations. Automatic sprinkler systems first detect and then immediately attack the fire, thereby restricting the growth of the fire and confining damage. Automatic sprinklers have a good performance record and it may be expected that the majority of fires in sprinkler-protected premises are controlled by the operation of four sprinklers or less. A common misconception is that if one sprinkler head operates then others, not in the fire area, will also operate. This is not the case in normal systems.

This section of Guide E considers the principles of sprinkler system design and identifies the relevant design codes. It is not intended to act as a design manual and specialist advice should be sought when a system needs to be designed.

8.1.2 Fire engineering using sprinklers

The use of a sprinkler system to automatically detect and fight a fire may be exploited as part of an engineered solution. The size of fire, and the rate of release of combustion products may be reasonably predicted where a specific standard is used. The prescriptive guidance of compartment size, fire resistance values etc. where sprinklers are used will depend upon the control of the release of heat from the fire given by sprinkler activation. This is discussed in some detail in section 10: *Fire dynamics*.

It is generally accepted that a fire will stop growing at the time of sprinkler activation. Therefore factors such as the type of risk, expected heat release rate, height of room and location of sprinkler relative to the ceiling are very important as they will directly influence the speed of sprinkler activation.

The spacing and location of sprinklers and the capability of the water supply and feed pipework are crucial in the prediction of sprinkler performance and for this reason the prescription of system engineering given in the various rules and codes should be used wherever possible and practicable. If bespoke or non-standard sprinkler designs are used or some of the system features do not meet the objectives laid down in the rules, their full impact upon the performance of the system's speed of reaction to fire and its ability to restrain fire growth must be taken into account.

For this reason much of this section of Guide E concentrates on the requirements of the rules and the principles upon which they are based. Where the nature of the risk falls outside the scope of the guidance in the rules or novel designs or techniques are employed the objectives of the standard system in terms of response time and water spray performance should be replicated if similar levels of control are to be expected.

8.1.3 Rules and standards

The principal rules applicable to sprinkler installations in the UK and many other parts of the world are the Loss Prevention Council's *Rules for Automatic Sprinkler Installations*[1], commonly known as the LPC *Rules*, which incorporate BS 5306: Part 2: 1990[2]. Prior to 1990, BS 5306: Part 2 took the form of a code of practice, rather than a specification, and the prevailing standard was the 29th edition of the Fire Offices' Committee *Rules for Automatic Sprinkler Installations*[3] (i.e. the 'FOC *Rules*'). The earlier edition of BS 5306: Part 2 made extensive reference to the FOC *Rules* and, when revised to form the 1990 issue, largely adopted the principal standards of the FOC *Rules*. However, building insurers required certain amendments which could not be included in BS 5306 and these are issued as LPC Technical Bulletins. The LPC *Rules* consist of BS 5306: Part 2: 1990 plus the Technical Bulletins.

This section concentrates on the provisions of the LPC *Rules* but some of the other rules which may be encountered are as follows:

— (USA) National Fire Protection Association (NFPA) Standard 13[4]

— Factory Mutual International (FMI) Standard 2-8N[5]

— Verband der Sachsesicherer (VdS) *Rules for sprinkler systems*[6]

— Comité Européen des Assurances (CEA) *Sprinkler systems planning and installation*[7-9]

NFPA standards are applied by most USA-based insurers and may be encountered anywhere in the world. They are likely to be specified in countries where American influence prevails. Factory Mutual is an international insurer which uses NFPA standards as the basis for its own standards. FMI Standard 2-8N is largely similar to NFPA Standard 13 but adjusted to account for FMI's loss experience and approach to risk management.

VdS is the German equivalent of the LPC and its rules are used extensively in Germany and in connection with German-insured risks. The CEA rules may be found in use mainly within Europe. Both are similar in format to the LPC *Rules*[1] but with differing requirements. The use of common standards throughout the European Union will increase as progress is made towards harmonisation of European standards.

A CEN (Comité Européen de Normalisation) provisional standard prEN 12845[10] was published as a final draft in August 2002. The format and content is similar to BS 5306: Part 2[2]. There are annexes at the rear of the document which deal with some of the issues contained in the Technical Bulletins of the LPC *Rules*[1]. Some of these are normative and some informative. It is expected that because of difficulties in achieving consensus at committee level there will be national and local interpretations and requirements which will apply when the standard is adopted by the authorities having jurisdiction.

Other rules may be encountered elsewhere within Europe. Some of these are loosely based on the 29th edition FOC *Rules* which were used as a model in many parts of the world.

8.1.4 Extent of sprinkler protection

Sprinklers are often resisted as part of the building services strategy for reasons such as cost, space considerations, aesthetic considerations and fear of inadvertent discharge. However, sprinkler protection should be as extensive as possible. Areas without sprinkler protection should be adequately separated from sprinklered areas and it is important to recognise that areas without sprinklers may be lost in the event of fire.

Sprinkler systems are designed to control fires at a very early stage in their development and not necessarily to halt the advance of an already established fire. Where it is appropriate to leave an area unprotected by sprinklers it is important to make other provisions for automatic fire detection and, if possible, other automatic firefighting systems.

Protection should be provided throughout the building under consideration, any building which communicates with it and any neighbouring building which represents an exposure hazard to the protected building. If a communicating building or other exposure risk is not to be protected, then the protected building must be separated from the risk of the unprotected building. This is usually accomplished by the nature of the structure between the risk areas but this may be supplemented by, for instance, an external drencher system.

Within any protected building there are usually areas where sprinkler protection would be hazardous, such as metal melt pans or frying ranges, and sprinklers should not be fitted in these situations. The impact of the absence of sprinklers should be fully considered and steps taken to mitigate the risk. This could take the form of alternative active fire protection systems, such as gaseous or water mist, or separation by means of a fire resisting construction. Additionally, there are some areas where sprinklers may not be essential, such as stairs, lifts, toilets etc. These will be scheduled in the rules as 'permitted exceptions' and usually a grade of fire resisting construction is stipulated between the protected and non-protected areas. Cut-off sprinklers — sprinklers fitted on the non-protected side immediately above a window, doorway or other penetration of the compartment wall — can sometimes be used to improve the efficiency of the separation.

8.1.5 Hazard classification

In order to match the capability of the sprinkler system with the type of risk with which it will have to cope, risks are grouped into hazard classifications. There are three main divisions:

— light hazard

— ordinary hazard

— high hazard.

The ordinary and high hazard classes are sub-divided to further qualify the type of risk. The classifications principally depend upon the quantity and type of combustible materials contained in the risk, the speed at which a fire is likely to develop and any processes which will produce particularly severe circumstances for fire propagation.

Premises may often contain a combination of different risk classifications. The allocation of the appropriate classifications can be complex and almost certainly will require qualified judgement. The final decision will often rest with the fire insurer or other authorities having jurisdiction.

There are certain risks, such as oil and flammable liquids and gas hazards, for which standard sprinklers may not be suitable. Special requirements apply in these circumstances and often specialist sprayers are used, sometimes in combination with foam solutions. The USA-based codes offer sound and detailed guidance for these types of risks.

The hazard classification will dictate the minimum amount of water which must be provided at the fire in the form of spray and this is normally expressed as the 'design density' (in mm per minute or litre·m^{-2} per minute). The expected maximum area of the sprinkler system which will be activated by the fire is also dictated and this 'assumed maximum area of operation' (AMAO) is expressed in square metres.

Typical LPC design densities and areas of operation are indicated in Table 8.1. Other rules will have slightly different combinations.

Table 8.1 Minimum design density and assumed maximum areas of operation of sprinklers

Hazard classification	Minimum design density / mm·min^{-1}	Assumed maximum area of operation (AMAO) / m^2
Light	2.25	84
Ordinary:		
— Group I	5	72
— Group II	5	144
— Group III	5	216
— Group III special	5	360
High	7.5–30	260–375

8.1.5.1   Light hazard

Light hazard risks will be non-industrial where the amount and combustibility of contents are low. This includes risks such as hospitals, hotels, offices, schools etc. However, this classification depends upon the size of the fire being very limited and the LPC *Rules* require that the maximum protected room size shall not be greater than 126 m^2 (surrounded by walls of 30 minutes fire resistance) or contain no more than six sprinklers. No areas of storage are permitted within this classification.

In practice these limitations are very restricting and often a risk initially listed as light hazard will be re-classified as ordinary hazard.

8.1.5.2   Ordinary hazard

Ordinary hazard risks will be commercial and industrial occupancies involving the handling, processing and storage of mainly ordinary combustible materials which are unlikely to develop intensely burning fires in the initial stages. This classification is further sub-divided into:

—   Ordinary Hazard Group I

—   Ordinary Hazard Group II

—   Ordinary Hazard Group III

—   Ordinary Hazard Group III special.

Examples of the four group occupancies are given in Table 3 of the LPC *Rules*.

The height to which goods may be stored in an ordinary hazard risk will depend upon the type of goods and the style of storage and these are given in Table 1 of the LPC *Rules*. Storage beyond the stipulated limits will require re-classification as high hazard. Although the LPC *Rules* considers only Ordinary Hazard Group 3 as suitable for protection of storage risks an argument can be made, in fire engineering terms, for lesser Ordinary Hazard Groups to be used when the area of storage is less than or equal to the AMAO and the storage area is enclosed with suitable grades of fire resisting construction. This is based upon the fact that the lower Ordinary Hazard Groups use the same 5 mm·min^{-1} density but with smaller AMAOs.

Each of the four ordinary hazard categories uses the same design density but with an increasing assumed maximum area of operation, related mainly to the expected speed of fire growth.

8.1.5.3   High hazard

High hazard risks will be commercial and industrial occupancies having abnormal fire loads due to:

—   the process taking place

—   the type of goods being stored

—   the height to which goods are stored.

The risks are further sub-divided as follows:

—   high hazard process risks

—   high piled storage risks

—   potable spirit storage

—   oil and flammable liquid hazards.

High hazard process risks

High hazard process risks are further sub-divided into Types 1, 2, 3 and 4 which reflect the likely fire intensity and, in the case of Type 4, fire development speed.

High piled storage risks

High piled storage risks present special problems and consequently the rules relating to their protection are complicated. The type of goods stored will fall into one of four categories, defined in Table 2 of the LPC *Rules*, and the style of storage, defined as eight different types, as scheduled in Table 1 of the *Rules*. The combination of category of goods and storage type will dictate the appropriate method of protection and the capabilities of that protection.

It must be taken into account that materials and storage methods are continually changing and all storage risks must be examined closely to ensure that an appropriate quality of protection is provided. The use of packaging materials may have a very significant impact on the classification of goods in storage. This is particularly significant in the case of expanded plastics which, when used as packaging, can easily convert an innocuous material into a high fire load.

In certain cases, the protection may be accomplished from roof level only but, where goods are stored in racks, intermediate rack level sprinklers may be necessary in addition to the roof level protection. The design density and assumed maximum area of operation for roof level protection, and the number of intermediate rack level sprinklers which must be taken into consideration in determining the capability of the system and the water supply, will be dictated by the *Rules*.

Another, more recent, method of protecting high piled storage risks is early suppression fast response (ESFR) systems. These use specially developed large capacity sprinkler heads fitted with quick response elements which are designed to operate very early in the development of the fire. They deliver very large quantities of water over relatively small areas of operation to effect extinguishment of the fire. The objective of extinguishing, rather than controlling, the fire is one of the major features of this type of system and, although the water volumes are large, the designed duration tends to be shorter so they can be a very effective alternative to systems involving roof plus in-rack sprinklers.

The rules for the spacing and location of sprinklers, feed methods and pipe sizing etc. are laid down in separate sections of the various rules and it will be found that these are fairly restrictive. For instance, the permitted angle of slope for the roof or ceiling is fairly shallow, and the maximum and minimum spacings between sprinklers are not very flexible. Since these rules were developed from specific fire tests for specific situations there is no scope for easement of the stipulated dimensions given in the guidance. If it is found that the detailed requirements cannot be fully met, then a more traditional protection-style system should be used.

Potable spirit storage

Potable spirit storage is given special consideration with separately identified storage types, design densities and assumed maximum areas of operation.

Oil and flammable liquid hazards

Oil and flammable liquids may be stored or used is such quantities, and in such a manner that standard sprinkler protection may not be suitable. In these cases a deluge-type installation using medium and/or high velocity sprayers may be appropriate. Also enhancement of the fire fighting capabilities with foam can be considered. The principles of deluge installations are given in section 8.1.7.7 but detailed consideration of these risks is outside the scope of this Guide. An alternative means of protection of these risks is water mist, which is considered in section 8.4.

8.1.6　　Sprinkler heads

Sprinkler heads are a crucial element in any sprinkler system. In most cases they will act to both detect a fire and release water, in the form of spray, in the appropriate quantities and spray characteristics to fight the fire effectively. Normally the sprinkler has a heat sensitive element, a glass bulb or a fusible metallic link or a combination of both, which, in combination with other elements of the sprinkler, seal the head until activated by the fire. However, sometimes it is desirable for fire detec-

tion and the consequent release of water to be activated by other means. In these circumstances the heat sensitive element and sealing mechanism are removed from the sprinkler and such units are termed 'open' sprinklers. The control of the water supply is by other means, such as a 'deluge' valve, which can be activated electrically or pneumatically.

The operating temperature of sprinkler heads will normally be not less than 30 °C above the highest expected ambient temperature. In most conditions this will result in a sprinkler head rating of 68 °C, indicated by the familiar red bulb. An exception is the case of high piled storage risks where intermediate rack sprinklers are installed and, although the rack sprinklers are normally rated to suit the ambient temperature, the roof level sprinklers are often rated at 141 °C so as to slightly delay their operation. The rack systems are expected to fulfil most of the fire fighting function.

So that sprinklers may be readily identified, the glass bulb or, in the case of fusible link sprinklers, the yoke arms are coloured according to the schedule given in Table 8.2.

Three sizes of sprinkler are generally available to suit the various applications, i.e. nominal orifice sizes of 10, 15 and 20 mm. Generally, 10 mm sprinklers would be expected on light hazard installations, 15 mm on ordinary and high hazard installations and 20 mm on high hazard installations. ESFR sprinklers can have sizes of 20 mm **or** more.

All sprinklers should be tested and approved by a recognised testing house. In the case of LPC installations this would be the Loss Prevention Certification Board (LPCB) and equipment would appear in the current *List of Approved Products and Services*[11], published by the LPCB. Some types of sprinkler head have limited uses and any restrictions or qualifications given in the LPCB list should be fully considered.

The following sections describe the major styles of sprinkler available.

8.1.6.1　　Conventional pattern

Sprinklers of this type give a spherical pattern of discharge with approximately 50% of the spray travelling upwards and 50% towards the floor. In addition to wetting the ceiling, the upward travelling water will collect and fall in larger droplets which have good fire penetration properties. Such 'general purpose' sprinklers are particularly useful where roof steelwork is exposed. They may be designed specifically for upright fitting or for use in pendent configuration. Some sprinklers, termed 'universal', are suitable for installation in either position.

Table 8.2　Schedule of colour coding of sprinkler heads

Glass bulb sprinkler		Fusible link sprinkler	
Temperature (°C)	Bulb colour	Temperature (°C)	Yoke arm colour
57	orange	55–77	uncoloured
68	red	80–107	white
79	yellow	121–141	blue
93	green	163–191	red
141	blue	204–246	green
182	mauve	260–302	orange
227–260	black	320–343	black

8.1.6.2 Spray pattern

Spray pattern sprinklers give a downward parabolic pattern of discharge with only about 20% of the spray travelling upwards. These sprinklers will be designed either for upright or pendent application.

8.1.6.3 Ceiling or flush pattern

These sprinklers are suitable for use on suspended ceilings and normally have the body of the sprinkler concealed within the ceiling with the heat sensitive element protruding below the ceiling. Recessed pattern sprinklers are those where the sprinkler body and all or part of the heat sensitive element are above the plane of the ceiling. Concealed pattern sprinklers are fully recessed into the ceiling with an additional cover plate at ceiling level. The cover plate is attached to the sprinkler body with fusible elements so that the cover plate reacts to the fire first and drops away to allow the sprinkler itself to react to the thermal conditions.

In some ceiling pattern sprinklers the deflector plates are not rigidly fixed to the sprinkler body but move downwards on chains or rods when the sprinkler is activated. In these cases there are restrictions applied to the circumstances of their use.

All ceiling style sprinklers are likely to react more slowly to fire conditions than more traditional designs, principally because the heat sensitive element is not located in the zone where the gases are hottest. The hottest gas layer is likely to be located 75–100 mm below a flat ceiling and the location of the sprinkler relative to this layer will have a bearing on the likely response time.

Care should be taken to ensure that only sprinklers designed to be recessed are fitted in such a way. There are two piece escutcheon plates available which are designed to allow fitting of the ceiling mounted sprinkler prior to the installation of the ceiling tile and it is possible to use these to effectively recess a sprinkler type which is not designed to be recessed.

8.1.6.4 Sidewall pattern

These sprinklers are designed to be sited along the walls and produce a spray pattern which is predominantly in one direction only. They should not be considered as an alternative to normal sprinklers but can be useful in certain circumstances, e.g. under flat ceilings and where headroom is restricted. They are not suitable for high hazard installations or above ceilings.

8.1.6.5 ESFR pattern

These sprinklers are quick acting, high performance devices specifically designed for use in high piled storage risks with protection from roof level only. They are not suitable for any other application.

The volume of water used with these sprinklers is significantly higher than normal sprinklers and consequently these will have large bore inlets (i.e. at least 20 mm). The spray pattern developed will be similar to that of a 'spray'

sprinkler but the droplet size is likely to be larger, giving very good plume penetration properties.

8.1.6.6 Other devices

Other devices which may be encountered include the following:

— Multiple controls which consist of valves, held in the closed position with a heat sensitive device and used to feed open sprinkler heads or sprayers.

— Medium velocity sprayers which produce a directional spray of fine droplets for controlling fires involving combustible liquids and gases having low flashpoints and to cool the surfaces of vessels.

— High velocity sprayers having open nozzles producing a directional spray of larger droplets for extinguishing fires in combustible liquids with higher flashpoints.

— Dry pendent sprinklers which take the form of special pipes with a valve at one end and a sprinkler head at the other. Operation of the sprinkler head at the bottom of the drop pipe opens the valve at the top end and allows water to pass down the pipe to the sprinkler outlet. They are used in situations where a pendent sprinkler is required on a system which is not normally charged with water, e.g. dry, alternate wet and dry or pre-action systems, and where the water which would normally be trapped in the drop pipe to the sprinkler head cannot be tolerated.

— Dry upright sprinklers operate on similar principles to dry pendent sprinklers but are less commonly encountered.

8.1.6.7 Thermal sensitivity of sprinkler heads

The speed at which the heat sensitive element of a sprinkler head will react to the local thermal conditions will depend upon many factors including the size and structure of the bulb or link, the material, shape and size of the sprinkler body and the type of fitting into which the sprinkler is fitted.

The speed at which they react can be measured and compared using standard apparatus and this is normally carried out during the approval procedure for any particular sprinkler head. The response time index (RTI) is a measure of sprinkler thermal sensitivity and sprinklers are graded according to the sensitivity range into which they fall. Three response classes are recognised:

— *standard response A*: corresponding to RTI values between 80 and 200

— *special response*: corresponding to RTI values between 50 and 80

— *quick response*: corresponding to RTI values of 50 or less.

Recessed, concealed and horizontal sidewall sprinklers are not classified and are referred to as 'unrated'.

It should be borne in mind that if sprinklers are to be used in a fire engineered solution and their speed of operation must be predicted the response time index (RTI) of the head must be used in the calculation. It follows that sprinklers which are unrated, and that includes most flush, recessed and concealed sprinklers, have no RTI and cannot be used.

BS 5306: Part 2[2] does not consider the thermal sensitivity of sprinkler heads but LPC Technical Bulletin TB20[12] deals with this matter in some detail and makes specific recommendations on the suitability of the various ratings of sprinkler heads for different types of risk.

As quick response sprinklers are likely to operate earlier in the development of a fire than would standard response sprinklers it follows that the control effect of the sprinklers is likely to take place when the fire size is less. If the fire size is less then the demand on the water supply should also be less and the hydraulic demand on the system should also be reduced. Similarly the smoke management system may be subject to a reduced demand if the fire size is restricted, see section 7: *Fire and smoke ventilation*. These factors can reduce the impact made by a fire incident on the building and, consequently, on the resulting costs. Although the design codes have not so far been changed to take account of these effects the benefits of quick response sprinklers may be exploited in fire-engineered solutions for appropriate projects.

8.1.7 Types of sprinkler system

The method of feeding the water supply to the sprinkler heads, the control of that supply and the method of raising the alarm must be suitable for the type of risk, its location and its environment.

Various types of system have been devised to meet the differing requirements and these are described below.

A common element for all system types is a means to isolate the system from the water supply; one or more valves are placed in the supply line such that the supply of water may be isolated by the fire brigade following a fire when they are satisfied that the fire is under control or extinguished. The same control valve is used to shut the system down for maintenance, alteration or extension.

The size of an installation should be limited in order that the area isolated during shutdown is not too extensive. Also, for those installations which are not charged with water at all times, the speed of delivery of water to the fire is a further consideration. For each type of installation, the maximum number of sprinklers permitted is stipulated in the rules.

In the case of systems which are in a 'dry' mode the speed of delivery of water in the event of fire should be carefully considered. LPC Technical Bulletin TB21[13] suggests a maximum pipe volume of 2.5 m³ or a delivery of water to the most remote single sprinkler within 60 seconds. This will be found to be onerous in terms of system design. In the case of an engineered solution, the delay in delivery of water from a sprinkler once it has operated must be fully taken into account. The limitation of fire size will not begin until water is delivered and the effectiveness of the sprinkler operation could be prejudiced if this delay is excessive.

8.1.7.1 Wet installations

This is the simplest and consequently the most reliable system, by far. It is also the most common. The entire system pipework is charged with water under its operational pressure and in the event of sprinkler head operation the water is discharged immediately.

Installations of this type are suitable for most risks but not where there is a danger that the water in the pipework may freeze or where the temperature may exceed 70 °C.

8.1.7.2 Alternate wet and dry installations

These systems are designed for areas which are subject to winter frosts. During the warmer months the system is operated as a wet installation but, prior to the onset of frosts, the system is thoroughly drained and the control valves set to 'winter' operation. In this mode the system pipework is charged with air under modest pressure. When a sprinkler head operates the air pressure is reduced which actuates the control valve allowing water into the system and thereby to reach the operating sprinkler head(s). As soon as there is no danger of freezing the system should be returned to wet operation.

The disadvantage of this type of system is the potential delay between sprinkler operation and the arrival of water to the fire area. Therefore the number of sprinkler heads which may be fed from this type of installation is restricted to a smaller number than that for wet systems. A slight relaxation in this restriction is allowed when an 'exhauster' or 'accelerator' is fitted to the valve set. Such devices detect the drop in air pressure resulting from sprinkler operation and operate to charge the system with water more rapidly than would otherwise be possible.

Alternate wet and dry installations are not suitable for high hazard storage risks nor are they to be used where the temperature may exceed 70 °C.

8.1.7.3 Dry installations

These should only be considered for areas where a wet or alternate wet and dry installation cannot be used. Installations of this type are permanently charged with air under pressure and the action of the system is identical to that described for winter operation of alternate wet and dry systems.

As well as being suitable for areas subject to permanent frost conditions, such as cold stores, they are appropriate for areas where the temperature is likely to exceed 70 °C, such as drying ovens.

8.1.7.4 Tail-end alternate/tail-end dry systems

If limited areas of a wet installation are subject to frost, either periodically or permanently, then it is possible to install a small alternate or dry system as an extension to the wet system. These are termed tail-end alternate or tail-end dry systems. The provisions and restrictions noted above for the appropriate full systems apply equally to these extensions.

8.1.7.5 Pre-action installations

This is a special type of dry installation which incorporates additional measures to pre-arm the system in the event of detection of the fire by another system. There are two different types of system but in both cases an electronic fire detection system must be installed in the same area as the sprinkler system. The detection system and its integration with the control system should comply with an appropriate standard to ensure that it will operate when required.

Type 1 systems

The pipework is fed through a special 'pre-action' valve and water is only released into the system pipework upon the actuation of the fire detection system, usually on the coincidence operation of two fire detectors. When the system is in its normal operating mode the system pipework is charged with low pressure compressed air which will escape in the event of damage to a sprinkler head or to the system pipework. This will raise the alarm but not allow water into the system. Simultaneous operation of the fire detection system and a sprinkler head is required before water can discharge from the system.

Such systems are particularly suited to situations where the inadvertent operation of a sprinkler head, or a damaged pipe, would have exceptionally expensive or disruptive consequences. However, the added complication, and reliance upon a fire detection system, reduce reliability. Consequently these systems should be considered only where there is no alternative. They should not be considered for high hazard risks.

Type 2 systems

These are alternate wet and dry or dry installations in which the detection system is used to charge the system with water at an early stage during fire development and prior to operation of the sprinkler heads. This is appropriate on large systems with a high volume and also where high hazards are involved and rapidly growing fires are likely to occur. In the event of failure of the detection system, the installation will operate as a conventional alternate or dry installation.

8.1.7.6 Recycling installations

The flow of water into the installation is controlled by a system of heat detectors installed in the same area as the sprinklers. The flow control valve is designed to open and close in response to the heat detectors and, after a pre-determined delay, can close down the water supply when the sprinklers have controlled the fire. The supply may be re-opened in the event of re-establishment of the fire. Such systems offer the obvious attraction of reduced water damage but there are also drawbacks and installations of this type should only be considered after full consultation with the authorities having jurisdiction.

8.1.7.7 Deluge installations

These are systems in which it is desired to operate all of the sprinklers simultaneously. The sprinklers, sprayers or nozzles are of the unsealed, or open, type and are attached to a system of pipework connected to a deluge valve or, for smaller systems, a multiple control. Sensing of the fire can be by electronic fire detection or by a 'dry pilot' system in the risk area in which sprinkler heads are fitted to pneumatic pipework. Normally it is possible to release the system manually at the control valve station or some other location. Installations of this type are normally found on oil or flammable liquid risks, gaseous risks, cooling from exposure risks and high hazard Type 4 process risks.

8.1.8 System components

8.1.8.1 General

Many of the components necessary in a sprinkler system are tested and approved by a recognised third party testing facility. In the case of LPC installations this is the Loss Prevention Certification Board (LPCB). These components include items such as:

— alarm valves
— accelerators and exhausters
— deluge valves
— adjustable drop pipes
— direct reading flow meters
— multiple controls
— pipe couplings and fittings
— pre-action systems
— re-cycling systems
— electrical alarm pressure switches
— sprinkler heads
— suction tanks
— vortex inhibitors
— water flow alarm switches
— water sprayers and systems
— fire pumps.

The approval list of products are usually updated annually and these should be checked before any item is specified. Standard items such as pipes, fittings, stopvalve and the like are usually referred to in the codes and rules by a recognised national or international standard.

It is most important that all components should be fit for purpose and of a quality that will not be detrimental to the longevity of the system or its potential to operate correctly in fire conditions.

The principal components of a typical sprinkler system are shown in Figure 8.1.

8.1.8.2 Control valves

Every installation will have a main stopvalve, usually located at ground floor level or entry level and often in a special chamber such that access to the valve is controlled. In any case, stopvalves located between the water source and the sprinkler head should be secured in their correct operating position with a strap and padlock.

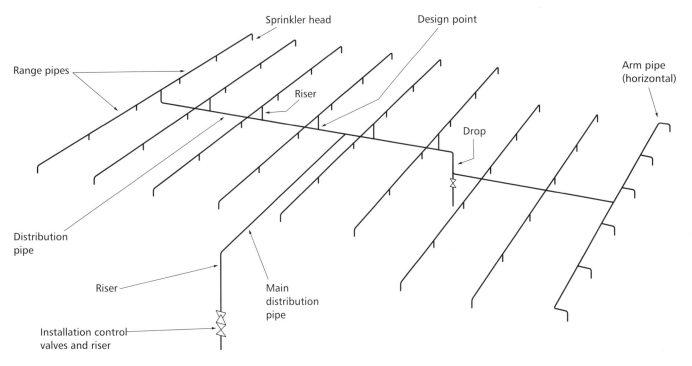

Figure 8.1 Principal components of a typical sprinkler system

As a general principle there should be no other stopvalves downstream of the main stopvalve but there are circumstances in which subsidiary stopvalves are appropriate and permitted. Such circumstances include:

(a) Immediately downstream of an installation valve set where it is undesirable to allow water to enter the system proper during testing and exercising of the valve set; for example, the case of a dry installation feeding a cold storage warehouse.

(b) On the feed to protection of a computer or similar area.

(c) To control the zones in life safety multi-zoned installations, including high rise and multi-storey systems where 'floor control' is required.

(d) On the feed to sprinklers in special locations where they must be isolated and temporarily removed to gain access to plant or machinery. The LPC *Rules* quote the hoods over the dry ends of paper making machines as an example of such a situation but sprinklers located under any large removable floor panels for major plant access may be equally applicable.

(e) On each zone of a multi-zoned installation, for instance in a multi-unit shopping centre.

(f) On life safety valve sets to facilitate isolation for maintenance whilst keeping the system operational.

In all circumstances the subsidiary valves must be secured in the open position and care must be taken to avoid situations where a section of sprinkler protection can remain isolated without detection. In life safety installations the valves must be electrically monitored. This method of improving valve security should be applied to any system where it is desirable to increase reliability.

Subsidiary stopvalves should be located on the same floor level that they supply and be situated where they are not subject to casual interference. For instance, on a high rise multi-storey installation the floor control stopvalve would normally be located in a special cupboard, clearly marked and secured, and situated in the firefighting lobby on each floor.

8.1.8.3   Pipework and fittings

The various types of acceptable pipe and fittings are usually defined within the applicable rules. The preferences of the authorities having jurisdiction, e.g. the fire insurer, local authority etc., must always be considered when choosing the materials and methods of installation. For instance, the use of plastic pipe on the underground feed main to an installation may not meet with the approval of a particular authority due to poor field experiences.

The anticipated use and life expectancy of the building may also influence the choice of materials. If the environment is corrosive then clearly the wet system components must be adequately protected. Alternate wet and dry systems are prone to more rapid internal corrosion than systems which are perpetually charged with water and the use of unprotected steel pipe may limit the life of the pipework to 20 years or less. The use of galvanised pipe may be considered as a means of extending the life of the pipework.

A more recent development has been the use of plastic (chlorinated polyvinyl chloride) pipes and fittings in above-ground (i.e. fire-exposed) situations. There are usually specific qualifications regarding their use. However, it is likely that the use of such materials will increase.

This material has proven to be particularly good for domestic and residential applications and retro-fitting in premises such as hotels, where the light weight and ease of installation are particularly important. It is likely that this material will be used more extensively in the future.

The use of welding is another area where consideration should be given to authority preferences. The practice of *in situ* welding is restricted within the LPC *Rules* to pipes of diameter greater than 50 mm but should be avoided if possible. These restrictions are due to the difficulties of quality control and the increased risk of fire on site (see section 12: *Fire safety on construction sites*). A strict quality control system for welded pre-fabrication is essential and techniques such as set-in sockets and 'cut and shut' direction changes should not be permitted.

The *Rules* offer many options for pipe materials and jointing methods but usually the choice made will be based upon a balance of material cost and availability, ease of installation, flexibility to take up site variances, experience and tradition and avoidance of future problems with maintenance. This tends to lead to a common approach within the industry and, for example, a typical wet installation in the UK would include:

— An underground feed main in high performance polyethylene (HPPE) pipework with fusion welded joints and fittings.

— Installation pipework downstream of the alarm valve in black medium grade steel tube to BS 1387[14], shop pre-fabricated as far as practicable. Mains over 50 mm diameter with welded branches and sockets, joined to adjacent pipework with mechanical grooved joints and to plant items with flanges. Pipework of diameter 50 mm or less fabricated with screwed joints to BS 21[15] and joined with screwed fittings to BS 143[16].

The use of more radical styles of pipework feed may be considered provided that all authorities having jurisdiction are consulted. An example of this would be the use of the circular hollow section roof structure to double as a sprinkler distribution network.

8.1.8.4   Pipework support

The components and materials for pipework supports are specified in the *Rules* but common sense, good engineering practice and clear objectives are all important. The likelihood that the system will be subject to significant dynamic thrusts and have to remain intact in fire conditions must be borne in mind when choosing materials. In corrosive environments the fixing components should be suitably protected.

Various fixing styles are available and even those not specifically identified within the *Rules* may be considered provided that they are genuinely equivalent to those specified in the *Rules*. All fixings must, however, be capable of being subjected to the test loads quoted in the *Rules*.

8.1.8.5   Alarms

Every installation should be provided with a water motor alarm gong, driven from a supply emanating from the control valve set. Consequently the gong must be reasonably close to the valve set. The maximum length of the pipe feed and appropriate sizes are specified in the LPC *Rules*[1]. Occasionally false alarms may be caused by fluctuations in town mains water pressure. This may be

overcome by fitting a 'retard chamber' to the alarm gong feed pipework or a small top-up or 'jockey' pump to raise the pressure on the downstream side of the alarm valve after weekly testing.

Often it is desirable to monitor the alarm condition of the valve set electrically or provide a repeat of the alarm at some remote location. This may be accomplished by fitting a pressure switch in the alarm gong feed pipework, located upstream of the isolating valve on the gong feed.

More detailed information on the flow of water into a particular area or zone can be provided by a water flow alarm switch. A suitably sized test cock must be provided downstream of the switch to test and exercise the unit. These switches are prone to failure if not regularly exercised, so a permanent connection from the test cock to a drain is desirable and may be required by the authorities. They may not be suitable for use on systems other than 'wet' systems as the mechanism of the switch may be damaged by the rapid actuation when water floods a 'dry' pipe.

Pressure switches are also used to activate pumps and compressors, to monitor system pressures and to raise alarms in given circumstances on specific systems, such as reduced trunk mains pressure in a life safety system or reduced air pressure in a pre-action installation. It is essential that all switches are of a type approved by a recognised testing house and that means are provided by which their performance may be tested.

Where premises are unoccupied at any time it may be desirable to install a system to transmit an alarm signal to the fire brigade or a remote manned centre automatically. This may be accomplished through the main fire alarm panel for the building.

All alarm systems and wiring should be in accordance with the provisions of BS 5839[17].

8.1.9   Installation planning

It is essential that the provision of sprinkler protection is properly planned in order that:

(a) the system fully meets the needs of the risk and is capable of controlling an outbreak of fire

(b) as many of the potential future uses of the building as possible are taken into account within the original design

(c) the specific requirements of the owner/occupier, local authority, fire insurers and other authorities having jurisdiction are met

(d) the local and national water by-laws are observed

(e) the sprinkler system forms an integrated part of the overall construction, fire detection and fighting and means of escape strategies for the premises

(f) the system is co-ordinated with the fabric of the building and other building services so as to minimise the aesthetic impact on the project.

Consultation with all interested parties should take place at the earliest time and the fire protection engineer should be involved as soon as possible when aspects such as building construction, space planning and services spaces may be influenced. The consequences of the operation in fire and non-fire conditions should also be considered and such matters as drainage of water resulting from sprinkler operation should be taken into account. The possibility of damage or interference to the system, both accidental and deliberate, should be 'designed out' wherever possible and contingency plans drawn up to deal with all eventualities should such damage arise.

In terms of the building itself, as many aspects as possible should be taken into account at the earliest possible stage in the building design process. These include, but are not limited to, the following:

— The occupancy and any processes which are to take place in the premises. This information will be used to determine the hazard classifications which will apply to the risk — it is not unusual for several different classifications to apply to various parts of the premises.

— The details of any goods on the premises and the heights and storage methods planned. Each type of goods will be given a category and the combination of category of goods, the storage method and height of storage will determine further the type and classification of protection.

— Details of town main sources, including full flow testing of the mains to establish their suitability to supply water for the installation, either directly or as infill to a water storage tank.

— Details of any existing water storage tanks, reservoirs, lakes, rivers etc. which may have potential as feeds to the sprinkler system.

— Potential locations of the installation control valves including consideration of fire brigade access in fire conditions and the need for disposal of test and system drain water.

— Potential locations of any main risers through the building and subsidiary control valve locations, where planned.

— Potential locations of storage tanks and pump house where these are proposed.

— Details of the planned electrical supply to the project, where an electric driven pump is necessary, to establish if this is of sufficient capacity and reliability.

— An outline of the principal routes of main distribution pipes such that any structural or architectural impacts may be taken into account early in the design process.

The effects of water run-off, resulting from the operation of the sprinkler system and any other firefighting operations, should be fully considered in the emergency planning. This will be especially crucial where soluble materials or chemicals are at risk or where synthetic foams are used in the firefighting system.

8.1.10   Installation design

8.1.10.1   Sprinkler spacing and location

The spacing and location of sprinklers is a most important element of the design of the system. It dictates the speed of response and the effectiveness of the sprinkler protection, and ultimately will have a major influence upon the severity of a fire incident and its impact on the building. The principles of design are relatively simple and are based on common sense but the most important factor concerning sprinkler performance is having a thorough understanding of the fundamentals of fire dynamics (see section 10: *Fire dynamics*).

A series of maximum values is given as a guide to the designer but these should not be taken as target values. For instance, in a high hazard risk the spacing of sprinkler heads may be reduced to a value significantly below the maximum in order to accomplish an improvement in the hydraulic demands upon the system. Similarly, the spacing in certain areas may be reduced to enhance performance in that area of the risk. The approach must be one of balance, based on sound engineering skills and experience.

Where sprinklers are being used as part of an integrated fire engineering strategy, the speed of sprinkler operation may be crucial to the strategy objectives. The spacing and location of sprinkler heads relative to the ceiling or roof must be carefully considered.

When measuring distances and areas on sprinkler spacing these are normally taken in the horizontal plane.

Spacing of sprinklers

The LPC *Rules*[1] prescribe the following maximum values for sprinkler head spacing of normal (i.e. non-sidewall) sprinklers according to classification of risk:

— light hazard: 21 m² per sprinkler

— ordinary hazard: 12 m² per sprinkler

— high hazard: 9 m² per sprinkler.

This area is calculated as that located between four adjacent sprinkler heads and is regardless of the spacing method used for the sprinklers (i.e. standard or staggered) for ordinary hazard risks.

The maximum allowable distance between sprinkler heads for 'standard' spacing is:

— light hazard: 4.6 m

— ordinary hazard: 4.0 m

— high hazard: 3.7 m.

In the case of light hazard risks, it is almost possible to use the maximum spacing in both directions (i.e. between ranges and along ranges) and not exceed the maximum areas whereas, in the case of ordinary hazard, a spacing of 4.0 m × 4.0 m is not permitted since this exceeds the maximum area coverage. If the spacing is 4.0 m in one direction then the maximum in the other direction must be 3.0 m. A spacing 3.6 m in one direction would allow a maximum of 3.33 m in the other and so on. Similarly, in the case of high hazard risks, the maximum spacings are 3.7 m × 2.43 m, 3.0 m × 3.0 m etc.

With ordinary hazard risks, 'staggered' spacing may be used whereby adjacent rows of sprinklers are offset. In this case the maximum distance between rows is still 4.0 m but the distance between sprinklers along the range may be increased to a maximum of 4.6 m. The 12 m² maximum area still remains, however, so a sprinkler spacing of 4.6 m along the range would restrict spacing in the other direction to 2.6 m. Situations in which staggered spacing is truly appropriate are rare and this layout should not be adopted without careful consideration of all aspects of the present and future needs of the area.

Other rules may require slight variations on the values specified in the LPC *Rules*.

A balanced spacing of sprinklers in both directions is likely to give the most effective firefighting arrangement as well as being more aesthetically pleasing.

In addition to the maximum distances between sprinklers there is also a minimum distance of 2.0 m in all cases to which the LPC *Rules* apply. This is to prevent 'washing', whereby water from one operating sprinkler cools the adjacent sprinkler and prevents or delays its operation. Some other standards will allow spacings down to 1.8 m between sprinklers.

Figure 38 of the LPC *Rules*[1], reproduced here as Figure 8.2, illustrates standard and staggered sprinkler spacing.

Another simple method of evaluating acceptable standard spacing is shown in Figure 8.3. Perimeter distances are, of course, subject to the maximum values discussed above.

For sidewall sprinklers, which are only suitable for light and ordinary hazard risks, the maximum area coverage is 17 m² per sprinkler for light hazard and 9 m² per sprinkler for ordinary hazard. This spacing is most suited to rooms of width 3.7 m or less where a single row of sprinklers spaced at a maximum 4.6 m (light hazard) or 3.4 m (ordinary hazard) centres is permitted. Where this room width is exceeded the spacing becomes more complex and is beyond the scope of this Guide. In any case sidewall sprinklers should not be considered as an alternative to normal sprinklers and should be used only if there is no alternative.

Sprinklers should be installed upright or pendent, as appropriate to the style of sprinkler, and perpendicular to the slope of the roof, i.e. with the deflector parallel to the slope.

In general, the spacing of sprinklers from the boundaries of rooms or spaces is limited to one half of the distance between adjacent sprinklers in the same direction. The general exception is the case of staggered spacing where the maximum distance is one half of the sprinkler spacing and one quarter of the sprinkler spacing on alternate rows.

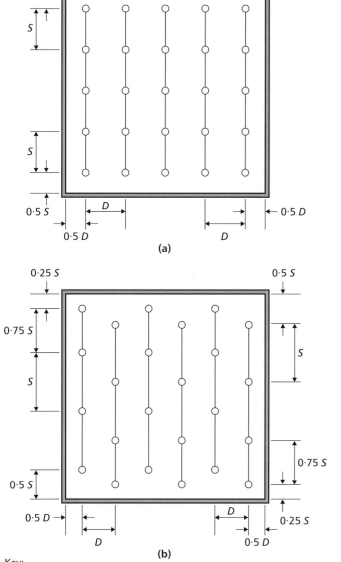

Key:
S is spacing between sprinklers on range pipes
D is spacing between range pipes
All dimensions shown are in metres

Figure 8.2 Sprinkler arrangements; (a) standard layout (rectangular matrix), (b) staggered layout for ordinary hazard systems where *S* is to exceed 4 m (reproduced from the LPC Rules[1] and BS 5306: Part 2[2] by permission of the Loss Prevention Council and the British Standards Institution)

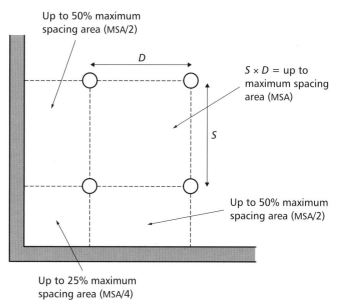

Figure 8.3 Calculation of perimeter distance

Particular exceptions are:

— ceilings with open joists

— roofs in which the rafters are exposed

— where the external walls are metal or asbestos cement with a combustible, bitumen, tar or pitch lining or if the external face is open.

In these cases the maximum distance is 1.5 m. It is generally accepted practice to consider normal external glazing as a combustible material since it is likely to fail in fire conditions.

An absolute minimum distance from walls or partitions is not given in the LPC *Rules*. Some USA standards call for a minimum distance of 100 mm. It is good practice, however, to avoid placing sprinklers closer than 150 mm to avoid spray disruption due to backwash.

The provision of atria in buildings may present special problems. Often these are too lofty for effective protection by sprinklers and the location of sprinklers at the edges of adjacent floors may require special consideration to enhance their ability to 'cut-off' the atrium from the protected floor.

It has been recognised for many years that sprinkler protection increases the life of glazing in fire situations and external drencher systems have been used to protect buildings from the effects of fire in adjacent buildings. Although not covered by existing codes, there is no reason why this practice should not be extended to provide protection for internal elements of buildings as part of a fire-engineered design. The location and spacing of the sprinklers would need to be determined for the particular situation but locating sprinklers within 600 mm of glazing should provide a good spray distribution over the glazing.

Systems have been designed for protecting atria which combine electronic flame detectors with open sprinklers or sprayers, fed on a zoned deluge system. Such systems are not covered by present codes. Therefore each system must be tailored to suit the particular objectives and circumstances, with the agreement of the appropriate authorities. The objectives would be to replicate the speed of sprinkler response and design density given by a 'standard' system for the risk involved. This has been achieved in some systems by using analogue infra-red flame detection linked to a microprocessor programmed to activate various stages of alarm from first detection of any fire through to activation of the deluge system when a fire of, say, 0.75 MW heat release rate has been detected.

Where sloping soffits or roofs are encountered the hot gases produced from a fire will tend to collect first at the highest point of the roof. Therefore the LPC *Rules*[1] require that, in general, sprinklers should be located within 750 mm, measured radially, from the ridge when the roof slope exceeds 1 in 3 or 18.5°.

The positioning of sprinklers in relation to the ceiling or soffit is also very important since this will affect the operating speed of individual sprinklers. The gas strata immediately adjacent to the soffit will be cooled by the fabric of the ceiling and therefore the *Rules* dictate that the sprinklers should be located between 75 mm and 150 mm below the soffit in order to place the sprinkler

within the zone of the hottest gases. Where the roof or ceiling is combustible and has either exposed common rafters or open joists the *Rules* require that the 150 mm dimension is not exceeded. Where the roof or ceiling is combustible but has a plane surface or is constructed of frangible materials such as asbestos cement sheeting or wired glass, the maximum dimension is extended to 300 mm. If the ceiling or roof is of non-combustible construction then in general terms the maximum distance should be no more than 450 mm. It should be noted, however, that the 75 mm to 150 mm dimension should be considered as a target in all cases and increased to the stated maximum only if the ideals cannot be achieved.

With sidewall sprinklers there is less room for tolerance and the deflectors must be between 100 mm and 150 mm below the ceiling with the sprinkler located between 50 mm and 150 mm from the wall face.

Downstand beams or other projections must be taken into account in the spacing and location of sprinklers. Where beams are in excess of 300 mm deep in the case of combustible ceilings, or 450 mm in the case of non-combustible ceilings, the beam must be treated as a boundary and the sprinklers spaced accordingly. It is possible that the 'beam rule' may be applied in the location and spacing of heads where the dimensions are less than those stated. This allows for the sprinkler to be placed in a specified relationship with the underside of the beam, related to the type of sprinkler and its horizontal distance from the beam. The dimensions are indicated in Table 77 and Figure 47 of the LPC *Rules*[1] but experience and judgement must be brought to bear when applying this guidance since there may be other factors which will influence whether to apply the beam rule or modify the dimensions.

The positioning of sprinklers in relation to trusses and girders is complex and concerns minimising the disruption of spray by the steel members. This is dealt with in sections 26.5.3 and 26.5.4 of the LPC *Rules*.

The relationship of sprinklers to columns is also important and the LPC *Rules* require that if a sprinkler is located within 0.6 m of a column then another sprinkler must be located within 2.0 m of the opposite side of the column. Again, common sense must be applied in interpreting this aspect of the *Rules*.

A clear space must be maintained below all sprinkler heads in order to allow the spray to distribute efficiently. In normal risks this is a minimum of 0.5 m but where storage risks are concerned this is increased to 1.0 m.

Supplementary sprinklers

Additional sprinklers must be fitted in situations where the spray from high level sprinklers may be disrupted. Typical examples include platforms, walkways, stairways, ducts etc. but any potential obstructions should be considered. The general rule applicable to such obstructions is that any item more than 0.8 m in width which is within 150 mm of a wall or partition, or otherwise any item more than 1.0 m in width, should have supplementary sprinklers provided below. In the case of circular ducts the equivalent dimensions are 1.0 m and 1.2 m respectively.

Where banks of services obstruct the spray from high level sprinklers additional sprinklers should be fitted. Experience and judgement will be necessary to determine whether or not this is required.

Other areas for which additional or supplementary sprinklers must be considered include escalators, lift and hoist shafts, silos, cyclones, machinery pits etc. but no area of the premises should be overlooked by the fire protection engineer. Care should be taken to ensure that other life safety codes or standards are taken into consideration where planning the extent of protection. For example, sprinkler protection would not be fitted in the shaft of a firefighting lift.

Suspended ceilings

Where suspended ceilings are fitted, the LPC *Rules* call for the void formed between floors and the ceiling below should be protected if it is in excess of 0.8 m deep and contains combustible materials or in not wholly formed of non combustible materials. With other rules this dimension may vary slightly.

If the suspended ceilings are of open cell construction (e.g. 'Formalux' or 'Magnagrid') then special rules apply which, in certain circumstances, allow for a single level of protection located within the ceiling space. Reference should be made to the LPC *Rules* for detailed requirements but, in simple terms, the ceiling must not obstruct more than 30% of the free area of the ceiling and any services or other obstructions should not increase this obstruction to more than 40%. There must be a gap between the ceiling and the soffit sufficient to allow the sprinkler to be located 800 mm above the ceiling line and the spacing of sprinklers above the ceiling is restricted to 9 m² per sprinkler with a maximum dimension between sprinklers of 3.0 m. This style of protection is not suitable for storage risks or high hazard risks.

Storage risks

High hazard storage risks may require the installation of intermediate level sprinklers. The positioning of these sprinklers is dictated by the method of storage and the category of goods being stored. The method of storage is divided into 10 types; types S1 to S8 inclusive relate to normal goods and types S9 and S10 relate to potable spirit storage. Four categories of commodities are scheduled, category I being the least hazardous and category IV the most hazardous.

The methods of storage and materials stored will continue to evolve and the fire safety engineer should be alert to these changes to ensure that the method of protection is appropriate to the risk. Simple schedules of goods and corresponding categories may not be sufficient where combustible packaging is concerned. Also the continuing challenge to store goods more efficiently is likely to have an impact upon the fire protection system. LPC Technical Bulletin TB17[18] provides a useful method of adjusting the categories of goods to take account of combustible contents or packaging.

The potential for commercial loss tends to be much greater where a storage risk is involved and the type of fire which can occur can be much more intense and spread more rapidly than in the case of non-storage risks. Consequently it is important to consider all aspects of the risk during design and it is likely that the fire insurers and other interested parties will wish to be fully involved in the specification of the system requirements.

It is not practicable to consider all combinations of storage types and categories of goods but a typical storage risk with intermediate sprinklers is illustrated in the following example.

Example: storage type S5

The most common storage method in high hazard storage risks is palletised beam pallet racking, termed S5 type storage. The terms used to describe the various features of this type of storage are illustrated in Figure 8.4.

For this example, category III storage is assumed, consisting of household goods including some foamed plastics and shrink wrapping.

Table 72 of the *Rules* stipulates the locations of sprinklers within the racking and, for this example, sprinklers must be located at every other tier, i.e. between tiers 2 and 3, 4 and 5, 6 and 7 etc., counting from the bottom, at the end of each protected level and at centres not more than 1.4 m along the rack. Normally, this means locating the sprinklers at every junction of longitudinal and transverse flue spaces. This is illustrated in Figure 8.4

Often the top tier of storage is placed on top of the racking and, provided that the roof level protection is not more than 3.0 m above the top of the storage, placement of the highest level of intermediate sprinklers at the top of the racking (i.e. at the base of the top tier) is usually acceptable. If the 3.0 m dimension is exceeded then provision must be made to locate the highest intermediate sprinkler at the top of the storage.

The provision of transverse and longitudinal flue spaces and the location of sprinklers within these spaces is essential to maintain the efficiency of intermediate sprinklers. If the flow of hot gases is restricted so as to prevent activation of the sprinkler heads, or correct distribution of the water spray is inhibited, the effectiveness of the sprinklers may be seriously impaired. Although the *Rules* are not specific a target clear gap of 150 mm should be designed into the logistics.

To assist the spray distribution within the rack a clear space of a least 150 mm must be maintained between the sprinkler deflector and the top of the adjacent stored goods.

8.1.10.2   Pipe sizing

The sizes of pipes in the installation must be chosen to accommodate the water flows appropriate to the design allowances of the system within the capacity of the water supply.

In general, the sizes of pipes will increase in the direction of the supply source and only in special circumstances would the opposite be appropriate.

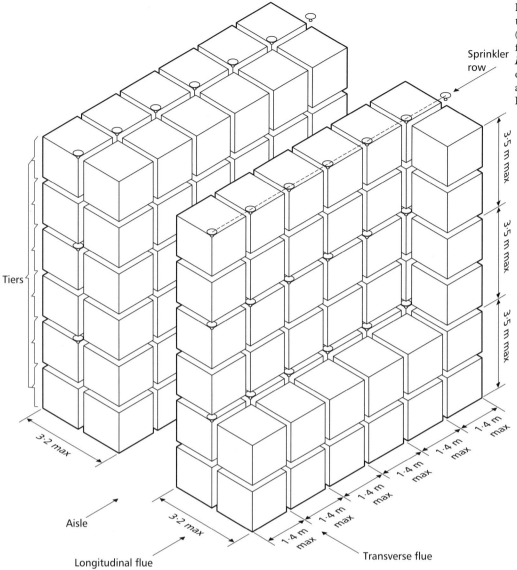

Figure 8.4 Sprinkler locations for type S5 storage, category III goods (beam pallet racking) (reproduced from the *LPC Rules*[1] and *BS 5306: Part 2*[2] by permission of the Loss Prevention Council and the British Standards Institution)

NOTE: Where the number of tiers is odd and the goods in the top tier are more than 3·0 m below the roof or ceiling sprinklers (or are otherwise not protected by them), the rows of sprinklers shall be provided above each even-numbered tier, and above the top tier.

Pipework systems

There are two principal styles of pipework design:

— 'Tree' or 'terminal' systems: the sprinkler heads are fed, singly or in groups, from dead-end range pipes linked to distribution pipes which are fed, in turn, from the water supply through main distribution pipes. This is the traditional method of feeding sprinkler systems. It is hydraulically very simple in that, in the event of system operation, only those range pipes which feed the operating sprinklers, and the distribution and main distribution pipes which feed those ranges, will contain flowing water.

— 'Gridded' systems: the sprinkler heads are fed from 'tie' pipes which are fed from more than one distribution main (often termed a 'track') which may or may not be directly linked to the water supply, see Figure 8.5. This type of system is hydraulically more complex than the tree system since generally each sprinkler is fed from more than one direction. Therefore all of the pipes in a

system may have water flowing through them simultaneously, even though the fire may only involve the sprinklers on one tie pipe.

Gridded systems can prove to be an economical method of sprinkler feed in certain circumstances since the hydraulic load may be spread over a greater number of pipes which can then be smaller in diameter than those in a tree system. Certain types of buildings, such as large high hazard risks with large bays and flat or slightly sloping roofs, are more suited to this system.

There are two methods of determining the sizes of pipes within these systems:

— 'pre-calculated' sprinkler pipe arrays

— fully hydraulically calculated pipe arrays.

'Pre-calculated' sprinkler pipe arrays

The range and minor distribution pipe sizes are determined in accordance with a schedule of sizes related to the

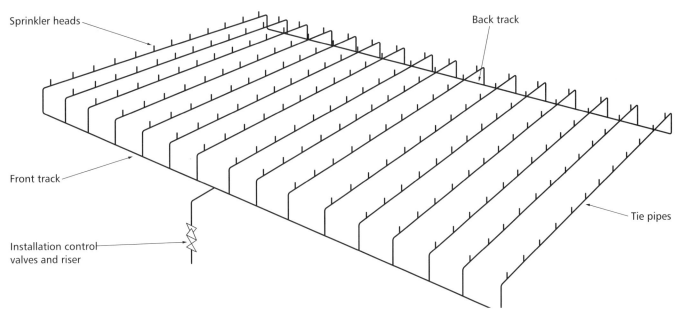

Figure 8.5 Component parts of a gridded system

number of sprinklers and their feed method. The sizes of the distribution and main distribution pipes are determined by simple hydraulic calculation to either:

(a)   keep within a predetermined maximum hydraulic loss, or

(b)   determine the minimum operating pressure capability of the water supply.

Systems for most hazards may be sized using this method except for gridded, deluge, early suppression fast response (ESFR) and intermediate rack systems. Each hazard has associated with it a set of pipe sizing tables for range and distribution pipe sizes, back as far as the 'design' points beyond which the sizes are determined hydraulically. The number of sprinklers which can be fed from the range pipes will vary according to the style of the range pipes.

Fully hydraulically-calculated pipe arrays

Fully hydraulically-calculated pipe arrays are arrays in which a detailed hydraulic analysis of the system is carried out to determine the precise hydraulic characteristics of the system and to balance the capacity of the water supply.

The basis of the calculation is to establish the demand of the hydraulically most unfavourable situation for the installation. The demand of the hydraulically most favourable situation must also be established where the water supply is limited and an overload on demand may be detrimental or could shorten the time during which the supply will be available (e.g. a storage tank and automatic pumped supply). This may involve multiple calculations since the most and least demanding situations may not be obvious.

The process involves establishing the individual sprinklers which are in the 'assumed maximum area of operation' (AMAO), which will be, as close as possible, rectangular in the case of the most unfavourable location, and square for the most favourable location. The number of sprinklers contained in the AMAO is calculated from the areas covered by individual sprinklers added together until the design area of operation is covered. The

minimum rate of flow through each sprinkler is obtained by multiplying the design density (litre·m^{-2} per minute) by the area covered by each sprinkler. Also, each sprinkler must operate at a minimum running pressure to ensure that the correct spray characteristic is established. These vary according to hazard and location, as follows:

—   light hazard, all types: 0.7 bar

—   ordinary hazard, all types: 0.35 bar

—   high hazard, intermediate rack systems: 2.0 bar

—   high hazard, other types: 0.5 bar

—   ESFR: varies according to the risk and type of sprinkler chosen.

The calculations may have to include sprinklers below ducts or other obstructions. Where intermediate rack sprinklers are involved the final calculations must include both roof and rack systems operating simultaneously, even if the most unfavourable rack location is not in the same area as the most unfavourable roof location.

The principal formula for the establishment of friction loss within the calculation process is the Hazen-Williams formula and the LPC *Rules*[1] allow the use of the full version or an abridged version to simplify the mathematical procedure. The equivalent lengths to be used to calculate friction losses in changes in direction and other obstructions to smooth flow are scheduled in Table 37 of the *Rules*. Losses or gains as a result of differences in elevation are accounted for using a simplified method in which 1.0 m head is taken as 0.1 bar. The balance tolerances to be achieved in the calculations are stipulated in the *Rules* which also schedule the information which must be provided to any approving authority for checking purposes.

Although the calculations may be performed manually, it is now more common to use computer techniques, particularly for gridded systems where the flow/pressure logic through the matrix of pipes is very complex. Where computer methods are employed, the input data must be checked, preferably by performing an independent calculation using quality-tested and calibrated software or by carrying out extensive manual cross checks.

The results of full hydraulic calculations must be plotted onto a water supply graph to ensure that the hydraulic demand of the system can be met fully by the water supply.

8.1.10.3   Fixings and pipe supports

The design of the location and type of fixings and pipe supports is very important. It must be appreciated that the full loading of a sprinkler system is only likely to occur in full fire conditions, at which time failure of any kind could have catastrophic consequences. The design must not only take account of the weight of the system and the water contained but also the dynamic reactions due to water flow through the pipes and its issue from sprinklers and nozzles, the dynamic shock of water charging a normally dry system, and reactions to outside factors such as building movement, thermal conditions, vibration and plant movement.

The fixings should be made direct to the building structure and, wherever possible, to non-combustible elements. There are occasions where fixing to a common suspension system is desirable but each case must be considered individually and account taken of all factors, particularly those likely in fire conditions. Other items or services should not be fixed to sprinkler pipes although it is acceptable to fix sprinkler pipes to an appropriately sized common suspension system. The sizes and types of material for clips, rods, brackets etc. are scheduled in the LPC *Rules*[1]. Almost any style of bracket may be used provided that the objectives are met. However, unacceptable procedures include the use of spring clips, open hooks, wood screws or nails into timber, explosively driven fasteners into wood or masonry, welding of the clip onto the pipe or toggle type fixings on pipes of diameter greater than 50 mm. The fixings must be sufficiently strong to withstand the test loads scheduled in Table 44 of the *Rules*.

The spacing and location of pipe supports is defined in the various rules but these requirements must be applied with care, bearing the objectives in mind.

Values given in guidance documents should be considered as maxima and closer spacing may be required in some circumstances. The pipes must be prevented from sagging and twisting and special rules apply when mechanical joints (i.e. grooved pipe and fittings) are used. Even closer attention should be given to maintaining the pipe in the correct position in the cases of dry, alternative wet and dry, pre-action or other dry type systems are involved.

Rise and drop pipes should be adequately supported, either directly or by fixing an adjacent horizontal part of the pipe.

There has been some uncertainty regarding the support of pipes feeding sprinklers located on a suspended ceiling, especially where these are fed by a combination feed pipe or rise from the distribution pipe, horizontal arm pipe and drop to the sprinkler head (i.e. 'universal arm' method). This method is used where accurate positioning of the sprinkler at the centre of a ceiling tile is required and, if

not correctly supported, will result in a gap between the sprinkler and the ceiling. The ceiling fabric should not be used to support the pipe which should be prevented from twisting. Therefore if it is possible for a pipe to twist or where a pipe must rely upon the ceiling for support, a fixing should be provided on the horizontal 'arm' pipe. This should be considered regardless of the distance between the sprinkler and the distribution pipe but this problem is more likely to occur with longer arm/drop combinations.

8.1.11   Water supplies

Adequate water supplies are one of the most important issues in connection with sprinklers and a full treatment is beyond the scope of this Guide. However, the following section identifies some of the salient points.

The concept of automatic fire protection collapses if water, in sufficient quantities, is not available for an adequate duration when required. Consequently, great attention must be given to the three aspects of water supply:

—   reliability

—   flow rate

—   capacity (i.e. duration).

In simple terms, the higher the hazard the higher the required flow rate and capacity, and the greater the need for reliability.

Water supplies are designated as follows, in order of increasing reliability:

—   single supply

—   superior supply

—   duplicate supply.

Any of the above may be suitable for light and ordinary hazard risks but only superior or duplicate supplies would normally be considered for high hazard risks.

Acceptable sources for water supplies include the following:

—   town mains

—   automatic booster pumps, drawing from town mains (where permitted)

—   automatic suction pumps drawing from a suitable source

—   elevated private reservoirs

—   gravity tanks

—   pressure tanks.

A single supply would normally be one of the following:

—   a town main fed from a single source

—   a single automatic suction pump drawing from a suitable source

—   a single automatic booster pump drawing from a town main fed from a single source.

Superior supplies include the following:

— a town main fed from more than one source and from both ends and not dependant on a common trunk main

— two automatic suction pumps drawing from a suitable source

— two automatic booster pumps drawing from a town main fed from more than one source and from both ends and not dependant on a common trunk main

— an elevated private reservoir

— a gravity tank

— a pressure tank (light and ordinary hazard risks only).

Combinations suitable for duplicate supplies are scheduled in Table 6 of the LPC *Rules*[1].

Acceptable water sources for suction pumps are detailed in the *Rules* and these include suction tanks, which may be of concrete or of proprietary manufacture and may or may not depend upon infill from a potable water supply, and also virtually inexhaustible sources such as rivers, canals and lakes. Care must be taken in choosing non-potable water sources and by far the most preferable option would be 'Type A' or 'Type D' suction tanks which should be suitable for service without major maintenance for fifteen years. Salt or brackish water would not normally be acceptable for sprinkler water supplies except with very special measures.

If a town main is intended to serve as a supply source or to provide an infill to a reduced capacity tank, extensive tests should be carried out on the mains to establish their capacity. Investigations should also be carried out to ensure that no deterioration is likely in the future. Where suction tanks are not dependent on inflow, an inflow rate of 75 litres per minute should be provided for refilling purposes.

The design capacities of tanks, both with and without infill, for the various hazard classes where pipes are sized on a pre-calculated basis are clearly scheduled in the *Rules*. A summary of those relating to ordinary hazard risks is given in Table 8.3.

Where suction or booster pumps are required, sufficient power to drive the pumps must be available at all times and particularly under fire conditions. Normally electrically driven pumps are considered more reliable than

diesel driven pumps but where insufficient power is available a diesel driven pump may be the only option. Where duplicate pumps are required each pump must be capable of satisfying the requirements on its own. If two electric pumps are provided independent electric supplies are required for each pump. For duplicate pumps, it is common practice to provide one electric and one diesel driven unit. If the capacity is too large to be provided by a single pump, three pumps may be used, each of which is capable of providing one half of the required capacity.

The pump flow and pressure ratings for pre-calculated pipe sizing are also stipulated in the LPC *Rules*. Values for light and ordinary hazard systems are given in Table 28 of the *Rules*.

Where the difference between the highest and lowest sprinklers exceeds 45 m, the system is classified as 'high-rise' and the system must be subdivided into sections each having a highest to lowest differential not exceeding 45 m. Each section must be fed from a separate set of pumps or from separate stages of a multi-stage pump, but these may draw from a common water storage facility sized to suit the highest demand.

For high hazard systems the values are based on the flow rate derived from pipe sizing tables given in Tables 16–19 of the LPC *Rules* multiplied by either 1.2 or 1.35, depending on the table chosen and the pressure derived from the hydraulic calculation, and the minimum pressures stipulated at the design point obtained from Table 16, 17, 18 or 19 of the *Rules*, as appropriate.

Where pipes have been sized by full hydraulic calculation then the flow/pressure characteristics of the pumps and the size of the storage tanks are based on these calculations.

The calculations for the hydraulically most favourable and unfavourable locations should be accurately plotted on a graph using a linear scale for pressure and a square law scale for flow. The resulting system demand curves should appear as a virtually straight line on the graph. The design site performance curve for the pump under two separate conditions, with the tank full and with the tank at its lowest operational level, should be plotted onto the same graph. The installation demand points must be covered by the pump curve when the tank water is at its lowest level so that the design flow rate is available through to the end of the operational period.

The circumstances of a full design size fire operating the sprinkler system in the most hydraulically favourable location must also be considered and the increased flow rate resulting from such circumstances must be catered for both in terms of pump driver power and tank capacity. The demand curves for this installation should be extended on the graph. The point at which the most favourable curve intercepts the pump curve at its highest point is known as Q_{max} and this value is used to calculate the tank size and pump duty.

Figure 8.6 shows the pump duty graph for a typical installation.

The tank capacity is determined by allowing for the flow of Q_{max} for the design duration of demand which is directly related to the hazard classification, as follows:

Table 8.3 Pre-calculated tank capacities for ordinary hazard risks[1]

Hazard group	Height between high and low sprinklers (m)	Capacity (m³)	Minimum capacity with infill (m³)
Group I	15	55	25
	30	70	25
	45	80	25
Group II	15	105	50
	30	125	50
	45	140	50
Group III	15	135	75
	30	160	75
	45	185	75
Group III special	15	160	100

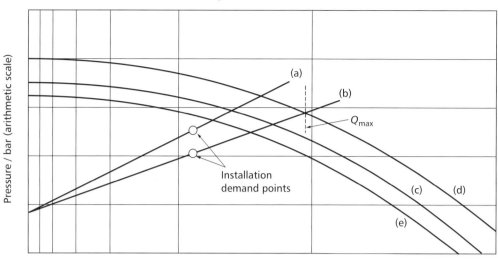

Figure 8.6 Pump duty graph for typical installation

(a) Hydraulically most unfavourable area
(b) Hydraulically most favourable area
(c) Pump performance low water level 'X' (at pump outlet)
(d) Pump performance normal water level (at 'C' gauge)
(e) Pump performance low water level 'X' (at 'C' gauge)

— light hazard: 30 min

— ordinary hazard: 60 min

— high hazard: 90 min

Sprinkler pumps must be arranged to start automatically in response to a drop in trunk main pressure and once started must run until switched off manually. The control and alarm features are specified in the *Rules*.

The conditions under which the pump is operating will be defined as either flooded suction or suction lift, depending on the relationship of pump centre line and low water level. Flooded suction conditions apply when not more than 2.0 m depth or one third of the effective capacity, whichever encompasses the smaller volume of water, is below the centre line the pump. With natural unlimited supplies such as rivers, canals, lakes, etc. the pump centre line must be at least 0.85 m below the lowest known or expected water level.

When pumps are considered as suction lift full priming facilities, including priming tank and pipework, must be provided. Separate suction pipes must be provided for each pump and the size of these pipes may be larger as a result of a decreased velocity limit imposed.

In addition to the main sprinkler pumps it is usual to provide a smaller capacity 'jockey' pump to make up small losses in the trunk main to prevent the operation of the main pumps in such circumstances. Unlike the main pumps the jockey pump is automatically switched off when the predetermined cut-out pressure is reached.

A typical arrangement of a single pump suction tank is shown in Figure 8.7.

In addition to the stipulated requirements, the LPC has published further requirements for automatic pump installations in LPC Technical Bulletin TB19[19].

8.1.12   Commissioning and testing

In common with all piped services the control of installation standards and proper commissioning and testing of the completed installations are very important. However, unlike other piped services, the completed installation will not normally be tested in full operational mode therefore even greater care should be exercised to ensure that the design objectives are met.

Notwithstanding the need to monitor the installation work during its progress, the commissioning and testing normally carried out is likely to consist of the following elements.

8.1.12.1   Pneumatic and hydrostatic testing of installation pipework

Dry pipework should be tested pneumatically to a pressure of 2.5 bar for not less than 24 hours. Wet pipework should be tested hydrostatically to a pressure of 15 bar or 1.5 times the working pressure, whichever is the greater, for a period of at least 1 hour.

With wet pipework it is common practice to carry out a preliminary pneumatic test prior to the hydrostatic test to establish that these are no major leaks or open ends.

The manufacturers of chlorinated polyvinyl chloride (CPVC) pipe and fittings recommend against pneumatic testing of their products and this should be borne in mind when choosing the most appropriate material, and specifying the testing regime, for a particular system. The manufacturer of the pipe and fitting should be consulted if there is any doubt in respect of the safety of pneumatic testing.

With systems which are normally dry, it may be appropriate to prove the capability of the system to deliver water to the remote ends of an installation within a reasonable time in response to the operation of a sprinkler head.

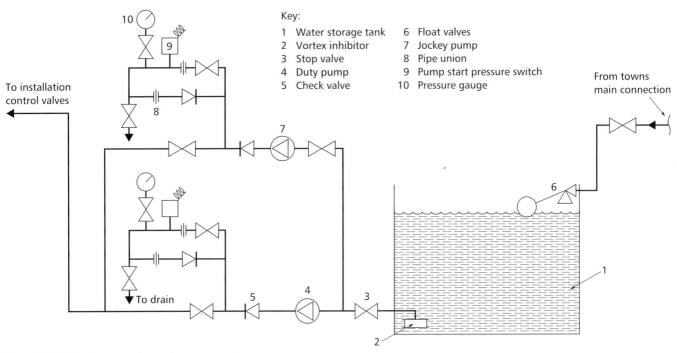

Figure 8.7 Typical pump suction tank arrangement

8.1.12.2 Water supply testing

The capability of the water supply should be tested, through the complete range of its design requirements, to prove that it will perform as required. Flow measuring devices must be provided at the installation control valves and also adjacent to pumps such that water flow and pressure can be accurately measured.

In the case of diesel driven pump sets additional tests should be carried out to prove the automatic starting sequence of the unit.

8.1.12.3 Alarms and monitoring facilities

All alarms and alarm connections associated with the installation should be tested and links to any remote locations proven. All valve monitoring functions should be proven.

When all tests have been carried out to the satisfaction of all authorities then a completion certificate should be issued by the installing contractor which may be similar in form to that illustrated in Figure 6 of the LPC *Rules*[1].

8.1.12.4 Third party certification

A voluntary scheme exists within the UK for the registration of sprinkler systems which are constructed to a recognised standard. This is administered by the Loss Prevention Certification Board (LPCB) and the scheme is termed LPS 1048, *Requirements for Certificated Sprinkler Installers, Supervising Bodies and Supervised Installers*[20]. Contractors who work within the scheme are listed as either 'Certificated' and can issue their own certificates of conformity for projects, or 'Registered Supervised' in which case their work is supervised by a Certificated Supervising Contractor who will issue the certificate for a completed project.

The facility to recognise and schedule areas of a project which do not fully conform to the letter of the rules is included and a schedule of 'non-compliances' is provided in the certification paperwork. A flaw within this scheme, however, is that those features which will be accepted as non-compliances and those which will not are not scheduled on any list. Therefore prediction of the likely status of the issues is difficult. It has been known, for example, for a certificate to be issued for a project where significant non-compliances have been accepted by all of the authorities having jurisdiction based upon a sound engineering approach and subsequently for the LPCB to withdraw the certificate on the basis that the non-compliances were not acceptable to the Board. Clearly, if a fire engineering solution is employed and sprinklers are used in a non-standard way as part of the strategy it is possible that the project will not be granted a certificate of conformity even if all of the authorities having jurisdiction are in agreement with the non-conformities.

The absence of a certificate of conformity should not necessarily be construed as condemnation of the sprinkler protection. The authorities having jurisdiction should be in agreement with all of the features of the sprinkler protection.

8.1.13 Maintenance of sprinkler systems

When the system is handed over to the user a comprehensive operation and maintenance manual should be provided which should contain:

— full documentation for the entire system, its components and all associated plant, alarms, utility supplies etc., including record drawings

— instructions for the day-to-day operation of the system and procedures to be adopted in fire conditions

— a full schedule of all maintenance and testing required to keep the system in full working order.

It is often wise for the user to have the testing, maintenance and servicing carried out under a service agreement with the installer or an accredited servicing company. The LPS 1048 scheme lists contractors considered to be suitable for maintenance of sprinkler systems and choosing a contractor from this list should bring an expectation of reliability and capability.

Care should be taken to ensure that all appropriate personnel are aware of the actions which are necessary in the event of fire and in the event of mechanical damage to a part of the system. When a system is shut down following either of these incidents the necessary repairs and replacement of sprinklers should be carried out and the system returned to an operational condition as quickly as possible. All interested authorities should be advised and the stock of replacement sprinkler heads held on site should be replenished as quickly as possible if any sprinklers have been used. Care should also be taken to ensure that in a fire incident all damaged components have been replaced. A thorough inspection by suitably qualified personnel may be necessary to establish the extent of the damage to the system.

8.1.14   Life safety systems

Although the origins of a sprinkler installation relate to the protection of property, the consequent control of fire means that any sprinkler system may be regarded, in part, as a life safety system in that the safety of the building occupants, those of adjacent properties and the firefighters may be improved if a sprinkler system is fitted. There are also circumstances in which a sprinkler system is installed specifically for life safety purposes and may form part of an integrated life safety strategy. There may be situations where concessions are made with regard to other fire safety measures on the basis that sprinklers are installed and, possibly, situations in which a risk will be considered unacceptable without sprinklers.

An example of the installation of sprinklers for life safety purposes is an enclosed shopping centre where sprinklers may be required within shop units to prevent the spread of fire and to limit the products of combustion, thereby assisting the safe escape of the occupants and making the fire brigade's task less onerous.

In such cases the reliability and integrity of the system becomes even more important than situations where only commercial risks need to be considered.

Where sprinklers are necessary for life safety the relevant authority may not necessarily require extensive protection but the points made elsewhere in terms of non-protected areas and the importance of correct separation must be borne in mind (see section 8.1.4). The LPC *Rules*[1] require that a separation rating of 1 hour for all items except doors, which must have a rating of 30 minutes, must be established between life safety protected and non-protected spaces.

Additional measures which should be considered for life safety systems are:

— they must be 'wet' systems

— they must be arranged into zones of not more than 200 sprinklers which cover only one ownership and one floor level

— water flow into each installation must be monitored and the device connected to a fire alarm panel; it may also be appropriate to monitor water flow into each zone by the use of water flow alarm switches

— the installation control valves must be arranged with either a valved by-pass or with a parallel duplicate valve set such that the valves may be maintained without interrupting the supply of water to the sprinkler system

— all stopvalves which are located in the path between water source and sprinkler head must be electrically monitored and tamper proof

— flushing valves are required in each zone

— the type of sprinklers suitable for such systems is restricted; ceiling, flush, recessed and concealed sprinklers are not suitable

— the water supply must be reliable and in the case of systems complying with BS 5588: Part 10[21] a duplicate supply is required

— additional information may be required on the block plan to indicate zone valve locations

— there may be restrictions in the extent of areas which may be shut down for maintenance, repair or alteration and strict notification procedures prior to shut down may be required.

8.1.15   Domestic and residential sprinklers

There is an increasing move towards the more widespread use of domestic and residential sprinkler protection. The potential to save lives in fires is greater in this field than any other area of sprinkler protection. The greatest resistance the use of sprinklers are cost and the perceived risk of unwanted operation.

With materials such as CPVC pipework and fittings becoming more readily available and a greater awareness of the potentials for sprinkler protection the use of sprinklers is gradually increasing.

The principles of sprinkler location, pipe feed and water supply resilience for these systems is similar to those for commercial and industrial risks discussed above but expected flow rates are fairly low, comparable with those in light hazard systems. The LPC *Rules* includes an Technical Bulletin TB14 to cover these risks and at the time of writing a draft British Standard DD 251[22] is being considered.

8.1.16   Approved contractors

The design, installation and maintenance of sprinkler systems should always be entrusted to those who are competent to do so. The LPC has established a list of firms which have been assessed to LPS 1048, *Requirements for Certified Sprinkler Installers, Supervising Bodies and*

Supervised Installers[20]. These companies will also have been assessed to BS EN ISO 9000: *Quality systems*[23].

Some of the companies listed are also authorised to supervise those installers which are not considered suitable to undertake work without supervision and are included in the LPCB's *List of Approved Products and Services*[11] as 'LPS 1048 Registered Supervised Installers'.

8.2 Foam systems

8.2.1 Introduction

This section is intended to provide the user with outline design criteria and descriptions for the main types of foam system. It has been produced with reference to BS 5306: Part 6[24], Sections 6.1: *Low expansion foam systems* and 6.2: *Medium and high expansion foam systems*. There are also the internationally used National Fire Protection Association (USA) Codes :

— NFPA 11: *Low expansion foam*

— NFPA 11A: *Medium and high expansion foam*

— NFPA 16: *Foam water sprinkler systems*

A CEN specification (prEN 13565[25]) is in preparation. At the time of writing (February 2003), Part 1, dealing with components, is awaiting formal vote, and Part 2, dealing with system design, is being drafted.

Foam systems are most commonly used to protect flammable liquid pool/surface fire hazards although the choice of foam concentrate and foam proportioning system will vary according to the type of system, the water supply pressure and whether a central supply is used to serve a number of hazard areas. Foam systems may also be used for Class A (ordinary combustibles) in some applications.

8.2.2 General

In a foam system, foam concentrate is 'proportioned' at a carefully controlled ratio into water to produce a 'foam solution'. This solution is the 'aspirated' with air to form bubbles, which flow on to surface of the flammable liquid.

Foam extinguishes fires by:

— smothering the fire by preventing air mixing with the flammable vapours

— suppressing the release of flammable vapours from the fuel surface

— separating the flames and heat from the fuel surface

— cooling the fuel surface and the sources of ignition.

To be effective foams must:

— flow freely

— form a tough cohesive blanket

— resist heat

— resist fuel pick-up

— retain water

Foam is not suitable for:

— live electrical hazards

— 3-dimensional running fuel fires

8.2.3 Types of foam concentrate

Foam concentrates are grouped and defined as follows. The performance characteristics of foam concentrates are shown in Table 8.4.

Protein foam (P)

Produced from hydrolysed protein (hoof and horn) giving a stiff foam which must be aspirated and with poor fire fighting properties.

Fluoroprotein foam (FP)

Protein foam with fluorochemical additives, must be aspirated, but flows freely, has good fire fighting properties and low fuel pick-up.

Film forming fluoroprotein foam (FFFP)

Has fire fighting properties between fluoroprotein and AFFF, giving faster fire knockdown than FP and better heat resistance than AFFF. It is more effective aspirated but can be used un-aspirated on spill fires.

Aqueous film forming foam (AFFF)

AFFF is a synthetic foam made using fluorochemical surfactants. As its name implies it releases an aqueous film which flows ahead of the foam resulting in quick fire knockdown, but at the expense of foam blanket durability. It is effective both aspirated and un-aspirated so it can be used with any water delivery nozzle such as a sprinkler or sprayer.

Alcohol resistant foam (AR)

Alcohol resistant foams are used on foam destructive flammable liquids that absorb water, such as methanol and alcohols. They provide a polymeric film to protect the water in the foam bubbles. Most foams are available in an

Table 8.4 Performance characteristics of foam concentrates

Foam type	Property		
	Speed	Heat resistance	Fuel pick-up
P	Poor	Excellent	Poor
FP	Fair	Excellent	Good
FFFP	Good	Good	Good
AFFF	Excellent	Fair	Good
AR	Good	Excellent	Good

AR version but care needs to be taken by the designers when selecting the foam proportioning system as AR foams have much higher viscosities than the ordinary foams which affects proportioner performance.

Synthetic/high expansion foam

Synthetic foams are produced from detergents and can be used to generate large quantities of bubbles particularly suitable for high expansion foam systems (see 8.4.5).

Class A foam

Class A foams are primarily wetting agents which reduce the surface tension of the water giving greater penetration and effectiveness on ordinary combustibles. It can also be aspirated to enable it to be used as a surface fire barrier.

They are generally available in either 3% or 6% strengths i.e. a 3% foam is 'proportioned' at 3 parts foam concentrate to 97 parts water; a 6% foam is 'proportioned' at 6 parts foam concentrate to 94 parts water. AFFF is also available at 1%.

Some foams are available in low temperature/frost protected versions where the concentrate can be used, typically, down to –18 °C. Standard foams freeze at +2 °C.

8.2.4   Foam proportioning

Foam proportioning is the means by which the foam concentrate is mixed with water at the required ratio (usually 3%). The proportioning options are described below.

8.2.4.1   Inductors (line proportioners)

An inductor is a venturi device where the inlet water pressure is converted to velocity and the jet discharges across an orifice thereby drawing in the foam concentrate through a metering orifice. The foam solution then enters a 'recovery section' where some of the pressure is restored. Inductors are single flow single pressure devices which need an inlet pressure of at least 5 bar and incur a 35% pressure drop across the device. They draw foam concentrate from an atmospheric storage tank.

8.2.4.2   Bladder tanks

A bladder tank proportioning system comprises a pressure vessel with a rubber bladder of foam concentrate inside it. Water is fed from the foam system inlet water supply, under pressure, into the shell of the vessel to pressurise the space between the vessel wall and the bladder. The water pressure thus squeezes the foam concentrate out of the bladder through a delivery pipe to a foam proportioner. The proportioner mounted in the pipework to the foam system mixes the water, flowing through the proportioner, and foam concentrate at the required ratio. Any bladder tank proportioning system will operate accurately over a wide range of flows and pressures. The range will depend upon the proportioner used and the foam concentrate.

Wide range proportioners are available which typically operate from 80 litres per minute of solution flow, up to over 5 000 litres per minute. These were specially developed for use in foam enhancement of sprinkler systems.

8.2.4.3   Balanced Pressure Proportioning

A balanced pressure proportioning system comprises a foam concentrate pump drawing from a atmospheric storage tank and pumping foam concentrate through pressure balancing valve into a proportioner. The pressure balancing valve senses both the foam and water pressures entering the proportioner and regulates the foam pressure down to match the water pressure. Like a bladder tank system it will operate over a wide range of flows and pressures depending upon the proportioner and the foam concentrate.

8.2.4.4   Water driven foam metering pumps

These units have a water motor, within the water line to the foam system, which drives a foam pump drawing from an atmospheric foam storage tank. The flow of the foam pump is matched to the speed and thus flow through the water motor to deliver the correct amount of foam concentrate into the water downstream of the water motor. These units will proportion accurately over a limited range of flows and pressures and are available in various sizes and capacities.

8.2.4.5   Premix foam units

Premix foam units are 'large fire extinguishers' consisting of a pressure vessel filled with the correct mixture of foam concentrate and water. They are linked to a gas supply (usually CO_2) which, went actuated, purges the foam solution from the vessel into the system. As these system have limited capacity they are used for protection of small hazard areas such as remote boiler rooms or oil storage rooms in buildings.

8.2.5   Types of foam system

8.2.5.1   Low expansion foam systems

Low expansion foam is foam solution aspirated between 1:1 and 20:1. These systems are used for the protection of cone roof and floating roof flammable liquid storage tanks, tanker loading and off-loading bays, process areas, oil fuelled machinery spaces, and aircraft landing and servicing areas. They are also used for protection of dykes and bunds.

8.2.5.2   Medium expansion foam systems

Medium expansion foam is foam solution aspirated between 20:1 and 200:1 although most operate at around 50:1. These systems are used for dyke/bund protection and for manual fire fighting on minor spills. Medium expansion foam has also proved an effective means of suppression of flammable and/or toxic vapours from spills to protect personnel and prevent ignition of flammable vapours.

8.2.5.3   High expansion foam systems

High expansion foam is foam solution aspirated between 200:1 and 1000:1. It is used for outdoor spills of liquified natural gas (LNG) at expansions up to 500:1. It is also used for protection of warehouses, tunnels, aircraft hangers and sometimes cable voids where water damage and/or water availability could be a problem. To be effective, high expansion foam must fill the hazard to above the height of the highest hazard. As a result it poses problems of breathing, hearing and disorientation for anyone within it, and difficulties for firefighters to find the seat of the fire.

8.2.6   Foam system discharge devices

8.2.6.1   Foam chambers

Foam chambers are used on cone roof storage tanks and contain a vapour seal to prevent escape of vapours. The foam chamber consists of a foam solution aspirator/foam maker and a chamber where the foam can expand before being discharged down the inside wall of the tank via a deflector plate.

8.2.6.2   Rimseal foam pourers

Rimseal foam pourers fit onto the top of floating roof tanks to protect the flexible seal area. They consist of a foam aspirator/foam maker and a foam chute to guide the foam down the inside wall of the tank.

8.2.6.3   Subsurface foam units

These aspirate the foam solution, under high back-pressure from head of fuel in the tank, then discharge the foam into the fuel where it floats to the surface. Semi-subsurface units exist where a tube deploys within the tank to deliver the foam to the fuel surface.

8.2.6.4   Foam water sprinklers

These are open nozzles mounted above process or fuel handling areas. They consist of an air induction body into which the foam solution discharges. The air, drawn in, mixes with and aspirates the foam before being spread evenly over a circular area by a deflector plate.

8.2.6.5   Water sprinkler and sprayers

Conventional sprinkler and waterspray systems can deliver fluorosurfactant-based foams which are effective with little or no aspiration, as AFFF, AR-AFFF, and also FFFP in some instances.

8.2.6.6   Branchpipes and monitors

Foam branchpipes and monitor nozzles work on the same principal as the foam water sprinklers, but do not always have a deflector plate. They can project foam over both horizontal and vertical distances but the plunging of the foam into the fuel can reduce their effectiveness. Smaller capacity units are hand-held whilst larger units, up to 6000 litres per minute and higher, are mounted on turrets/monitors which can rotate and elevate. They are used for area protection such as bunds, process and handing areas, aircraft hangers and helicopter decks.

8.2.6.7   Foam inlet systems

These consist of a fire brigade 'pumping-in breeching' on the outside of a building, piped to foam spreaders within a small hazard area such as a basement fuel oil storage room. The fire brigade pump aspirated foam into the system via the breeching.

8.2.6.8   Medium expansion foam generators

Medium expansion foam generators consist of a body with a mesh screen on the outlet and a foam solution nozzle mounted axially in the (air) inlet. The solution is sprayed onto the mesh and the induced air flow blows the solution into bubbles. They are mounted above and beside the hazards they protect.

8.2.6.9   High expansion foam generators

High expansion foam generators consist of a body with a mesh screen on the outlet and one or more spray nozzles in the (air) inlet. Some units also have some form of fan, driven by either foam solution motor or an electric motor. They should be mounted above the level that the foam is required to reach and usually draw fresh air to produce the foam.

8.2.7   Foam system design

Foam systems are required to deliver foam at or above a minimum density in litres per minute/m^2 (lpm/m^2) for a minimum time. These vary according to the type of hazard, the discharge device and the foam concentrate used, but are laid down in the BS and NFPA standards. Experience and judgement is required to correctly and effectively engineer foam systems.

The minimum application rates for foam pourer systems are shown in Table 8.5.

Rimseal foam pourers require 12 lpm/m^2 for seals where the foam is contained by a 'dam' and 20 lpm/m^2 without.

Foam deluge (spray) systems apply a density of 4 lpm/m^2 with un-aspirated foam or 6.5 lpm/m^2 with aspirated foam.

Table 8.5 Minimum low expansion foam solution application rates for tanks (foam chambers and subsurface) and bunds

Type of foam concentrate	Flammable liquid	Minimum application rate / (litre per minute/m^2)
Any	Hydrocarbon	4
AR	Foam destructive	6.5

Foam enhanced sprinkler systems use the assumed maximum area of operation (AMAO), see section 8.1.5, as the design basis.

The duration of foam discharge varies according to the type of system and the hazard. Sprinkler, deluge, and other spill fire hazards require a 10 minute supply of foam. Fuel in depth hazards such as tanks have longer discharge times of between 30 and 65 minutes depending on the volatility of the fuels.

8.2.8 Components and materials

Foam concentrates and foam solutions will attack galvanising, so piping is usually black steel although some foam concentrates require stainless steel or copper alloy. Foam systems have operating pressures similar to those of sprinkler systems so the same pipe, fitting and valve standards apply.

All pipework must be adequately supported and be pressure tested to 1.5 times the maximum working pressure after installation.

8.2.9 Testing

To verify that the foam system is functioning correctly each system should be tested as part of the commissioning process and annually thereafter. Ideally each system should be allowed to discharge foam to check the correct functioning and coverage of the discharge devices (cone roof tank foam chambers discharge away from the tank so as not to contaminate the tank itself). During the test, a sample of the foam should be taken to check that the foam proportioning system is mixing at the correct ratio.

Annually the foam proportioning system should be tested, at maximum flow, to verify that it is proportioning accurately. In addition a sample of foam concentrate should be analysed to check that is still effective. Modern foam concentrates can be expected to have a shelf life of 10 to 20 years depending upon the type of foam and the storage conditions. However premix foams have a limited life and should be replaced every 1 to 3 years depending upon through testing of a sample.

8.2.10 Documentation

Each system should be provided with the following documentation:

— scaled plan and section drawing of the hazard and the foam system, including proportioners and their location, piping and discharge devices, valves and pipe hanger spacings

— isometric view of the agent distribution piping system showing the lengths, sizes, and node references relating to the flow calculations

— flow calculations giving pipe and nozzle sizes

— name of owner and occupant

— location of building in which the hazard is located

— location and construction of the protected hazards

— foam concentrate information including agent used, proportioning concentration and quantity provided

— specification of the water and foam supplies used, including capacity, pressure and quantity

— description of occupancy and hazards protected

— description of discharge devices used including orifice size/code (where applicable)

— description of pipes, fittings and valves used, including material specification.

8.3 Gaseous systems

8.3.1 Introduction

This section is intended to provide outline design criteria for, and descriptions of, the main types of gaseous clean agent fire suppression systems. It has been produced with reference to BS ISO 14520: *Gaseous fire fighting systems*[26] and BS 5306: Part 4: *Fire extinguishing installations and equipment on premises — Specification for carbon dioxide systems*[27].

At the time of writing (February 2003), a CEN/ISO specification (prEN ISO/DIS 14520[28]) is in preparation.

Other standards, such as NPFA 2001[29], may be used although they tend to use lower safety factors.

8.3.2 General

Gaseous systems are those in which the fire extinguishing agent is applied in a gaseous form. They are an effective means of attacking fires in electrical risks such as electronic data processing (EDP) facilities, control rooms, and communications equipment; ordinary 'Class A' hazards such as record stores, as well as flammable liquid fires in plant enclosures and flammable liquid stores.

Since the end of halon production, modern systems have used agents from one of two classes: halocarbon or inert. Halocarbon agents act largely by heat absorption but also have some chemical effect on the flame combustion reactions. Inert agents reduce the oxygen level below that at which fire combustion can continue.

The protection objectives are:

— extinguish fire

— limit the spread of fire

— limit fire damage

— prevent re-ignition

— enable speedy reinstatement of operations

Secondary benefits are:

— limited smoke generation

— no fire agent clear up; these are referred to as 'clean agents'.

8.3.3 System configuration

8.3.3.1 General

Gaseous systems comprise one or more containers of agent. Each container having its own release valve that can be electrically, pneumatically or manually operated. These are connected to normally empty steel distribution pipework on which nozzles are mounted to give a uniform build up of agent concentration upon discharge. When agent is released from the containers it flows through the pipework and discharges from all nozzles simultaneously. Small systems (generally single containers) may be pre-engineered so that no flow calculations and specific nozzle sizing is required. However, most will be engineered systems where the pipe and nozzle sizing is calculated to ensure the correct gas distribution and discharge time.

8.3.3.2 System release

The opening of the container valves must be initiated by a separate actuation system. As most systems operate automatically this is usually an electrical fire detection and actuation system giving an electrical signal to actuate the container valve. Manual release is also included. The detection system initiates evacuation alarms and the shutdown of plant and equipment likely to provide sources of re-ignition and or fuel.

Fire detection should be generally in accordance with current British Standards. For typical electrical applications this would consist of each hazard area having two zones of smoke detection arranged so that one detector would sound an alarm; two detectors would initiate specific 'pre-discharge alarm' sounders and a timer (adjustable to suit evacuation times). At the end of the 'pre discharge time' the separate distinctive discharge alarm would sound and agent would be released.

Further guidance on detection systems falls outside the scope of this document. Refer to section 6.

8.3.3.3 Total flooding systems

A total flooding system is one where the hazard is contained within an enclosure of reasonable integrity. The agent is discharged into the enclosure to build up a fire extinguishing concentration throughout, and to maintain it for a sufficient period (hold time) to allow sources of re-ignition to cool.

All the halon-alternative gaseous clean agents, both halocarbon and inert, are considered suitable for surface fire hazards. Only CO_2 has design criteria and standards for deep-seated fire risks.

8.3.3.4 Local application

A local application system is one where the hazard is small in relation to its surrounding enclosure so the gaseous system discharges only onto the hazard.

None of the halon-alternative gaseous clean agents, both halocarbon and inert, are approved for local application use. Only CO_2 has design criteria and standards for local application.

8.3.4 Agents

8.3.4.1 Safety

Agents placed on the market undergo an assessment of their safety issues. In UK this is carried out by the Halon Alternatives Group (HAG) of the Department for Environment, Food and Rural Affairs (DEFRA). It has produced a report, *Review of the Toxic and Asphyxiating Hazards of Clean Agent Replacements for Halon 1301*[30], which is regularly updated.

The decomposition products generated by the hydrocarbon clean agents in the presence of very high amounts of heat can be hazardous. All of the present halocarbon agents contain fluorine so the main decomposition product is hydrogen fluoride (HF) which is toxic and corrosive, even at low concentrations. The amount of agent that can be expected to decompose depends upon the size of the fire, the particular agent and its concentration, and upon the volume of the room, the degree of mixing, and ventilation.

Inert agents do not decompose, therefore no toxic or corrosive decomposition products are produced.

However, combustion products from the fire itself can be substantial and could, under some circumstances, make the area untenable for human occupancy.

8.3.4.2 Environment

Whilst all the halocarbon and inert agents referred to have zero ozone depletion potential (ODP), other environmental effects such as global warming and atmospheric lifetime may be relevant, see Table 8.6.

8.3.4.3 Halocarbon agents

Although a number of halocarbon agents have been developed, only a few are in general use. The principle one being FM200 with limited usage of FE13 and CEA-410. Their minimum design concentrations (the fire extinguishing concentrations plus a 30% 'safety factor') are given in Table 8.7, based upon BS ISO 14520[26].

Halocarbon systems discharge in 10 seconds, the same as halon, in order to achieve a rapid build-up to the extinguishing concentration. This does not represent the extinguishing time, which can be somewhat longer, but is

Table 8.6 Environmental implications of gaseous agents

Agent	Ozone depletion potential (ODP)	Global warming potential (GWP)	Atmospheric lifetime / years
Halon 1301	10	6900	65.0
FM200	0	2900	36.5
CEA-410	0	7000	2,600
FE 13	0	11700	264
Inergen	0	0	0
Argotec	0	0	0
Argonite	0	0	0
CO_2*	0	0	0

* The CO_2 used for fire protection systems is recycled from the waste gases from other processes and would otherwise have been discharged to atmosphere. Fire protection is considered a non-emissive use as relatively few systems are discharged

done in order to minimise the decomposition of the agent by the fire.

8.3.4.4   Inert agents

Several inert agents or mixtures of inert agents are widely available. These use argon ('Argotec'), a 50/50 mix of nitrogen and argon ('Argonite'), and a 52/40/8 mix of nitrogen, argon and CO_2 ('Inergen'), the CO_2 being used to stimulate higher oxygen intake in low-oxygen environments. Their minimum design concentrations (the fire extinguishing concentrations plus a 30% 'safety factor') are given in Table 8.7, based upon BS ISO 14520[26].

Inert systems discharge over one minute although fire extinguishment is normally expected within that time.

CO_2 is always used at toxic (lethal) concentrations unlike the other inert agents which are usually at non-harmful oxygen levels. The minimum design concentrations (the fire extinguishing concentrations plus a 'safety factor') are given in Table 8.7 based upon BS 5306: Part 4[27].

Table 8.7 Minimum design concentrations for gaseous agents

Agent	Minimum design concentration / %		
	Surface fire (ordinary combustibles*)	Heptane	Limit in automatic mode in normally manned areas
FM200	7.5	8.6	9
CEA-410	6.5	7.7	40
FE13	19.5	15.6	50
Inergen	36.5	43.9	43
Argotec	38.5	48.8	43
Argonite	37.8	42.0	43
CO_2	34.0	34.0	5

* Where plastic fuel hazards may be involved a design concentration of not less than 90% of that for heptane should be used (unless the agent has completed testing against such fuels)

8.3.5   Design

The amount of agent stored for discharge is calculated by multiplying the net volume of the enclosure (length × width × height minus the volume of any permanent impermeable building elements) by a 'flooding factor'. The 'flooding factor' is based upon the maximum ambient room temperature. It ensures that the design concentration of the agent is achieved at the end of the discharge and makes allowance for the loss of some agent due to venting during the discharge.

Dedicated systems can be provided for each hazard enclosure. Alternatively, a single 'central bank' of cylinders can protect a number of different hazards by actuation of the appropriate number of containers and the use of directional valves to divert gas to the required hazard area. Such central banks should be sized to be able to protect the largest single hazard. This is acceptable in most situations on the basis of having only one fire in one area at a time.

Where continuity of protection is needed a reserve bank of containers can be installed and connected in to the main bank, with a change-over switch in the detection and control system.

For 'pre-engineered systems' no hydraulic/pneumatic calculations are required as the pipe sizes and lengths, and nozzle sizes, are predetermined. Most systems are 'engineered' systems whereby the pipe routes are set out to suit each individual hazard enclosure and specific layout drawings produced. The sizes of the pipes and nozzles are then determined by hydraulic or pneumatic calculation. The calculations must reflect the pipe layout as installed.

8.3.6   Components and materials

Gaseous system piping should normally be galvanised steel as a minimum, rigidly bracketed to prevent swaying or other movement during discharge of the system. At the end of pipe runs there should be a short 'dead-end' section of pipe to act a 'dirt trap' to protect the nozzle orifices from clogging with any debris in the system.

Open sections of piping should be low pressure gas-leak tested after installation to 3 bar. Closed sections of pipe, i.e. between the containers and normally closed directional valves, should be hydraulically tested to 1.5 times their working pressure.

As the nozzles are individually sized to provide the required flow rate at each nozzle point in the system, it is important that care is taken to ensure that the correct nozzle size is mounted at each nozzle point.

8.3.7   Enclosures

Enclosures must have sufficient structural strength and integrity to contain the agent discharge. Venting may be required to prevent excessive over-pressurisation of the enclosure.

A fan integrity test should be carried out to determine the integrity of the enclosure to enable an agent retention time (hold time) determination. The test may also be used to establish the leakage/natural vent area.

Where required vents must be installed to limit the build-up of pressure within the enclosure during discharge. These should exhaust to outside to avoid dispersing fire products to other areas on the building.

Upon fire detection, forced air ventilation systems should shutdown or close automatically where their operation could impair the operation of the fire fighting system. Dampers in ductwork must be closed.

All services within the protected enclosure (e.g. fuel and power supplies, heating appliances etc.) should be shut down prior to agent release.

8.3.8　Testing

Testing is usually limited to functional testing of detection and alarm devices, plus actuation devices, without releasing agent.

If required, inert agents and CO_2 may be discharge tested, but halocarbon agents should not be released due to their environmental impact.

8.3.9　Inspection and maintenance

Users should, on a weekly basis, review the hazard area and its integrity, visually check the agent distribution system and check the agent container pressure gauge readings.

At six monthly intervals, trained, specialist fire systems personnel should verify that the agent containers remain fully charged, and test the detection, alarm and actuation functions.

Specialists should re-check the integrity and agent retention capabilities of the enclosure annually. They should also check that the protection remains appropriate and effective for the hazards within the enclosure.

8.3.10　Documentation

Each system should be provided with the following documentation:

—　scaled plan and section drawing of the enclosure (including raised floors and suspended ceilings) and the extinguishing system, including containers and their location, piping and nozzles, valves and pressure reducing devices, and pipe hanger spacings

—　isometric view of the agent distribution piping system showing the lengths, sizes, and node references relating to the flow calculations

—　flow calculations giving pipe and nozzle sizes

—　name of owner and occupant

—　location of building in which the hazard is located

—　location and construction of the protected enclosure walls and partitions

—　agent information including agent used, extinguishing concentration and maximum concentration

—　specification of the containers used, including capacity, storage pressure and quantity of agent

—　description of occupancy and hazards protected

—　description of nozzle(s) used, including inlet size, orifice port configuration, nozzle orifice size/code and pressure reducing device orifice/code (where applicable)

—　description of pipes, fittings and valves used, including material specification

—　enclosure pressurisation and vent calculations

—　description of the fire detection, actuation and control system.

8.4　Water mist systems

8.4.1　Introduction

This section is intended to provide outline design criteria for, and descriptions of, the main types of water mist fire suppression systems. It has been produced with reference to NFPA 750: *Standard on Water Mist Fire Protection Systems*[31]. Water mist is defined by NFPA as 'fine water sprays for the efficient control, suppression or extinguishment of fire using limited volumes of water'. Fine sprays are those where 99% of the droplets are less than 1000 microns diameter.

'Water fog' is not a formally recognised term and should be regarded as a marketing device.

Water mist may be used for fire control and suppression in enclosures, up to 5 m high, with low to medium levels of ordinary combustibles, such as might be found in hotels, shops, and offices. It may also be similarly used in electronic data processing (EDP) areas and cable tunnels to prevent fire spread. Water mist can provide fire extinguishment of flammable liquid fires as might be encountered in turbine enclosures, industrial cooking equipment, and other machinery spaces.

8.4.2　General

Water mist systems, as their name implies, deliver water in very small droplets. However, in order to be effective for fire suppression, these droplets must also be delivered at high momentum otherwise air currents and fire convection plumes will blow them away before they are able to be effective.

Water mist suppresses fire by a combination of cooling, plus steam smothering and oxygen dilution at the flame front. It stops the spread of fire by blocking radiant heat transfer, and also cools, and to some degree, washes harmful smoke particles out of the air. This combination of properties can significantly increase the safety of personnel during evacuation and fire fighting.

The creation of very small droplets of water produces a high surface area of droplets relative to the amount of water, thus enabling high heat absorption and high surface contact with smoke particles. The small droplets are also light in weight making them more buoyant and able to remain airborne longer to continue absorbing heat. The low mass of the individual droplets means that they can more readily be converted to steam and, in doing so, absorb a considerable amount of heat. It also undergoes a volumetric expansion of 1620 to 1 thereby displacing air away from the flame front, where the combustion and evaporation takes place. Water has excellent heat absorption properties, requiring 4.18 kJ of heat to raise the temperature of 1 kg of water from 1 °C to 100 °C, and 2240 kJ to convert it to steam.

A principle feature of all water mist systems is the relatively low quantities of water they use compared with other water-based firefighting systems, with consequent low levels of water damage and post-operation clean-up.

Whilst it is not envisaged that water mist systems should discharge onto live electrical equipment, as this should be shut down when a fire is detected, tests have shown that there is little or no electrical transmission until a water layer is formed, which can take some time to occur. Where sensitive electrical equipment may be involved, de-ionised water can be used to reduce conductivity.

As the water mist droplets have low mass, such systems are not generally suitable for outdoor applications or for use where high air movements may be encountered. It must also be taken into consideration that, whilst water mist droplets are buoyant and can be drawn in by combustion air flows, they do not permeate into and through narrow openings/equipment as do gases.

8.4.3 System configurations

Water mist systems may be configured using quick response frangible bulb elements, similar to sprinkler heads, so that only those nozzles in the immediate vicinity of a fire operate; in this respect the system may be regarded as equivalent to a sprinkler system. Alternatively, the system may employ all 'open' nozzles so that water mist discharges from every nozzle when the system is activated.

Systems may be designed for protection of an enclosed volume similar to a 'total flooding' gaseous system, or they may be engineered to provide local application protection of a particular hazard within a larger enclosure.

Water mist systems can be arranged with pumped water supplies taking water from potable or even sea water sources or, for small systems, stand-alone cylinders with water purged from them by gas under pressure.

8.4.4 Types of water mist system

Systems can be classified as high, intermediate, or low pressure according to their operating pressures. High pressure systems are those which operate at pressures above 80 bar. Intermediate pressure systems operate between 15 and 80 bar, and low pressure systems operate at pressures up to 15 bar.

The different operating pressures mean that the droplets are generated by different means, produce different droplet size ranges, and different mechanisms for imparting momentum to the droplets.

8.4.5 Design

All designs are based upon full scale fire testing of fuels and hazard configurations similar to that to be protected. With water mist systems the performance of each manufacturer's system is a function of their particular and unique nozzle operating parameters, the enclosure, the fire and the ventilation. As a result, each manufacturer's design for a particular hazard will be specific to that manufacturer and its fire test results.

Where water mist is being considered for an application for which directly relevant test data cannot be provided, then fire tests will be required to provide the design basis and validate the approach to be taken. NFPA 750[31] calls for a 30 minute water supply for general fire hazards, but permits shorter duration where fire test data supports it. This typically applies to flammable liquid risks where rapid extinction can be achieved and re-ignition prevented by the cooling effect of the mist.

It is therefore important to establish the fire test design basis for the protection of any particular hazard for which water mist protection is envisaged. It is also important that the design and installation of such systems is only entrusted to those with direct access to, and understanding of, the fire test data and a knowledge of the technology.

8.4.6 Components

8.4.6.1 Nozzles

Water mist nozzles produce mist by one of the following means:

— orifice plate

— spinner or internal swirl chamber

— gas atomisation

— deflector

The design of the nozzles is primarily intended to generate fine droplets and impart momentum to deliver them through the fire plume.

Distribution over a prescribed floor area is not a feature of water mist design or performance.

8.4.6.2 Piping

The internal hygiene of all water mist systems is of paramount importance in order to ensure that the small orifices employed in the nozzles do not become blocked. To this end inherently corrosion-resistant piping is used with stainless steel and copper being commonly used throughout. Some low pressure systems, using larger orifice nozzles, may be found using galvanised steel piping, although careful consideration of the need for filtration is necessary in such cases.

8.4.6.3 Control valves

All systems require control valves to enable the flow of water to be initiated and monitored.

8.4.6.4 Cylinder water supplies

Cylinders storing water need to be corrosion resistant i.e. stainless steel, or lined and at atmospheric pressure. (Stored pressure with lined cylinders can lead to gas permeation behind the lining with subsequent failure of the system.

8.4.6.5 Pumped water supplies

Pumps must be capable of meeting the maximum design flow and pressure and have dedicated and reliable power supplies. Duplicate supplies, providing redundancy, may be needed for critical hazards. Criteria similar to those used for sprinkler system may be applied, although type approved equipment is not available. For higher pressure pumped systems positive displacement pumps are used.

8.4.7 Installation and testing

During installation every pipe must be thoroughly purged of debris and scale internally during installation, and flushed after installation. All pipework should be hydraulically tested to 1.5 times the maximum operating pressure. Control valves should be functionally tested, as should the operation of the water supplies.

Open nozzle systems should be discharge tested where possible and all nozzles and strainers checked for cleanliness afterwards.

8.4.8 Inspection and maintenance

Regular inspection and maintenance must be carried out by those specifically trained and experienced in water mist systems.

References

1 *Rules for automatic sprinkler installations* (London: Loss Prevention Council) (1990)

2 BS 5306: *Fire extinguishing installations and equipment on premises*: Part 2: 1990: *Specification for sprinkler systems* (London: British Standards Institution) (1990)

3 *Rules of the Fire Offices' Committee for automatic sprinkler installations 29th edition* (London: Fire Offices Committee) (1973) (*withdrawn — superseded by reference 1*)

4 *Standard for the installation of sprinkler systems* NFPA 13 (Quincey, Mass: National Fire Protection Association) (2002)

5 *FM Standard 2-8N* (Norwood, MA: Factory Mutual International) (1989)

6 *Rules for sprinkler systems* (Cologne: Verband der Sachversicherer (VdS)) (1987)

7 *Sprinkler systems: Planning and installation* CEA 4001 (Paris: Comité Européen des Assurances) (2000)

8 *Specifications for Sprinkler systems — Requirements and test methods for K57, K80, K115 and K160 sprinklers* CEA 4023 (Paris: Comité Européen des Assurances) (1999)

9 *Specifications for Sprinkler systems — Requirements and test methods for ESFR sprinklers* CEA 4024 (Paris: Comité Européen des Assurances) (1999)

10 prEN 12845: 2002: *Fixed firefighting systems — Automatic sprinkler systems — Design, installation and maintenance* (Brussels: Comité Européen de Normalisation) (2002)

11 *List of Approved Products and Services* (London: Loss Prevention Certification Board) (published annually)

12 *The selection of sprinkler heads* LPC Technical Bulletin **TB20** (London: Loss Prevention Council) (1994)

13 *Supplementary requirements for sprinkler installations which can operate in the dry mode* LPC Technical Bulletin **TB21** (London: Loss Prevention Council) (1994)

14 BS 1387: 1985 (1990): *Specification for screwed and socketed steel tubes and tubulars and for plain end steel tubes suitable for welding or for screwing to BS 21 pipe threads* (London: British Standards Institution) (1990)

15 BS 21: 1985: *Specification for pipe threads for tubes and fittings where pressure-tight joints are made on the threads (metric dimensions)* (London: British Standards Institution) (1985)

16 BS 143 and 1256:2000: *Threaded pipe fittings in malleable cast iron and cast copper alloy* (London: British Standards Institution) (2000)

17 BS 5839: *Fire detection and alarm systems for buildings*: Part 1: 1988: *Code of practice for system design, installation and servicing*; Part 1: 2002: *Code of practice for system design, installation, commissioning and maintenance*; Part 2: 1983: *Specification for manual call points*; Part 3: 1988: *Specification for automatic release mechanisms for certain fire protection equipment*; Part 5: 1988: *Specification for optical beam smoke detectors*; Part 6: 1995: *Code of practice for the design and installation of fire detection and alarm systems in dwellings*; Part 8: 1998: *Code of practice for the design, installation and servicing of voice alarm systems* (London: British Standards Institution) (dates as shown)

18 *Categorization of goods in storage* LPC Technical Bulletin **TB17** (London: Loss Prevention Council) (1992)

19 *Automatic sprinkler pump installation* LPC Technical Bulletin **TB19** (London: Loss Prevention Council) (1993)

20 *Requirements for Certificated Sprinkler Installers, Supervising Bodies and Supervised Installers* LPS 1048 (London: Loss Prevention Council (1993)

22 BS 5588: *Fire precautions in the design, construction and use of buildings*: Part 10: 1991: *Code of practice for shopping complexes* (London: British Standards Institution) (1991)

23 DD 251: 2000: *Sprinkler systems for residential and domestic occupancies. Code of practice* (London: British Standards Institution) (2000)

24   BS EN ISO 9000: 2000: *Quality management systems. Fundamentals and vocabulary*; BS EN ISO 9000-1: 1994: *Quality management and quality assurance standards. Guidelines for selection and use* (London: British Standards Institution) (dates as indicated)

25   BS 5306: *Fire extinguishing installations and equipment on premises*: Part 6: *Foam systems*: Section 6.1: 1988: *Specification for low expansion foam systems*; Section 6.2: 1989: *Specification for medium and high expansion foam systems* (London: British Standards Institution) (dates as shown)

26   prEN 13565: *Fixed fire fighting systems. Foam systems*: Part 1: *Requirements and test methods for components* (draft) Document no. 99/540412 DC (London: British Standards Institution) (1999)

27   BS ISO 14520: *Gaseous fire-extinguishing systems. Physical properties and system design*; Part 1: 2000:*General requirements*; Part 2: 2000: *CFDOWN3I extinguishant*; Part 3: 2000: *FC-2-1-8 extinguishant*; Part 4: 2000: *FC-3-1-10 extinguishant*; Part 6: 2000: *HCFC Blend A extinguishant*; Part 7: 2000: *HCFC Blend 124 extinguishant*; Part 8: 2000: *HCFC 125 extinguishant*; Part 9:2000:*HFC 227ea extinguishant*; Part 10: 2000: *HFC 23 extinguishant*; Part 11: 2000: *HFC 236fa extinguishant*; Part 12: 2000: *IG-01 extinguishant*; Part 13: 2000: *IG-100 extinguishant*; Part 14: 2000: *IG-55 extinguishant*; Part 15: 2000: *IG-541 extinguishant* (London: British Standards Institution) (dates as shown)

28   BS 5306: *Fire extinguishing installations and equipment on premises*: Part 4: 2001: *Specification for carbon dioxide systems* (London: British Standards Institution) (2001)

28   prEN ISO/DIS 14520: *Gaseous fire extinguishing systems. Physical properties and system design*: Part 5: *FC-5-1-14 extinguishant* (draft) Document no. 98/540920 DC (London: British Standards Institution) (1998)

29   *Standard on clean agent fire extinguishing systems* NFPA 2001 (Quincey, MA: National Fire Protection Association) (2000)

330   *Review of the toxic and asphyxiating hazards of clean agent replacements for halon 1301* (Petersfield: Halon Users National Consortium/Refrigerant Users Group) (2001) (www.hunc.org)

31   *Standard on water mist fire protection systems* NFPA 750 (Quincey, MA: National Fire Protection Association) (2000)

9 Firefighting

9.1 Introduction

Firefighting is the term that is used to describe all attempts at attacking a fire whether those attempts are by the occupiers of buildings or by a company or local authority fire brigade. Because firefighting involves people, it is necessary to not only consider the practicalities of equipment and techniques but also the legislation that applies and the objectives and procedures that have been developed.

BS 5588: *Fire precautions in the design, construction and use of buildings*[1] is intended to safeguard the lives of occupants in a fire and can also protect the building. Those parts of BS 5588 that deal with specific occupancies caution that:

> 'An intelligent appreciation of the recommendations of this code are essential'.

BS 5588: Part 5: *Code of practice for firefighting stairs and lifts* cautions that:

> 'Individual recommendations of this code should not be applied in isolation because of their interdependence and joint contribution to the provision of a relatively safe environment for firefighting'.

This section of Guide E recognises the interdependence of the fire safety standards within buildings and firefighting operations and their joint contribution to the provision of a relatively safe environment. The current prescriptive standards are commented upon and means of calculating realistic provisions for firefighting are proposed. The proposals cover firefighting by occupiers of buildings and by fire brigades.

9.1.1 General objectives: first aid firefighting by occupiers

When firefighting is undertaken by the occupiers of a building, there is usually a single immediate objective: to extinguish the fire in the shortest possible time. The outcome of an attack on a fire by occupiers will depend on the ability of trained staff to undertake a dynamic risk assessment based on the following factors:

— availability of appropriate equipment

— appreciation of the size of the task

— physical ability

— training assimilated

— skill level.

9.1.2 General objectives: firefighting by fire brigades

When firefighting is undertaken by a fire brigade, the objectives will vary with the situation on arrival and the speed of development of the fire related to the speed at which firefighting action can be initiated.

The objectives of a fire attack by a fire brigade can be listed as:

— ensuring safety of fire crews

— rescue

— finding the fire

— stopping spread

— surrounding the fire

— extinguishment

— damage limitation and environmental issues.

Methods of achieving those objectives include:

— establishing water supplies (or other firefighting medium)

— gaining access

— searching in smoke

— protecting the search team(s)

— maintaining a line of retreat

— holding defensive bridgehead(s)

— firefighting

— ventilation

— salvage operations

— environmental control.

9.1.3 Life safety objectives: firefighting by fire brigades

Although the first priority of a fire brigade attendance is to carry out any rescues, in a properly designed and maintained building the built-in fire safety provisions should enable all the people in the building to escape without fire brigade assistance.

The Home Office guidance document *Out of the Line of Fire — modernising the standards of fire cover*[2] contained a list of fires that have caused new fire safety legislation to be enacted within the UK. These include the following:

— Eastwood Mills, Keighley (1956)

— Hendersons Department Store, Liverpool (1960)

—   Top Storey Club, Bolton (1961)

—   Rose and Crown Hotel, Saffron Waldon (1969)

—   Woolworths, Manchester (1979)

—   Bradford City Football Ground, Bradford (1985)

—   Kings Cross Underground Station, London (1987)

These multiple-death fires all occurred in areas with the highest level of fire service attendance, i.e. multiple pumps and special appliances within a five minute attendance time. Subsequent multiple fire deaths in non-domestic property have also occurred in areas with the highest level of fire service attendance in the UK, in Europe, the United States and Asia. It is clear from these examples that the best method of safeguarding life from fire in non-domestic property is by built-in fire protection measures rather than an enhanced fire service attendance.

9.1.4   Property protection objectives

The broad requirements of the Fire Services Act[3] (as outlined below) have not been translated into detailed definitions of risks and objectives. Accordingly, individual fire brigades have devised broad objectives that are expressed in terms such as 'To save life and protect property'.

From the inception of professional fire services in the 17th century, society's fear of fire has resulted in an attitude that the only acceptable response to an outbreak of fire is to extinguish it as soon as possible, irrespective of other considerations. Although the modern fire service has embraced and even taken the initiative in developing new techniques and undertaking new responsibilities, the attitude of 'attack at all costs' still persists today.

Fire safety legislation is designed for life safety rather than for property protection. This means that provided that people can escape from the building, nothing needs to be done to protect the structure. Recent fires in out-of-town superstores, large food processing plants and high-bay warehousing have resulted in the total destruction of the buildings and their contents. There have been no casualties or fatalities amongst staff or members of the public. The people who died in these fires were firefighters who had been sent into the buildings to do an impossible job. It is shown in sections 9.2.2 and 9.3.2 below that there is no requirement for fire brigades to 'attack at all costs' and that fire brigades that follow that philosophy are potentially in breach of health and safety legislation.

There are other considerations if the decision is taken to fight a fire in premises such as those mentioned above. Large numbers of fire engines are required, not only to fight the fire but also to establish one or more water relays to get water to the scene. This denudes the surrounding area not only of clean water but also of normal fire cover. Run-off water from firefighting may pollute watercourses and open land. The action of applying water to the fire will inhibit combustion and cool the products of combustion thereby creating heavier and more concentrated airborne toxic products that will settle on land in higher concentrations than would have been the case with more complete combustion.

Whether an attack on a fire is by the occupiers of a building or by a fire brigade, two items are required:
—   an appropriate extinguishing medium
—   sufficient knowledge, skill and protection to apply the medium when and how required.

The size of fire that can be successfully controlled by firefighting attack is dependent not only on the passive and active fire safety measures installed in a building but also the speed and 'weight' of attendance of the fire brigade and the effective implementation of the fire attack plan.

Accordingly, the property protection objectives of firefighting should vary according to the building, the level of installed fire protection and the availability and actions of the fire brigade.

9.2   Legislation

9.2.1   Fire safety legislation

See section 2 for detailed consideration of legislation concerning fire safety.

In terms of firefighting, neither the Building Regulations[4] nor the Building Standards (Scotland) Regulations[5] require anything to be done except for the purposes of securing reasonable standards of health and safety for persons in or about the building. Part B of Schedule 1 to the Building Regulations (paragraph B5(1)) requires that:

> 'The building shall be designed and constructed so as to provide reasonable facilities to assist fire fighters in the protection of life.'

Within the UK, the Fire Precautions Act[6] and the Fire Precautions (Workplace) Regulations[7], are the two main Acts that require the provision of adequate means for fighting fires in buildings.

Other legislation relating to hospitals, houses in multiple occupation, licensed premises, cinemas, theatres etc. also requires the provision of first aid firefighting equipment.

9.2.2   Fire service legislation

All industrially developed countries have legislation that describes the shape and size of fire brigades. Such legislation may be municipal, regional or national.

Within the UK, the Fire Services Act[3] applies to all parts of England, Wales and Scotland. Although the Act does not apply to the Isle of Man, the Channel Isles or Northern Ireland, the standards applied in the UK are generally followed in those Islands and the province.

There are two principal bodies mentioned in the Fire Services Act, 'Fire Authorities' and 'Fire Brigades'. A Fire Authority is the political body (usually a county council or joint board) that is responsible for the provision of a Fire Brigade and for the enforcement of fire safety legislation. That Authority delegates the administrative management of the Fire Brigade and the enforcement of fire safety legislation to the Chief Fire Officer and Officers of the Fire Brigade.

At national level the UK fire service is monitored by the Fire Service Inspectorate under HM Chief Inspector of Fire Services. This body, which until 2001 came under the Home Office, is now the responsibility of the Office of the Deputy Prime Minister (ODPM). A statutory advisory body, the Central Fire Brigades Advisory Council, makes recommendations to the Secretary of State on fire service matters.

The Act governs the duty of a Fire Authority to make provision for firefighting purposes and the formation of the Central Fire Brigades Advisory Council. It also gives certain powers to firefighters when they are on duty.

It is the duty of a fire authority (amongst other things) to:

— secure the services for their area of such a fire brigade and such equipment as may be necessary to meet efficiently all normal requirements (Section 1(I)(a))

— secure efficient arrangements for dealing with calls for the assistance of the fire brigade in case of fire and for summoning members of the fire brigade (Section 1(I)(c))

— secure efficient arrangements for obtaining, by inspection or otherwise, information required for firefighting purposes with respect to the character of the buildings and other property in the area of the fire authority, the available water supplies and the means of access thereto, and other material local circumstances (Section 1(I)(d))

— take all reasonable measures for ensuring the provision of an adequate supply of water, and for securing that it will be available for use, in case of fire (Section 13).

Powers of firefighters in extinguishing fires include:

— To enter and if necessary break into any premises or place in which fire has or is reasonably believed to have broken out, or any premises or place which it is necessary to enter for the purposes of extinguishing a fire or of protecting the premises or place from acts done for firefighting purposes, without the consent of the owner or occupier thereof, and may do all such things as he may deem necessary for extinguishing the fire or for protecting from fire, or from acts done as aforesaid, any such premises or place or for rescuing any person or property therein (Section 30(I)).

— The senior fire brigade officer present shall have the sole charge and control of all operations for the extinction of the fire (Section 30(3)).

— Any water undertakers shall, on being required by the senior fire brigade officer present to provide a greater supply and pressure of water for extinguishing a fire, take all necessary steps to enable them to comply with such requirement (Section 30(4)).

— The senior fire brigade officer present may close to traffic any street or may stop or regulate the traffic in any street whenever in the opinion of that officer it is necessary or desirable to do so for firefighting purposes (Section 30 (5)).

It should be noted that there is nothing in the legislation that imposes a duty on fire authorities or fire brigades to save life, render humanitarian services or extinguish fire.

Under Section 13 of the Fire Services Act it is the duty of a fire authority to:

'take all reasonable measures for ensuring the supply of an adequate supply of water, and for securing that it will be available for use, in the case of fire'.

Section 14(1) of the Act provides, for the purpose of complying with Section 13, that a fire authority:

'may enter into an agreement with statutory water undertakers … for securing that an adequate supply of water will be available in the case of fire'.

Section 14(2) provides, for the purpose of complying with Section 13, that if a fire authority considers that the existing supply of water:

'would be likely to be inadequate in case of fire, may enter into an agreement with the undertakers … for the provision of such additional supply of water as may be specified in the agreement'.

Section 15 provides, for the purpose of complying with Section 13, that a fire authority shall:

'have power by agreement:

(a) to secure the use, in case of fire, of water under the control of any person other than statutory water undertakers;

(b) to improve the access to any such water;

(c) to lay and maintain pipes and to carry out other works in connection with the use of such water in case of fire.'

It can be seen from the above that the duty for ensuring the supply of water in the case of fire is the responsibility solely of a fire authority. It is also clear that, if it is considered that the supply is inadequate, it is the responsibility solely of a fire authority to enter into an agreement with the undertakers for the provision of additional water supplies.

The fire authority can also enter into an agreement with 'any person other than statutory water undertakers' for the provision of additional water supplies. However, this is, as stated, by agreement. The fire authority cannot require those 'other persons' to provide additional supplies.

Those sections of the Fire Services Act that apply to the responsibility of a fire authority to provide water have not been tested in court. However, in interpreting the legislation, fire brigades generally link the reference in Section 1(I)(a) to 'normal requirements' to Sections 13, 14 and 15, requiring them to provide water for firefighting. By linking these sections of the Act, fire brigades can claim to provide the necessary water by utilising the water carried on fire pumps, by pre-planned water relays or the provision of water carriers, and thereby avoid the expense, to the fire brigade, of installing mains supplies.

This author is not aware of any legislation that enables a fire authority or fire brigade to require the developer, owner or occupier of premises to provide additional water supplies for firefighting by private mains or any other method.

9.2.3　Health and safety related legislation

There is a general duty placed on employers and employees under health and safety at work legislation for the safety of the workforce and others. Of the several regulations and guidance documents that have been published to assist employers and their servants in establishing safe places and systems of work, two can be directly related to firefighting:

— Management of Health and Safety at Work Regulations 1999[8] and the associated *Approved Code of Practice and Guidance for the Management of Health and Safety at Work Regulations*[9]

— the Personal Protective Equipment at Work Regulations 1992[10] and the associated *Personal Protective Equipment at Work Regulations 1992 — Guidance on Regulations*[11]

These regulations set standards for places of work and the people who work there and include standards for:

— a safe environment

— adequate clothing

— safe procedures

— adequate training

9.2.3.1　Management of Health and Safety at Work Regulations

The Health and Safety Commission's *Approved Code of Practice and Guidance for the Management of Health and Safety at Work Regulations*[9] is the source document for many of the more detailed occupational guides. This Code advises on the need for 'suitable and sufficient risk assessment' and states that employers are 'expected to take reasonable steps, e.g. by reading HSE guidance, the trade press, company or supplier manuals etc. to familiarise themselves with the hazards and risks in their work'. The assessments are for the purpose of identifying measures which need to be taken to establish a safe work environment.

Regulation 3 of the Management of Health and Safety at Work Regulations 1999[8], places a duty on employers to carry out an assessment of the risks to which employees are exposed whilst at work. Such a risk assessment should, amongst other things:

— be suitable and sufficient

— address what actually happens during the work activity

— record significant findings.

9.2.3.2　Personal Protective Equipment at Work Regulations

Regulation 4 of the Personal Protective Equipment at Work Regulations 1992[10] ('PPE Regulations') requires that every employer shall provide employees with suitable personal protective equipment (PPE).

However, the guidance to the PPE Regulations stresses that there is 'a hierarchy of control measures', and PPE should always be regarded as the 'last resort' to protect against risks. Safe systems of work should always be considered first (Regulation 3 above).

9.3　Application of health and safety legislation

9.3.1　Application of health and safety legislation to firefighting by occupiers

Clearly, if firefighting equipment is to be provided for use by the occupiers of a building, the equipment must be suitable for the risk, and able to be used by the occupiers. As it would be unrealistic for someone to dress in protective clothing for the purpose of attacking a fire in a building, the assessment of the size of fire that an occupier can attempt to attack must be based on an assumption that the person will be wearing clothing that is normally worn in the premises throughout the working day.

It follows that sufficient training must be given to enable the occupier not only to operate the equipment satisfactorily but to decide at what point first aid firefighting should cease and the evacuation of the premises be undertaken (see also 9.4.5 below).

9.3.2　Application of health and safety legislation to firefighting by fire brigades

It is recognised that when a fire occurs in a building and a call is made to the fire service, the responding firefighters will attempt any rescues and will attack the fire in order to save as much of the property as possible.

Clearly there are risks inherent in firefighting operations. Accordingly, measures which are considered necessary to enhance life safety should take account of not only the occupants of a building but the safety of fire fighters who may be called to deal with an incident in that building.

The personal protective equipment available to all fire fighters includes a tunic and over trousers of fire retardant material, safety boots, helmet, flash-hood and gloves. Breathing apparatus is available to safeguard the individual when working in a hostile environment.

The Home Office and fire service organisations have taken account of health and safety legislation and have produced several guidance documents in respect of best operating practices and firefighter safety. Recent publications from the Home Office on safe working practices include *A Guide to Operational Risk Assessment*[12] and *Dynamic Management of Risk at Operational Incidents*[13].

The *Guide* updates earlier advice on dynamic risk assessment and includes a flow chart. The main tasks and questions identified on the flowchart are:

— Evaluate the situation, tasks and persons at risk.

— Select systems of work.

— Assess the chosen systems.

— Are the risks proportional to the benefits?

— Can additional control measures be introduced?

Also within the *Guide* is an acknowledgement that there is no requirement to extinguish a fire or to fight a fire aggressively if circumstances suggest that the risk would be out of proportion to the objective. This attitude is encapsulated in the following statement from the Home Office *Guide*:

'The maxim highlighted below demonstrates the correct attitude towards safety:

— We may risk our lives a lot, in a highly calculated manner, to protect saveable lives.

— We may risk our lives a little, in a highly calculated manner, to protect saveable property.

— We will not risk our lives at all for lives or property that are already lost.'

The fire service operational application of health and safety legislation accepts that fires should not be attacked 'at all costs'. It is the sole responsibility of the officer in charge of any incident to ensure that the people under his/her command are not risking their lives at all for lives or property that are already lost.

9.4 First aid firefighting equipment and training for occupiers

9.4.1 Fire buckets

Portable fire extinguishers have largely taken over from fire buckets in most premises. However there are still some applications where fire buckets filled with sand are useful and may be required by legislation. This is particularly so in premises that store or use flammable liquids and in petrol filling stations. For all premises where legislation requires the provision of sand filled fire buckets, the advice of the appropriate licensing authority should be sought.

9.4.2 Fire extinguishers

BS 5306: Part 8[14] contains recommendations on the selection and installation of portable fire extinguishers that can be carried by one person.

The classification and rating of different types of fire extinguisher, contained within BS EN 3[15], enables the distribution of of fire extinguishers in buildings to be determined according to their extinguishing capability and size.

Fire extinguishers that conform to BS EN 3 are marked with a figure and a letter. The figure denotes the maximum size of test fire they are capable of extinguishing and the letter denotes the class of fire e.g. 8A or 13A for an extinguisher designed to attack Class A fires; 89B or 144B for an extinguisher designed to attack Class B fires.

Examples of how to apply the minimum recommended distribution standards for fire extinguishers are given in Annex B to BS 5306: Part 8[14]. These examples take account of:

— the class of fire likely to occur (what is the fuel)

— the size of fire likely to occur

— the area to be covered.

However, when planning the provision of fire extinguishers for a building, three other factors need to be considered:

— the physical capabilities of the occupiers to carry and operate different sizes of fire extinguisher

— the distance to be travelled with the fire extinguisher

— the necessity of maintaining a route to safety so that the operator can turn away from the fire and escape.

The result of considering these other factors may be the provision of a number of small fire extinguishers at several locations rather than a few large extinguishers at a small number of locations.

9.4.3 Hose reels

9.4.3.1 General

A hose reel consists of a length of small-bore rubber tubing wound onto a reel or drum, connected to a permanent water supply and with a shut-off nozzle at the end of the hose. Hose reels are considered as a first-aid firefighting measure and are designed for the use of the occupants of the building in fighting an outbreak of fire when this is first discovered. As well as being available for the occupants of the building, often the fire brigade will also make use of hose reel installations. Hose reels provide a more resilient firefighting measure than water extinguishers due to the greater water flow rates achievable and the availability of continuous supply.

Hose reels may be installed as a replacement for, or in combination with, water-type extinguishers but should ideally form part of the integrated firefighting measures for the building as a whole. This may mean that other types of extinguishers or other hand appliances are available for first-aid firefighting in addition to the hose reels.

The initiative to provide hose reels will generally be made by the local authority or fire brigade, or at the request of the building owner/occupier or their insurer. For areas other than London, where they may be required by the local authority for 'Section 20' buildings[16], there are no rules as to the numbers required but they must form part of a balanced fire strategy for the premises and due consideration must be given to the types of fire upon which they are likely to be used and the risk to those using them.

9.4.3.2   Rules and standards

The standard most likely to be applied for installation of hose reels in the UK is BS 5306: Part 1[17] which covers not only hose reels but also hydrant systems and foam inlets.

The manufacturing standard for hose reels is BS 5274[18]. Hose tubing should be manufactured to BS 3169[19]. The inlet valves to hose reels should be either stopcocks to BS 1010[20] or gate/globe valves to BS 5154[21].

9.4.3.3   Types of hose reel

A number of different types of reel are available:

—   *Fixed*: in which the reel or drum rotates from a fixed position and the hose is usually fed through a guide that allows the hose to be pulled from the reel without fouling. The reel can be fixed to the wall or floor, sometimes with a pedestal to position the reel at the correct height. There are occasions when it is desirable to conceal the reel and there are options to use a fixed reel hidden behind a panel in which there is a small opening, sometimes with a hinged flap, through which the hose is pulled for use.

—   *Swinging*: in which the reel is hinged at one side and can be rotated such that the reel may be positioned to allow the hose to be run out without the need for a guide.

—   *Swinging recessed*: similar to the swinging type but designed to fit into a recess. Both recessed and swinging recessed can be housed in a cabinet which can prove to be more attractive in sensitive environments.

Two different operating methods can be provided for virtually all hose reels:

—   *Manual operation*: whereby the isolating valve, which is located on the feed to the reel, is kept closed in normal circumstances and must be opened prior to running out the hose.

—   *Automatic operation*: rotation of the reel operates a valve, built into the reel mechanism, which admits water to the hose. The isolating valve on the feed is kept open and normally a lock shield valve used to discourage casual interference.

With all types of reel the control nozzle on the free end of the hose is kept in the closed position and opened only when the location of the fire is reached. Some manual reels may have an interlocking device such that the supply valve must be opened before the hose can be run out.

9.4.3.4   Hose reel components

The internal diameter of hose tubing may be 19 mm or 25 mm. The maximum hose length available is 45 m, in the case of the 19 mm tubing, and 35 m for 25 mm hose, but consideration should be given to the persons likely to use the equipment and the difficulty, and physical strength required, in pulling out the hose along a potentially tortuous route. Normally hose lengths are 35 m or less.

The nozzles should be of a shut-off type to give either a plain jet or combination jet/spray discharge pattern. Modern nozzles are likely to be of the latter type and the actuation is by screw control. Older plain jet nozzles are usually controlled with an on/off cock.

9.4.3.5   Spacing and location

Although hose reel lengths are usually 35 m or less, the actual length should be determined on the basis of a risk assessment, taking account of the building design, the people who occupy it and the distribution of goods within it. In a large warehouse with wide, straight aisles and a physically strong workforce, the length can be increased to 60 m (the same length that is carried on one reel on a fire pump). In a residential care home with a single night-time supervisor and corridors to negotiate, a length of 20 m might be the maximum that could be handled.

The distribution of hose reels within a building should be based on the following concepts:

—   every part of every room should be within 6 m of a hose reel nozzle

—   the maximum length of every reel should be based on an assessment of the routes in the building and the people who may have to use the equipment

—   the reels should be located so that when running out the equipment or attacking the fire, the operator can always turn away from the fire and escape.

Where hose reels are located on escape routes it is preferable that they are located within recesses so that they do not obstruct the means of escape. Often hose reels fitted in such locations are fitted with non-lockable doors which must be clearly marked as to the contents and open fully to 180° to avoid impeding the operation of the reel.

9.4.3.6   Water supplies

The water supply should be capable of giving a minimum flow of 30 litres per minute at the nozzle and sustaining simultaneous operation of two reels in the most hydraulically unfavourable positions. The length of jet should be approximately 6 m at the minimum delivery rate.

The required operating reel inlet pressures should be sought from the manufacturers but BS 5306: Part 1[17] gives approximate values of 1.25 bar (125 kPa) for a reel with a 30 m hose and 6.35 mm nozzle, and 3 bar (300 kPa) where the nozzle size is 4.8 mm.

The supply may be achieved in one of the following ways:

— direct from the town main

— by using booster pumps on the town main (where this is permitted by the water undertaking)

— by pumping from a suction tank.

It may also be possible for a hose reel water supply to be taken from the trunk main feeding an automatic sprinkler installation but this requires the specific approval of those responsible for the sprinkler installation, the fire insurers etc.

Where pumps are provided they should be duplicated with one duty and one standby unit, usually electrically driven. They should come into operation automatically upon detection of a drop in system pressure or water flow. There should also be audible and visual alarms upon actuation of the equipment. There are many standard hose reel pump packages available which conveniently combine all the necessary equipment on a single base plate.

Where direct boosting of the supply is not permitted a tank or tanks having a capacity of 1125 litres must be provided which must have an automatic infill from the town main having a minimum diameter of 50 mm.

The supply pipework must be sized such that the required flows and pressures are continuously available at the hose reel nozzles. Normally a minimum of 25 mm diameter pipework would be used to supply a single reel and an average system would not normally require a main feed pipe larger than 50 mm diameter.

Care must be taken to ensure that pipes are not subject to frost conditions and insulation and/or trace heating should be provided where appropriate.

9.4.3.7 Labels

The location of all hose reels should be clearly marked so that they may be readily found in an emergency.

Operating labels for the reels should be easy to read in adverse conditions and should bear simple instructions on the action necessary to operate the reel.

Labels on recess doors should be in red letters at least 50 mm high.

9.4.3.8 Testing

All system pipework should be flushed and hydrostatically tested prior to commissioning. Each hose reel should be fully run out and flow tested and the performance of the water supply should be proven by simultaneously operating the two most hydraulically unfavourably located reels and measuring the flow rate and length of jet.

In the case of supplies involving pumps the test should first be carried out using the duty pump and then repeated after simulation of electrical or mechanical failure of the duty pump to prove the capability of the standby pump.

When all tests have been completed all hose reel tubing should be drained and all reels returned to their normal operating condition.

9.4.3.9 Maintenance

Hose reels should be regularly inspected and tested to ensure that they operate correctly and that the hose is in good condition. All pump sets should be properly serviced along with their electrical control equipment. Any changes to the architecture or occupancy, which could alter the effectiveness of the hose reels, should be noted and remedial action taken as appropriate.

It is recommended that the inspection and maintenance is carried out at least annually and at that time a full test of the water supply as described in section 9.4.3.6 should be carried out.

9.4.4 Fire points

In is important that firefighting equipment, fire notices and fire alarm operating points are always conspicuous to the occupiers of buildings. The best method of achieving this is to group these items at fire points. Fire points should be on exit routes and be distinctively marked. Fire equipment manufacturers can supply proprietary fire points that consist of a base for the holding of fire extinguishers and a highlighted backboard that identifies the fire point. Alternatively, fire points may be identified by marking an area of wall behind the fire point.

In those cases where it is appropriate to locate individual fire extinguishers throughout an open office area, beside a particular risk or on different levels of plant they are best located on a column and identified by a band around the column. The colour(s) of the band to match the markings used to identify the fire points.

9.4.5 Training

There are several training needs that must be fulfiled before people who occupy a building are able to attack a fire in safety. Training needs include:

— identifying the largest fire capable of being attacked in the location in which it might occur

— appreciating the hazards of heat and smoke within a room and along escape routes

— maintaining a safe escape route

— the use of fire buckets/extinguishers/hose reels.

By way of illustration, consider the different types of fire that may occur in the following types of occupancies:

— the kitchen of a restaurant

— a factory where furniture is waxed by hand

— a workstation in a modern office

— a commercial printing press.

The shape and size of the premises that would be used for the above purposes would be different, the size of fire that could develop and the speed of development would be different, the volume of smoke and its rate of production would be different and the techniques used to fight the fire would be different. Training that is limited to the use of fire extinguishers in an open space is totally inadequate.

Accordingly, the training should, as near as possible, reflect the premises and circumstances in which a fire might occur and take account of the action necessary to attack the fire while maintaining an acceptable level of personal safety.

9.5 Firefighting equipment and training for fire brigades

9.5.1 Fire brigade equipment

The standard vehicle of the UK fire service is known as a fire pump. It has built-in high and low pressure pumps, portable pumps, a variety of branches and nozzles, hydraulic rescue equipment, breaking-in and cutting gear, ladders, breathing apparatus, flood lighting, standard protective clothing and chemical protection suits. All such vehicles carry a quantity of water (typically between 1000 and 2000 litres) and foam compound (to produce firefighting foam). Many vehicles also carry thermal imaging cameras. These vehicles may be known by various names such as 'water escape', 'water ladder', 'water tender ladder', 'rescue pump' etc. However, for the purposes of planning for fire brigade attendance at a building, it is sufficient to refer to any such vehicle as a 'pump'.

The extent and duration of operation of a single pump and crew are limited by a number of factors including:

— total length of hose carried

— quantity of water carried

— availability of additional water from hydrants

— ability to implement safe working practices with limited crew

— duration of breathing apparatus sets.

9.5.1.1 Hose and water

The complement of hose carried on a pump and the quantity of water carried varies significantly between countries, regions and municipalities. However, within the UK the following complement of hose and water is typical of most pumps.

Fire brigades use two types of delivery hose: hose reels and layflat delivery hose.

Hose reels typically have a diameter of 19 mm or 25 mm. It is usual for UK fire brigade pumping appliances to have two hose reels fitted, each being approximately 60 m long (these may be in a continuous line or in three lengths each of 20 m). The two reels can be connected to form a single line 120 m long. A hose reel can be operated at pressures up to 40 bar (4000 kPa) and deliver up to 230 litres of

water per minute in a variety of configurations from jet to wide angle spray to fog.

Layflat delivery hose is usually of 45 mm or 70 mm diameter. UK fire brigades usually carry a selection of the two diameters of layflat hose 16 × 70 mm and 4 × 45 mm (plus high-rise). The nominal length of layflat delivery hose is 18 m or 25 m. Layflat delivery hose is particularly susceptible to damage at the ends where the fabric of the hose is fastened to the couplings. Because of this it is standard practice to purchase hose in lengths of 25 m and to cut back any damage rather than repair near a coupling. For planning purposes it is reasonable to assume that each length of hose is 20 m long. In addition, to the hose in lockers, many (though not all) fire brigades also carry a 'high rise pack'. This pack typically contains 2 × 45 mm hose, 1 × hand controlled branch with a 12.5 mm nozzle, wrench, door wedges, fire blanket etc.

With all hose, the description of the hose from the hydrant to the pump and from the pump to the branch (i.e. the hand-held equipment to which the nozzle is attached) is a 'line' with each individual piece of hose being described as a 'length'. Where, for example, four lengths were joined, it would be described as a single line of hose of four lengths (approximately 80 metres long). When it is necessary to reduce frictional loss, and thereby increase flow, lines are usually 'twinned'.

The water carried in the tanks of the fire pumps varies between 1000 and 2000 litres. With a 12.5 mm nozzle at 2.5 bar (250 kPa) nozzle pressure the delivery will be approximately 160 litres of water per minute. (*Note*: these figures should be taken as a guide only; modern multi-flow nozzles for use with 45 mm hose can deliver 360–750 litres per minute). The water that is carried means that there should be no delay in the first jet/spray being applied to the fire. With a 1000 litre tank and a delivery flow of 160 litres per minute, the water would be exhausted within 6 minutes. With a hose reel working at maximum flow the water would be exhausted within 4 minutes. The significance of these figures for preplanning is that if the fire cannot be extinguished within that time, additional water supplies need to be established in order to maintain an unbroken attack on the fire.

9.5.1.2 Breathing apparatus

Although there are some fire brigades in the UK that use long duration oxygen breathing apparatus, these are for specialised risks within those areas. All fire brigades now use compressed air breathing apparatus (BA). This has a nominal duration of 40 minutes but this time may be substantially reduced due to the arduous and hot conditions experienced in firefighting.

Two terms are important in preplanning for the use of BA in a building: 'donning' and 'starting-up'. The term donning simply means fixing the set securely on the back of the wearer with all straps adjusted and the facemask hung around the neck. The term starting-up is when the facemask is fitted over the head, and pre-entry tests for gas tightness etc. have been completed. Starting-up a BA set must always be carried out in clean air.

The link between starting-up in clean air and duration is significant as these two factors determine the distance within a building that it is possible to penetrate while wearing BA. Clean air is taken to be outside a single compartment building or within a firefighting shaft. In a large building, such as a multi-storey shopping complex, clean air could be within a ventilated mall or protected corridor separated from the remainder of the complex by a ventilated, protected lobby. Accordingly, while it is permissible to travel through several floors of a building to the floor below the fire floor before starting-up a BA set, in the case of a large single storey building it is necessary to start-up outside the building.

The 40 minutes duration is timed from the moment the set is started-up to the time at which the wearer exits the building and reports back to the entry control officer. The duration is nominal because of the differing physiological needs of individuals and the variation of effort expended in undertaking different tasks. It is usual that the first BA team to enter will have the most onerous job. They have to find the fire and lay a hose line. Relief teams need to follow the hose line to take over from the first team and advance the jet as the fire is attacked. Accordingly the duration of the BA of the first team and the distance penetrated might be significantly less than for succeeding teams.

The continued use of BA at a fire is a considerable logistic exercise. For example, if it is assumed that the travel time from the entry point to the fire is 10 minutes and each team maintains a full duration of 40 minutes, a fresh team of two BA wearers needs to be sent into the building at 20-minute intervals to maintain a single point of fire attack.

9.5.1.3   Single pump

Fire brigades have a considerable variety of modern equipment at their disposal to protect firefighters, to gain entry to premises and to attack fire. This equipment, together with detailed operational preplanning, should ensure that an effective fire attack could be mounted if an early call is received to an incident. However, for planning purposes, it should be assumed that a single pump and crew are only able to mount a single point of fire attack. As most fires require attacking from at least two directions in order to prevent spread, the preplanning should be based on the attendance time of at least two pumps.

9.5.2   Fire brigade training

Because firefighters work in premises in which they are unfamiliar and in areas where the risks are variable and changing, a series of operational practices has been developed to ensure best practice in fire attack coupled with an acceptable level of safety. These operational practices are contained in fire service manuals, technical bulletins and other documents generated by the Home Office, technical bodies and individual fire brigades.

All firefighters are trained in the use of the equipment that they are likely to use and the standard operating procedures. Fire officers follow a progression of training courses appropriate to their rank and responsibility in order to exercise their operational command responsibilities effectively.

9.6   Standards of fire cover

Standards of fire cover are for the purpose of planning the number and location of fire stations and the duty system worked. That planning assumes that the fire appliances are at their home station when a fire call is received. Apart from this assumption being necessary for planning purposes, it is a fact that in the vast majority of occasions fire appliances are, in fact, at their home station when a fire call is received.

Attendance patterns in the UK are determined by the application of a series of prose descriptions and formulae[22] that categorise the risk in a geographical area and determine response times and attendance times. From these standards it is possible to calculate the maximum travel distances between fire stations and whether the fire station needs to be staffed by wholetime or retained personnel.

Application of the formulae results in buildings being graded as to fire risk. The fire grading of buildings which predominates within an area of five half kilometre squares results in that area being categorised as: A, B, C, D or remote rural. Each of these risk categories attracts a particular predetermined attendance.

9.6.1   Determination of maximum attendance times

The minimum requirements, in terms of 'weight' and speed of attendance of personnel and equipment, that have been set by the UK Home Office are dependent on the risk categorisation of the area in which the incident occurs[23]. In assessing emergency attendance times, the call handling time (the elapsed time from when a caller is connected to a fire control to when all relevant information has been obtained) is not taken into account. The formula for attendance times therefore consists of two inputs: response time (i.e. the elapsed time from the turnout system being operated to when the fire appliance is leaving the fire station) and travelling time from the fire station to the address of the incident.

Maximum attendance times are shown in Table 9.1. It should be noted that these are maximum attendance times, not target times for all parts of a station ground of a particular risk category. It is implicit in the standards that attendance times should be achieved on 100% of occasions.

Table 9.1 Maximum attendance times (UK)

Risk category	Attendance time (minutes)		
	1st pump	2nd pump	3rd pump
A	5	5	8
B	5	8	—
C	8 to 10	—	—
D	20	—	—
Remote rural	No time specified		

9.6.2   Size of crews

Although the 'normal' number of people that form the crew of a standard pump in the UK is five, the actual number can vary between a minimum of four and a maximum of six. The crew of five is termed the 'confidence level' and this level must be maintained on 75% of occasions[24].

9.6.3 Actual attendance times and confidence levels

All UK fire brigades are required to publish 'best value performance indicators'. These show the percentage of occasions that the brigade met standards of (a) 'weight' of attendance (pumps), (b) attendance times (whole time manned) and (c) attendance times (retained manned).

The figures are generally published annually by individual fire brigades and are usually available on each brigade's website.

The risk category of the area is immaterial when assessing probable fire brigade attendance at a specific location as the risk category gives a maximum attendance time to the whole of the area, not the average minimum attendance to a particular building. For example, in a risk category 'D' area the minimum 'weight' and speed of attendance is one pump in 20 minutes. However, there may be a two-pump station within a one-minute attendance time of some buildings within that area.

For planning purposes it is essential that the actual attendance times to the area in which the development is to be located are obtained from the local fire brigade.

9.6.4 Implications of different standards of fire cover, equipment and training

When planning a total fire safety package for a building, the actual standards of fire service equipment available, the training and competence of the firefighters and the weight and speed of attendance to the area where the building is to be constructed need to form part of the considerations. These are dealt with in section 9.13.

9.7 Fire service water supplies

Fire brigades use water from a variety of sources to supplement that carried on pumping appliances. This section is intended to show the use of different systems by fire brigades and the way in which they are included in preplanning for fire attack.

9.7.1 Fire hydrants

Fire hydrants are the most common way of obtaining supplementary supplies of water for firefighting. They are fitted onto water mains and provide a means by which fire brigades can connect hose to those mains by use of a standpipe and thereby obtain water for firefighting. The prescriptive standard for the locating of hydrants on a site are that they should be not more than 60 m from an entry to any building and be not more than 120 m apart. The benefits of hydrants are their ready availability in urban areas and the constant, unlimited supply of water that they provide. The disadvantage is that some hydrants on old mains do not give sufficient flow for large jets, although this can sometimes be rectified by the attendance of a 'turn-cock' from the water undertaking.

9.7.2 Fire tanks

Fire tanks can be static above-ground tanks located within commercial premises or underground tanks forming part of a hydrant system.

Water may be extracted from them either by gravity feed to a fire pump or by lifting via a suction hose.

9.7.3 Open water

Fire brigades class as 'open water' any potential supply that can be used for firefighting including the sea, docks, rivers, streams, lakes, ponds, swimming pools, mill lodges, reservoirs, ornamental ponds etc. Open water always requires lifting via a suction hose.

9.7.4 Water relay

When the water supply is some distance from the fire, or the nearest supply is insufficient, fire brigades utilise a system of hose and pumps to relay the water from the supply to the location of the fire. Relaying water is a time consuming task that places onerous demands on personnel and equipment.

9.7.5 Operational planning implications

The availability of water and the method of obtaining sufficient quantities for a fire attack will have a significant impact on the speed at which a fire attack can commence and the time for which it can be sustained.

9.7.6 Fire mains in buildings

Fire mains in buildings are either 'wet' (i.e. permanently filled with water) or 'dry' (i.e. maintained empty and filled by the fire brigade when they attend an incident). Some fire brigades now require the installation of 'charged-dry mains', see section 9.7.6.3. Fire mains in buildings may be rising, falling or horizontal.

9.7.6.1 Dry rising mains

Dry rising mains are systems in which a pipe is installed vertically through a building with an inlet breeching provided at street level, through which the fire brigade can pump water. Outlets, with hand-controlled valves, are provided at each floor level (except the ground floor) to which the brigade can attach firefighting hoses. These valves are known as landing valves. A schematic of a dry riser is shown in Figure 9.1.

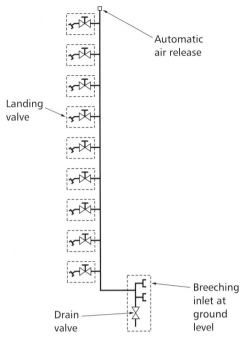

Figure 9.1 Schematic of typical dry riser installation

Dry rising mains should comply with Parts 2, 3, 4 and 5 of BS 5041[25].

The landing valves should be sited within a ventilated lobby of a lobby approach stairway or within a stairway enclosure or in any other position agreed with the fire authority. Normally only one landing valve will be provided at each level on each riser but in special circumstances two may be appropriate. Where deep basements are encountered it may be appropriate to provide landing valves at these lower levels.

The valves should be installed with their lowest point about 750 mm above floor level. It may be desirable to enclose the landing valves in a box or open recess in which case it is essential that there is sufficient space for both operating and maintaining the valve. It is preferable that dry riser landing valves are housed in a box that complies with BS 5041.

All valves should be protected from interference by thieves and vandals and those not in lockable boxes secured closed by straps and padlocks.

Breeching inlets for dry risers should be located in an external wall as close as possible to the riser position but with due regard to fire brigade access, danger from falling materials, exposure to the fire etc. There should be a road, suitable for fire appliances, within sight and a maximum of 18 m from the inlet.

Breeching inlets and inlet boxes should comply with BS 5041. The box should be positioned with its lower edge between 400 mm and 600 mm above ground level. Where a 100 mm dry riser is provided a two-way breeching inlet should be fitted and for 150 mm risers, a four-way inlet should be provided.

A drain valve should be incorporated into the breeching inlet but, if the main feeds landing valves below the inlet level or the pipe route forms a trap for water for any other reason, an additional drain valve must be provided and identified both at the valve location and at the inlet.

An automatic air release valve should be fitted at the highest point on dry risers to permit the riser to be charged with water without the need to open any landing valves.

In buildings fitted with dry risers there should be access for a pumping appliance to within 18 m of each fire main inlet.

Fire brigade pumping appliance carry either 1000 litres or 2000 litres of water for immediate use on arrival at a fire. The quantity of water carried by the predetermined attendance at a fire where a dry riser is to be used and the availability of a supplementary water supply are critical for planning purposes. Tables 9.2 and 9.3 and Example 9.1 show the importance of preplanning for fire attack.

Example 9.1

If it is assumed that one length of 70 mm diameter delivery hose is run from the pump to the riser inlet (1 × 20 m × 70 mm), and three lengths of 45 mm delivery hose is necessary from the riser outlet to the fire (3 × 20 m × 45 mm). The water requirements are:

— for 70 mm diam. hose: 3.846 × 20 = 76.92 litres

Table 9.2 Water requirements per metre length of pipe

Hose type	Diameter of hose / mm	Volume per metre length / $m^3 \cdot m^{-1}$	Volume per metre length / $litre \cdot m^{-1}$
Hose reel	19	0.0283	0.283
	25	0.0490	0.490
Layflat	45	0.1589	1.589
	70	0.3846	3.846
Riser	100	0.7850	7.850
	150	1.7662	17.662

Table 9.3 Example 9.1: total water requirement to fill riser and hose lines (20 m × 70 mm plus 60 m × 45 mm)

Height above access level / m	Water requirement / litre		
	Riser	Hose lines	Total
2.5	19	173	192
5	39	173	212
7.5	58	173	231
10	78	173	251
12.5	98	173	271
15	117	173	290
17.5	137	173	310
20	157	173	330
22.5	176	173	349
25	196	173	369
27.5	215	173	388
30	235	173	408
32.5	255	173	428
35	274	173	447
37.5	294	173	467
40	314	173	487
42.5	334	173	507
45	354	173	527
47.5	373	173	546
50	393	173	566
52.5	413	173	586
55	432	173	605
57.5	452	173	625
60	471	173	644

— for 45 mm diam. hose: 1.589 × 60 = 95.34 litres

Total water requirement to fill hose lines = 172.26 litres.

If it is further assumed that the diameter of the riser is 100 m (i.e. a flow of 7.85 litres per metre), the total water requirement to fill both the riser and the hose lines will be as shown in Table 9.3.

From Table 9.3 it can be seen that if the fire brigade pumping appliance is carrying 1000 litres of water and the riser outlet to be used is at the 60 m level, it leaves 356 litres available for an immediate attack (approximately two minutes, at a conservative estimate). Accordingly it is necessary for a supplementary water supply to be available immediately on arrival of the predetermined attendance.

9.7.6.2 Wet rising mains

A vertical pipe, similar to a dry rising main, runs through the building with landing valves at each level except the ground floor. Instead of an inlet breeching, the pipe is connected to a permanent water supply, see Figure 9.2. This may be a direct connection to the town main, where this is permitted and of sufficient capacity, but more commonly consists of a water storage and pumping facility.

Wet risers are suitable for buildings of all heights but are essential when the highest floor is more than 60 m above ground level. This is due to the excessive pressure at which the fire brigade would need to pump and the delay in delivering water to the highest point in the riser.

The benefit of wet rising mains is that a supplementary water supply may not be necessary. If a supplementary water supply is necessary the time available to obtain the supply is extended.

For wet risers, landing valves should comply with BS 5041: Part 1[25].

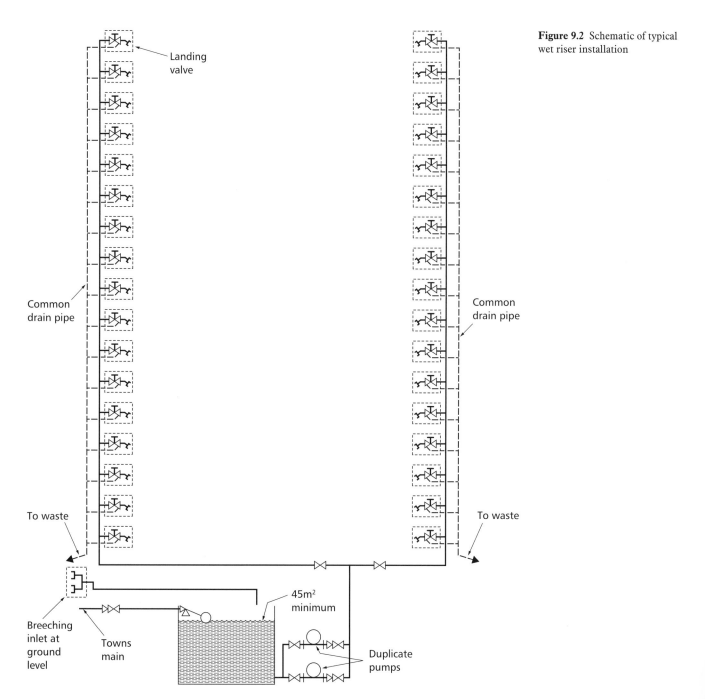

Figure 9.2 Schematic of typical wet riser installation

Landing valve

Common drain pipe

To waste

Breeching inlet at ground level

Towns main

45m² minimum

Common drain pipe

To waste

Duplicate pumps

Landing valves for wet risers are often more cumbersome than those for dry risers and an open recess is often preferred. In any case the opening for the valve should give not less than 150 mm clearance on both sides and not less than 230 mm below the centre line of the outlet. A clearance of 200 mm above the hand wheel must be maintained. The depth of opening must be kept as short as practicable but such that the edge of the female coupling is no more than 75 mm behind the face of the wall. These requirements are shown in Figure 9.3.

All valves should be protected from interference by thieves and vandals and those not in lockable boxes should be secured in the closed position by straps and padlocks.

Because of the need to provide sufficient pressure in the upper sections of wet risers, the pressures in the lower parts of the riser may be excessive. If this is the case it may be necessary to limit the delivery pressures so as to avoid dangerously high pressures in firefighting hoses. The running pressure should be controlled to a minimum of 4 bar (400 kPa) and a maximum of 5 bar (500 kPa) at each landing valve. When the nozzle of the hose is shut off, the pressure in the hose should not exceed 7 bar (700 kPa). Pressure control can be achieved by the provision of a pressure relief connection built into the delivery side of the landing valve that is permanently connected to a waste pipe. The valve can be calibrated to give an adjustable inlet/outlet pressure differential to cope with the various locations in the riser.

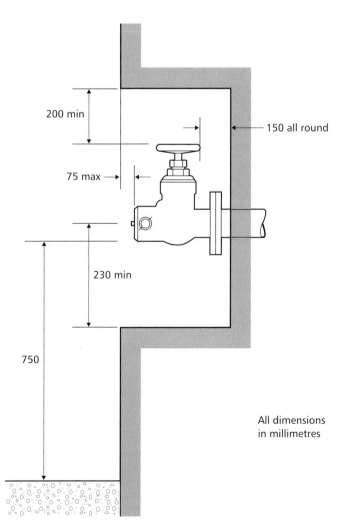

Figure 9.3 Fixing height and recess requirements for landing valves

An alternative type of landing valve for wet risers incorporates a 'dead shut off' pressure reducing valve and requires no drain connection.

A dependable supply of water must be available for wet risers, which is capable of supplying three landing valves in simultaneous operation in the most unfavourable hydraulic location. This equates to a minimum flow rate of 1500 litre·min^{-1} and a minimum running pressure of 4 bar (400 kPa) at the highest landing valve must be maintained.

With the agreement of the water authority, the town main can provide a suitable supply provided that it is capable of meeting the above requirement and is sufficiently reliable. However, it is usually necessary to supplement the supply with water storage and pumping facilities.

A storage tank with a minimum capacity of 45 m^3 should be fitted and provided with an automatic town main infill connection to replenish the tank contents such that the combination of the storage and infill give a capacity of 1500 litre·min^{-1} for 45 minutes (i.e. 67.5 m^3). Therefore, if a reliable infill of 375 litre·min^{-1} can be provided, the minimum 45 m^3 tank may be used.

Duplicate automatic pumps, one duty pump and one standby, should be provided, each capable of the full duty and supplied from a different power source. The pumps should come into operation upon detection of a drop in pressure or water flow. Audible and visual alarms of pump operation should be provided.

An emergency tank filling connection may be necessary to take account of circumstances when the automatic infill is out of action. This should take the form of a breeching inlet and 100 mm pipe to discharge over the wet riser storage tank.

Breeching inlets for or tank filling connections on wet riser installations should comply with the same standards as for dry risers.

9.7.6.3 Charged dry rising mains

There are no standards specific to charged dry rising mains. However, fire brigades typically require the main to comply with the standards for a dry rising main with the addition of a 300 litre header tank.

As with a wet rising main, the benefit of a charged dry rising main is that additional time is available to obtain a supplementary water supply.

9.7.6.4 Prescriptive standards for the number and location of rising mains

Prescriptive standards for the number and location of rising mains recommend a dry rising main where the highest floor of a building is between 18 m and 60 m above ground level. Above this height it is inappropriate to fit dry rising mains because of the limitations of fire brigade pumps.

It is further recommended that one riser should be provided for every 900 m^2 of floor area at each storey the distance along which hose can be laid does not exceed

60 m. If the internal layout is not known a direct distance of 40 m may be used for planning purposes.

9.7.6.5 Horizontal mains/internal hydrants

Horizontal mains are installed in any large building and are a common feature in large shopping complexes. They are invariably wet mains and are often referred to as an internal hydrant system.

9.7.6.6 Fire brigade equipment requirements

Whatever type of fire main is installed in a building, the equipment that firefighters are required to carry to the landing valve or internal hydrant outlet is the same. This is significant when considering a calculated approach to designing facilities to assist firefighting in buildings as against the prescriptive measures in some guidance documents.

9.8 Fire service access: external to the premises

9.8.1 Requirements and recommendations for external access provisions

The functional requirements for external access and facilities for the fire service are contained within the Building Regulations[4] under requirement B5, which states:

'(2) Reasonable provision shall be made within the site of the building to enable fire appliances to gain access to the building.'

In the Secretary of State's view the requirement of B5 will be met for external access if, amongst other things, the building is provided with:

'Sufficient means of external access to enable fire appliances to be brought near to the building for effective use.'

Access for fire appliances is only required in the interests of the health and safety of people in and around the building.

There are two separate elements that are dealt with in Building Regulations Approved Document B[26] and BS 5588[1]:

— vehicular access to a proportion of the perimeter of buildings

— access to the perimeter for ladders.

9.8.2 Prescriptive standards for access to building perimeter

9.8.2.1 Buildings not fitted with fire mains

General recommendations for access to the perimeter of a building that is not fitted with fire mains are as follows.

If using portable or ground ladders, the fire appliance should be able to approach as near as is safe in order to minimise the distance which the ladders have to be carried. Once in position at the face of the building a clear space is needed for crews to manoeuvre the ladder into position, set up an entry control point, take hose up the ladder and for the safe handling of casualties. If using a vehicle mounted ladder or aerial platform the fire appliance will be larger and heavier than a standard fire appliance and will need to get closer to the building. Additional space will be required to allow for the movement of projections from the vehicle and consideration needs to be given not only to adjacent buildings but to aerial links, overhead cables etc.

Approved Document B[26] recommends that fire service vehicles should have access to within 45 m of the door to single family dwelling houses and every dwelling entrance door in blocks of flats/maisonettes that do not have fire mains fitted.

For building up to 2000 m² with a top storey up to 11 m above ground level, fire service vehicles should have access to 15% of the perimeter; or within 45 m of every point on the projected plan area.

For other buildings not fitted with fire mains, the recommended access facilities are given in Table 9.4.

There are also precise measurements recommended for hard standing for high reach fire appliances as shown in Table 9.5.

The hardstanding should be capable of withstanding point loads to accommodate jacks. The actual value should be checked with the local fire brigade.

In the case of a single and multi-storey shopping complexes without a fire main, fire appliance access should be provided within 18 m of a sufficient number of entry points so that no point in the building is more than 60 m from an entry point.

9.8.2.2 Buildings fitted with fire mains

If fire mains are fitted in a building, the recommendations in the above tables need not be complied with in the case of a multi-storey building if:

— access for a pumping appliance is available within 18 m of the inlet of a dry fire main and in sight of the inlet

— access for a pumping appliance is available within 18 m of the entrance to a building giving access to a wet fire main and within sight of the inlet for emergency replenishment

Table 9.4 Prescriptive recommendations for access facilities

Total floor area of building / m²	Height of floor of top storey above ground/ m	Percentage of perimeter for which vehicle access must be provided / %	Type of appliance
Up to 2000	Over 11	15	High reach
2000 to 8000	Up to 11	15	Pump
	Over 11	50	High reach
8000 to 16000	Up to 11	50	Pump
	Over 11	50	High reach
16000 to 24000	Up to 11	75	Pump
	Over 11	75	High reach
Over 24000	Up to 11	100	Pump
	Over 11	100	High reach

Table 9.5 Prescriptive recommendations for hard standing facilities

Measurement	Value for stated type of appliance / m	
	Turntable ladder	Hydraulic platform
Maximum distance of near edge of hardstanding from building	4.9	2.0
Minimum width of hardstanding	5.0	5.5
Minimum distance of further edge of hardstanding from building	10	7.5
Minimum width of unobstructed swing	N/A	2.2

In the case of a single storey building fire appliance access should be provided within 45 m of a sufficient number of outlet valves.

In the case of a single and multi-storey shopping complexes fire appliance access should be provided within 50 m of a sufficient number of outlet valves.

9.8.3 Comment on prescriptive standards for external access

The recommendations Approved Document B[26] and BS 5588[1] for access to the perimeter of a building and the access for ladders do not take account of the structure of the building, the occupancy of the building, the fire service attendance time, equipment and training available or the means of achieving the objectives of rescue and firefighting.

As noted in 9.1.3 above, the best method of safeguarding life from fire in non-domestic property is not by an enhanced fire service attendance but by built-in fire protection measures. The means of escape provisions in new buildings within the UK are such that all occupiers should be able to make their escape through their own unaided efforts. If conditions reach a critical point too quickly for people to make their own escape from a modern building, it is probable that the reactive attendance of the fire brigade would be too slow to assist.

The requirement for access for ladders should be based not on an assumption that ladders will need to be deployed, but on an assessment of whether ladders are likely to be needed for life safety and firefighting for life safety purposes. If it is considered that ladders are required, then the means of escape provisions and internal access routes may need to be reassessed. If the nearest vehicle-mounted ladder or aerial platform is more than ten minutes travelling time away, its ability to provide a meaningful contribution to life safety and firefighting should be seriously questioned. The longest ladders carried on fire pumps are 10.5 m or 13.5 m in length. They are typically able to reach second floor and third floor window cills. The access requirements that are related to an 11-metre floor height are therefore not logical.

In particular, the suggestion of rescue by ladder or hydraulic platform from a modern building should be treated with extreme caution. Rescue by this means is difficult and dangerous, not only for the firefighter undertaking the rescue but also for the trapped person. Rescue by ladder generally consists of a firefighter guiding the trapped person down the ladder. For this to be possible it is necessary for the trapped person to have a particular level of physical ability. Rescue that involves the carrying down of people is even more hazardous and, in most instances, not physically possible unless the trapped person weighs less than the firefighter.

The requirement for access to the perimeter of a building should be based not on a percentage of the perimeter of the building but on the location of access doors, the internal layout of the building in the vicinity of those access doors, the availability of water supplies and the fire attack plan.

The dimensions for the relationship between building and hardstanding/access roads for high-reach fire appliances (as shown in Table 9.5) are potentially hazardous as fire appliances parked in close proximity to a building could be at risk from partial or total collapse or flame spread from a window.

9.8.4 Application of calculated external access provisions

The external access provisions for a building should be planned to complement the internal access requirements for a fire attack plan. External access should not therefore be related to a prescriptive percentage of the building perimeter but to specified access doors, external water supplies and internal facilities.

It may not be necessary to provide access for portable ladders or vehicle mounted ladders or aerial platforms if the building has any of the following characteristics:

— does not have windows

— has windows that are double or triple glazed

— has windows that are fixed shut

— has windows higher than the highest reach ladder or platform capable of reaching the address within 30 minutes

— has sufficient protected staircases or firefighting shafts.

External access and hard standing for a pumping appliance should be provided to within one hose length (18 m) of each door that has been designated as a fire service access point. If a rising main is installed, the inlet should also be within one hose length (18 m) of the hard standing. A hydrant should be sited within a calculated distance of each pumping appliance hard standing. That distance should be based on the functional requirement to either establish a water supply to the fire pump within one minute of arrival or to ensure that if the first attack utilises the water from the tank of the fire pump a feed from another water supply can be established before the pump tank is emptied

The detailed application of calculated external access provisions is dealt with in section 9.13.6.

9.9 Fire service access: within the premises

The functional requirements for internal access and facilities for the fire service are contained within the Building Regulations[4] under requirement B5, which states:

'(1) The building shall be designed and constructed so as to provide facilities to assist fire fighters in the protection of life.'

In the Secretary of State's view the requirement of B5 will be met for internal access if, amongst other things, the building is provided with:

— sufficient means of access into, and within, the building for firefighting personnel to effect rescue and fight fire

— sufficient internal fire mains and other facilities to assist firefighters in their tasks

— adequate means for venting heat and smoke from a fire in a basement

These access arrangements and facilities are only required in the interests of the health and safety of people in and around the building.

There are three separate elements that are dealt with in Approved Document B[26]: general access, provision of firefighting shafts and venting of heat and smoke from basements.

9.9.1 Prescriptive standards for access within single storey and small buildings

For building up to 2000 m² with a top storey up to 11 m above ground level, fire service vehicles should have access to 15% of the perimeter or within 45 m of every point on the projected plan area or footprint of the building.

In a single storey buildings fitted with a wet fire main, fire service pumps should be provided with access to within 45 m of each of a sufficient number of outlet valves so that no point in the building is more than 60 m from an outlet, measured along a route suitable for laying hose.

9.9.2 Prescriptive standards for access within single and multi-storey shopping complexes

In single storey shopping complexes up to 30 000 m² and/or having one dimension not greater than 190 m, if a wet fire main is installed, fire service pumps should be provided with access to within 50 m of each of a sufficient number of outlet valves so that no point in the building is more than 60 m from an outlet, measured along a route suitable for laying hose. If a wet fire main is not installed, fire service pumps should be provided with access to within 18 m of each of a sufficient number of outlet valves so that no point in the building is more than 60 m from an entry point, measured along a route suitable for laying hose.

In multi-storey shopping complexes fitted with dry rising mains, fire service pumps should be provided with access to within 18 m of, and within sight of, each inlet. The distance from the fire pump hard standing to the top landing of a firefighting shaft should not exceed 30 m. A further recommendation is that firefighting shafts should be located such that every part of every storey, other than fire service access level, is no more than 60 m from the fire main outlet where the building layout is known, or 40 m if the layout is unknown.

In multi-storey shopping complexes fitted with wet rising mains, fire service pumps should be provided with access to within 45 m of and within sight of each inlet. The distance from the fire pump hard standing to the top landing of a firefighting shaft should not exceed 45 m. A further recommendation is that firefighting shafts should be located such that every part of every storey, other than fire service access level, is no more than 60 m from the fire main outlet.

Table 9.6 Prescriptive access provisions

Description of building	Recommended prescriptive access provisions				
	Firefighting stair	Firefighting lift	Firefighting lobby with rising main	Unventilated lobby with rising main	Escape stair
Floor height over 18 m	Yes	Yes	Yes	—	—
Floor height between 11 m and 18 m	—	—	—	Yes	Yes
Top storey over 7.5 m and area not less than 900 m² (factory, shop or warehouse)	Yes	—	Yes	—	—
Two or more basement levels, each with a floor area exceeding 90 m²	Yes	—	Yes	—	—
One or more basement levels with any floor area of 900 m² or more	—	—	—	Yes	Yes
Hospitals:					
— five or more storeys high	Yes	Yes	Yes	—	—
— basement at more than 10 m below access level	Yes	Yes	Yes	—	—
— floor over 3 storeys, area not less than 600 m²	Yes	—	Yes	—	—
— two or more basement storeys each exceeding 1000 m²	Yes	—	Yes	—	—

Table 9.7 Number of firefighting shafts

Largest qualifying floor area / m²	Minimum number of firefighting shafts
Less than 900	1
900 to 2000	2
Over 2000	2 plus 1 for every additional 1500 m² or part thereof

9.9.3 Prescriptive standards for access within multi-storey buildings

In buildings with a floor level more than 18 m above fire service vehicle access level, firefighting shafts are recommended, which include a firefighting lift, ventilated lobby and a rising main.

In buildings with a floor level between 11 m and 18 m above fire service vehicle access level, a firefighting shaft containing an escape stair, unventilated lobby and a rising main are recommended.

In buildings used as shops, factories or warehousing where the topmost storey exceeds 7.5 m, and any floor has an area not less than 900 m², or where there are two or more basement levels each with a floor area exceeding 90 m², firefighting shafts are recommended, which include a ventilated lobby and a rising main.

In buildings with one or more basement levels with any floor area of 900 m² or more, firefighting shafts are recommended, which contain an escape stair, unventilated lobby and a rising main.

In hospitals without a hospital street:

— if five or more storeys high or with a basement at more than 10 m below access level, firefighting shafts are recommended, which include a firefighting lift, ventilated lobby and a rising main

— if a floor over 3 storeys with an area not less than 600 m², or two or more basement storeys each

exceeding 1000 m², firefighting shafts are recommended, which include a ventilated lobby and a rising main

The above recommendations are summarised in Table 9.6.

Table 22 of Approved Document B[26] recommends a minimum number of firefighting shafts, related to the 'largest qualifying floor area'. This table is reproduced as Table 9.7.

Further recommendations are:

— access to a firefighting shaft can be directly from open air

— access to a firefighting shaft can be by way of a protected corridor 18 m in length

— firefighting shafts should be located such that every part of every storey, other than fire service access level, is no more than 60 m from the fire main outlet

— firefighting lobbies should have a clear floor area of not less than 5 m² and not more than 20 m² for lobbies serving up to four lifts

9.9.4 Comment on prescriptive standards for internal access

Attendance by fire brigades is time based and travel by firefighting lift is time based (i.e. speed should be sufficient to run the full travel of the building in 60 seconds[27,28]); however, the prescriptive standards for travel within floors is distance based.

It is probably reasonable for travel within floors to be distance based for means of escape purposes because of the mixed abilities of the occupancy of buildings and the varying standards of fire safety management procedures. When planning for access by firefighters it is possible to assess internal travel on a time basis and thereby develop a 'time line' from the transmission of the call to the fire brigade to the time at which firefighting commences.

It is thought that the prescriptive standards that limit the floor area of firefighting lobbies was introduced to restrict the possibility of furniture or other goods being placed in the lobbies. While this can be a factor in some high-rise buildings, the size of the lobbies has not prevented people placing furniture or other goods in them. In a well managed building, the floor area of firefighting lobbies need not be restricted to the prescriptive standards.

9.9.5 Application of calculated internal access provisions

For planning purposes, all firefighters can be assumed to have a similar general standard of fitness. The speeds at which they are able to traverse a given distance in clear visibility are dependent on the layout of the building, the level of PPE being worn, the weight of equipment carried or hose being run out.

The detailed application of calculated external access provisions is dealt with in section 9.13.9.

9.10 Smoke and heat exhaust ventilation for firefighting access

9.10.1 Prescriptive standards for smoke and heat exhaust ventilation for firefighting

There are many guides and methodologies for calculating smoke development rates for a variety of occupancies for the purposes of ensuring adequate evacuation times. However, such techniques are not used for fire service access to buildings. The following sections describe current prescriptive standards for smoke and heat exhaust ventilation for firefighting in different building types.

9.10.1.1 Large compartment single storey buildings

There are no national requirements or standards for smoke and heat exhaust ventilation for firefighting in large compartment single storey buildings.

Some local Acts allow the local building control authority (not the fire authority or fire brigade) to demand 'effective means of removing smoke in case of fire'. The local Acts also allow the same authority to demand that:

— compartments typically do not exceed 7000 m³

— automatic fire alarms are installed

— fire extinguishing systems are installed

— access for fire brigade appliances and personnel is provided.

As there is no definition of what constitutes 'effective means of removing smoke in case of fire' and few guidance documents produced in support of those Acts, every development is treated individually.

9.10.1.2 Firefighting staircases

Prescriptive ventilation provisions for firefighting staircases are as follows:

— an openable vent with an area of not less than 5% of the horizontal cross sectional area of the stair enclosure located at the top of the enclosure

— openable vents with an area of not less than 15% of the horizontal cross sectional area of the stair enclosure located at each storey level

With a floor height below 18 m there is no requirement for firefighting staircases. If there is a floor above 18 m, all levels of firefighting staircases require ventilation.

9.10.1.3 Firefighting lobbies

As noted in Table 9.6, prescriptive ventilation provisions for firefighting lobbies vary with the size and use of the building.

Unventilated lobbies are acceptable if the building has a floor height between 11 m and 18 m or has one or more basement levels with any floor area of 900 m² or more

Ventilated lobbies are required if the building has a floor height over 18 m or, in the case of a factory, shop or warehouse; a top storey over 7.5 m and a floor area not less than 900 m².

Ventilated lobbies are also required if the building has two or more basement levels, each with a floor area exceeding 90 m².

In the case of hospitals, ventilated lobbies are required if the building has:

— five or more storeys

— basement at more than 10 m below access level

— floors over 3 storeys with an area not less than 600 m²

— two or more basement storeys each exceeding 1000 m².

The recommendations for natural ventilation of firefighting lobbies varies between one 1 m² opening at high level to one 1 m² opening at high level and another 1 m² opening at floor level to not less than 25% of the horizontal cross sectional floor area of the lobby and sited at high level.

As with staircases, in spite of the recommendations for ventilation of lobbies being in the chapter of BS 9999[29] which deals with firefighting access and referring to firefighting shafts, the figures quoted for ventilation vary dependent on whether the evacuation of the building is planned to be single stage or phased.

With a floor height below 18 m no ventilation is required for firefighting lobbies. If there is a floor above 18 m, all levels of firefighting lobbies require ventilating.

9.10.1.4   Basements

Section 19 of the Approved Document B[26] deals with the venting of heat and smoke from basements and paragraph 19.1 confirms the functional requirement for the provision of means of venting smoke. That paragraph states that:

'The build-up of smoke and heat as a result of a fire can seriously inhibit the ability of the fire service to carry out rescue and firefighting operations in a basement. The problem can be reduced by providing facilities to make conditions tenable for fire fighters.'

Book 11 of the *Manual of Firemanship*[30] also deals with fires in basements and lists the 'special hazards' presented; these include difficulty in:

— venting heat and smoke

— gaining access

— appraising the fire conditions

— communicating with people below ground

— applying extinguishing media.

Recommendations for the venting of heat and smoke from basements is somewhat vague with the only quoted figure being that the combined clear cross-sectional area of all smoke outlets should be not less than $1/40$th of the floor area of the storey they serve.

In Approved Document B[26], mechanical extraction from basements may be provided only if the basement storey(s) are fitted with a sprinkler system. Mechanical extraction from basements should give at least 10 air changes per hour and should be capable of handling gas temperatures of 300 °C for not less than one hour. The mechanical extraction system should come into operation automatically on activation of the sprinkler system or on actuation of an automatic fire detection system.

9.10.1.5   Basement car parks

The prescriptive recommendations for basement car parks are as follows:

— *Car parks with open sides*: each storey to be naturally ventilated by permanent ventilation openings having an aggregate vent area not less than 5% of the floor area of which at least 2.5% should be equally provided between two opposing walls.

— *Car parks with enclosed sides*: each storey to be naturally ventilated by permanent ventilation openings having an aggregate vent area not less than 2.5% of the floor area of which at least 1.25% should be equally provided between two opposing walls.

If mechanical extraction is to be installed, it should provide at least 10 air changes per hour in fire conditions and should be capable of handling gas temperatures of 300 °C for not less than one hour. The ductwork and fixings to have a melting point of not less than 800 °C.

There is no requirement to fit a sprinkler system and the above standards apply whether or not a sprinkler system is installed.

There is no requirement for the mechanical extraction system to come into operation automatically on activation of the sprinkler system or on actuation of an automatic fire detection system. However, as mechanical extraction systems in basement car parks are designed to operate at 6 air changes per hour in non-fire conditions it is implied that this rate will be increased automatically on detection of a fire.

9.10.1.6   Loading docks and covered service roads

For loading docks and covered service roads the recommendations are that a clear air layer should be maintained below the smoke of not less than 1.75 m above any point on the loading dock floor or roadway or the smoke should be exhausted at 10 air changes per hour. There are no temperature requirements for the fans or any ductwork.

9.10.2   Comment on prescriptive standards for smoke and heat exhaust ventilation for firefighting

The prescriptive measures for all applications of smoke and heat exhaust ventilation for firefighting are inconsistent within themselves, conflict with other standards, do not take account of the fire load in a building or the installed fire protection systems and do not address the practical requirements for firefighting.

The necessity to ventilate large compartment single storey buildings for firefighting access is dependent on the objectives of firefighting, the nature of the goods within the premises, the rate of smoke production, the size of the smoke reservoir created by the volume of the building, and the time line for fire brigade attack.

If staircases in a building with a floor height below 18 m do not require ventilation, there may not be any reason to ventilate these lower levels in a building with a floor height above 18 m.

If lobbies in a building with a floor height below 18 m do not require ventilation, there may not be any reason to ventilate these lower levels in a building with a floor height above 18 m.

The assumed build-up of smoke and heat in basements and the stated increased difficulties for firefighting do not relate to the reality in modern construction. If firefighters access a basement via a firefighting shaft the conditions should be no worse than accessing an upper floor that has sealed windows. It follows that natural venting of heat and smoke from basements should comply with the same standards as that calculated as necessary for a similar occupancy on an upper floor.

It is unclear why the provision of a mechanical extraction from basements is dependent on the installation of a sprinkler system when there is no requirement to install sprinklers in a basement car park. It is also unclear why the system should be capable of handling gas temperatures of 300 °C for not less than one hour when a sprinkler system would be expected to operate at 70 °C and thereafter keep all smoke temperatures below this level.

In basement car parks it is not clear why the fans must be capable of handling gas temperatures of 300 °C for not less than one hour but the ductwork and fixings must have a melting point of not less than 800 °C.

The requirements for the mechanical extraction system in basements and basement car parks to come into operation automatically on activation of the sprinkler system or on actuation of an automatic fire detection system is at odds with standard firefighting practice.

Within the UK, firefighters have traditionally kept a fire 'bottled-up' until such time as covering branches are in place. Therefore, if smoke and heat exhaust ventilation systems (SHEVS) are to aid firefighting, it is considered to be inappropriate for the system to operate before covering branches have been put in position by firefighters.

This policy is stressed in book 12 of the *Manual of Firemanship*[31] where it states the following:

> 'Ventilation generally has little effect on the rate of burning of a fire in a large building in its initial stages, though it would eventually cause an unattended fire to burn more rapidly than it would otherwise do. If unwisely or incorrectly performed, however, ventilation can lead to the rapid spread of the fire within the building and endanger people present. Releasing the fire can also put neighbouring structures and combustible roof coverings at risk.
>
> Accordingly, firemen should not start ventilation until they are sure it is safe and have branches in position to guard against the risk of fire spread. Subject to the necessary precautions, however, it is important that they should start ventilation as soon as possible.'

This standard operating procedure was reiterated in volume 2 of the Fire Service Manual(32), where it states the following:

> 'Tactical ventilation can only occur once the fire service attends a fire.' (page 21)
>
> 'In the majority of instances, tactical ventilation should not be used until the fire has been located and, in all cases, an assessment must be made of the likely effects of ventilation.' (page 22)
>
> 'Arrange for the outlet vent or vents to be covered by manned charged hose lines.' (page 67)

In addition to fire service publications, the draft BS 7346 Part 4[33] contains the recommendation: 'Pre-installed smoke ventilation for warehouse scenarios (or anything describable as 'high hazard' in sprinkler terms) are recommended to be operable on fireman's switch'.

In addition, if it is necessary for an early suppression fast response (ESFR) sprinkler system to be installed in the building, it is a requirement of LPC Technical Bulletin TB25[34] that 'ESFR sprinkler protection may be used in conjunction with manually operated smoke ventilation systems, suitable only for smoke ventilation purposes, operated by the fire brigade.'

None of the prescriptive measures take account of the commodities within the buildings and the potential for the production of smoke. Equally, no account is taken of the installation of automatic fire suppression systems and the effect such systems would have on limiting the quantity and the buoyancy of smoke produced from a fire.

When considering smoke and heat exhaust ventilation from a building it is important to define the objectives of providing the ventilation, as this will have a marked effect on the system chosen and therefore the cost of installation and continued maintenance.

In issues of life safety, it is accepted that, where extended evacuation times are a consideration, smoke and heat exhaust ventilation systems, whether mechanical or natural, should operate immediately a fire is confirmed in order to maintain a clear layer for a given fire size and time. For life safety purposes it is usual for the actuation of the system to be automatic.

If SHEVS are for the purposes of property protection or for firefighting access, further considerations are required. The detailed application of calculated ventilation provisions is dealt with in section 9.13.10.

9.11 Implications of installed sprinkler systems

Approved Document B[26] (ADB) and Health Technical Memorandum HTM 81[35] link the installation of an automatic sprinkler system to a reduction in the recommended number of firefighting shafts, and standards of fire resistance.

ADB allows a variation in other fire safety standards if an automatic sprinkler system is installed including:

—   phased evacuation in buildings with floors above 30 m

—   doubling of compartment sizes

—   reduction of foundation standards for portal steel buildings

—   reduction of space separation to boundaries by half

—   an increase in the areas of unprotected openings

—   a variation on the method of venting smoke from basements.

In addition to the above publications, Home Office guidance document *Guide to fire precautions in existing places of work that require a fire certificate*[36], also recognises the value of an automatic sprinkler system in high risk factories. That document states that the installation of an effective automatic sprinkler system may reduce the fire risk categorisation of a factory from 'high' to 'normal'.

It is clear from the above, that the regulatory and advisory bodies consider the installation of an automatic sprinkler system to be of significant benefit to the standard of fire safety within a building. However, in view of current statistical evidence and test results, it is considered that the installation of an automatic sprinkler system should have much greater implications than the prescriptive relaxation of the fire safety standards referred to above.

The impact of an automatic sprinkler system on a fire should be assessed as a potential compensatory feature of all prescriptive fire safety provisions.

9.12   Relationship between firefighting attack and fire safety engineering

9.12.1   General

The objectives of a firefighting attack are directly related to the circumstances described or limited by fire safety engineering techniques applied to a building. The time of containment of a fire, provided inherently by the building design or by fire protection measures, is an essential first step in determining the extent of protection necessary.

By way of example, as noted in 9.10.1.1 above, some local Acts allow the local Building Control Authority to demand 'effective means of removing smoke in case of fire'. However, there is no indication what this requirement means in terms of the time for which a clear layer must be maintained, the height of that clear layer, or the temperature of the smoke. It has been suggested that the 2000 revision to Approved Document B[26] regarding the size of compartments for shops was made largely in response to a number of high profile fires in home improvement ('DIY') superstores. However, the compartment sizes apply to all shops. A DIY store will typically contain high racking stacked with large quantities of combustible materials (timber products, fabrics etc.) and significant quantities of flammable solvents. In a large supermarket much of the merchandise (e.g. fresh produce, canned items, soft drinks etc.), will be difficult to ignite and will not contribute to the development and spread of a fire Although some types of merchandise will be flammable (e.g. crisps, hanging clothing etc.) they will generally be displayed on separate gondolas or racks. The height of the gondolas will usually be about 2 m and the aisle separation between adjacent units is typically 2.5 m.

There are between 5000 and 6000 fires annually in the UK in 'retail distribution buildings'[37]. The vast majority of these fires are extinguished by hand-held fire extinguishers or hose reels. Those fires which develop beyond that stage are almost exclusively caused by deliberate ignition and often by ignition of waste outside the building.

The low risk to life presented by supermarkets is confirmed by the available records which indicate that in the UK retail sector no customer or member of staff has died as a result of a fire in the sales area of a single storey, custom-built supermarket. The nature of products stocked in supermarkets and the mode of their display is such that rapid fire spread that could trap the occupants is extremely unlikely. There is no historical evidence to suggest that a potential problem exists in single storey supermarkets in respect of life safety.

The two types of occupancy represented by supermarkets and DIY outlets present very different circumstances for firefighting. The DIY outlet is, in reality, a high-bay warehouse with high storage racking. Most of the commodities are combustible and will also include flammable liquids. The type, quantity and configuration of stock has the potential to allow fire to develop with great rapidity. The high rack storage also presents a collapse hazard to fire fighters.

In spite of this demonstrable difference in risk, the prescriptive fire safety measures are the same for both occupancies.

9.12.2   Application of fire safety engineering techniques

Fire safety engineering techniques should be applied to all large or complex buildings to establish the circumstances that are likely to develop from the initiation of a realistic design fire. If, because of the shape and size of the building and the type and configuration of the contents, it is determined that tenable conditions will be maintained for sufficient time to ensure evacuation and/or commence a fire attack, additional fire safety provisions may not be necessary.

Where the predicted conditions do not allow time to ensure evacuation and/or commence a fire attack, fire safety engineering techniques should be used to determine what additional fire safety provisions may be necessary.

Note: UK legislation is usually only related to health and life safety.

9.13   Building specific fire service pre-planning

9.13.1   Fire attack plans

An effective fire brigade has good operational practices, reliable equipment and sound operational leadership.

The three essential elements of strategic planning are the availability of resources, the development of operational plans (to determine when those resources are to be used) and the development of procedures (to determine how those resources are to be used).

As noted in 9.2.2 above, it is a requirement of the Fire Services Act 1947 that fire authorities make efficient arrangements for obtaining information required for firefighting purposes with respect to the character of the buildings and other property in the area of the fire authority.

The detail to which individual fire brigades comply with this requirement is a matter for interpretation. However, it is considered that, in the case of a large building, it would be reasonable for the fire brigade to have:

—   identified the main fire risk areas

—   mapped fire attack zones utilising fire resisting walls and doors or identifying general floor areas

— identified optimum entry points and hydrant locations

— located positions for stopping jets and the routes to those locations

— outlined primary and secondary positions for special appliances such as control unit and damage prevention unit and areas for breathing apparatus servicing and BA main control

— linked damage prevention measures to fire attack

— identified fuel and power cut-offs.

9.13.2 Actual speed and 'weight' of fire brigade attendance

While the risk category of an area will give the maximum attendance times (as described in 9.6.1 above), it is the actual speed and 'weight' of attendance that is important when preparing a fire attack plan. The risk category of an area should therefore be discounted for building specific pre-planning.

There are three time intervals that are significant when considering the attendance of firefighting resources to a building:

— the time from ignition to discovery

— the time from discovery to calling the fire service

— the attendance time of the fire service.

A fire service attendance time is the sum of the response time (the time taken from receipt of a call by fire control to the time at which the fire pump turns out of the fire station) and travelling time.

The response from a wholetime staffed fire station is generally within one minute of receipt of call, the maximum response time allowed from a part-time staffed fire station is five minutes. In practice the response time is never more than four minutes and even this, extended, response time would be unusual for most part-time staffed fire stations

Automatic fire detection and alarm systems should ensure that the time from ignition to discovery would be very short. The routing of all alarms to an indicator board and from there to a central monitoring station should ensure that there is no delay in the fire service being called. UK fire brigades operate sophisticated computer aided mobilising systems which ensure the rapid transmission of an alarm to the appropriate station(s). Statistics maintained by each fire brigade mean that there will usually be historical data available of the average attendance times to all parts of a fire station ground.

9.13.3 Link between fire safety provisions and objectives of fire attack

The objectives of a fire attack can be more narrowly defined in all buildings if full details of the passive and active fire safety measures installed are made known to operational fire crews.

In a building that is divided into compartments and sub-compartments by fire resisting construction, the objective might be to prevent spread from a single sub-compartment. In a multi-storey building the objective might be to limit the fire to a single floor.

Even in large single compartment buildings, it may be possible to localise the objectives of a fire attack if the rate at which a fire is likely to grow is known and early detection and a rapid call to the fire brigade can be guaranteed.

In the case of a large single compartment building it might be necessary to assess the impact of a fire in each part of the compartment (each section of racking or each gondola etc.) in order to define firefighting objectives.

The installation of an automatic sprinkler system or a smoke and heat exhaust ventilation system will enable firefighting objectives in all buildings to be more precisely defined.

9.13.4 Identification of fire risk areas

The chances of fire starting within a new building and, once started, the speed at which it is likely to spread is principally dependent on the occupancy of the building and the presence of heating and machinery.

Even buildings that are superficially similar present different risks of fire starting and spreading.

All areas of special fire risk should be identified so that extra consideration can be given to the means of containing any fire that occurs, the identification of fire firefighting objectives and the necessity for additional protective clothing, extinguishing media and equipment.

9.13.5 Fire attack zones

Fire attack zones can be mapped for all building types and occupancies. The comments in 9.13.3 in respect of large single compartment buildings mean that sections of the building could be identified as fire attack zones.

With buildings that are divided into compartments or sub-compartments, the fire attack zones could be individual rooms or larger areas or whole floors dependent on the installed fire protection measures and the time line for fire attack.

Once fire attack zones have been determined it is possible to identify optimum positions for stopping jets to be located.

9.13.6 Optimum entry points and locations for hard standing

The prescriptive recommendations that specify access to a percentage of the perimeter of a building do not address significant features such as construction and entry points. The prescriptive recommendations for perimeter access to a building should therefore be discounted for building specific pre-planning.

The identification of optimum positions where stopping jets are to be located will enable a calculation to be made as to the maximum hose lengths it is possible to deploy, following arrival of the fire service predetermined attendance, before the potential fire grows to a size that affects more than one fire attack zone. The maximum hose lengths able to be deployed will indicate the positions of the fire service entry points.

Current codes recommend maximum actual hose lengths of 60 metres or 40 metres in a straight line if the internal layout of a building is not known. These distances are suitable as a general guide but may be extended or reduced because of the fire protection systems installed in a building.

When the fire service entry points have been fixed, the locations for external access and hardstanding can be determined. Unless there are unusual risks of exposure from a fire within the building, locations for hardstanding will usually be within 18 m of each entry point.

The area of hardstanding at each access point should be large enough to accommodate the assessed number of fire pumps without causing an obstruction on access routes.

The routes to each hard standing from the site entrance should be such that attending fire pumps do not have to pass an area of danger.

9.13.7 Water supplies

9.13.7.1 External supplies

In most cases there will be a need to plan for water supplies to supplement the quantity carried on the fire appliances.

The prescriptive recommendations for distances between hydrants and proximity to entry points do not address the water requirements for firefighting or the specific identification of fire attack entry points. The prescriptive recommendations for hydrants on a site should therefore be discounted for building specific pre-planning.

There are two elements that are significant in calculating water supplies: the speed with which the additional supplies can be fed into the fire pump and the quantity necessary for the assumed duration of the fire.

The time available to obtain additional supplies can be calculated using a similar technique to that described in 9.7.6.1, i.e:

$$t = (W_p - W_h) / D$$

where t is the time available to obtain additional supplies (min), W_p is the quantity of water in fire pump tank (litres), W_h is the quantity of water in hose lines from pump to branch (litres) and D is the discharge rate from nozzle (litres min^{-1}).

Note: the discharge rate from the nozzle is dependent on the size of nozzle and the pressure used.

The time available to obtain additional supplies must then be converted into a travel distance from a hydrant to the fire pump.

Within the UK, each length of delivery hose is fitted with male and female instantaneous couplings. It is, therefore, possible to run-out hose only in the direction of the flow of water, whether delivering water to a fire pump or from the pump to the fire.

For planning purposes the following assumptions can be made:

— each length of hose is 20 m long

— one length can be run out in 10 seconds in a straight line

— an additional 1 min to be added to the travel time to ship a standpipe, key and bar and to flush the hydrant

— two firefighters are available

Using the above figures, it is possible to establish a water supply from a hydrant to a pump via one line of four lengths (total distance 80 m) within two minutes. It is considered that two minutes should be considered the maximum time it should take for the predetermined attendance to obtain supplementary water supplies. If the immediate supply is not 'unlimited', additional supplies, from other pressure-fed or open water sources, should be able to be obtained within half an hour of the arrival of the predetermined attendance. This must be discussed with the fire brigade as part of a comprehensive fire attack plan.

There is little research data to use as a guide as to the quantity of water used for firefighting. An internal guidance note for fire safety produced in 1989 by a large chemical company included the comment 'experience shows that stored goods with a very high fire load require up to 5 m^3 firefighting water per tonne'. As 1 m^3 of water weighs 1 tonne, this assessment suggests that 5 tonnes of water are required for 1 tonne of product. Although not clear in the guidance document, this quantity is thought to be that required to extinguish completely the most hazardous material used in that industry.

The means used to extinguish fires in the UK is recorded by all fire brigades for all primary fires. Unfortunately, the Home Office Research, Development and Statistical Directorate ceased to publish these data after 1990. However, up to that date, 89% of all fires were extinguished without the use of jets.

The document *In the Line of Fire*[38] concluded that 90% of all fires within the UK were extinguished by up to a single hose line.

Even allowing for the problems with the availability of reliable, detailed statistics, it can be stated, from the available data, that 90% of all fires can be dealt with by up to a single hose line and 89% of all fires can be dealt with without the use of jets. In most cases the period during which the extinguishing medium was applied to almost extinguish the fire was estimated to be equivalent to 20 minutes continuous application.

The maximum flow from a hand-held jet is usually 1100 litres per minute. If a safety factor of three is applied to the above statistics, there would be a requirement for a flow of 1100 litres per minute to be maintained for one hour at each fire attack entry point. A total requirement of 66 000 litres.

9.13.7.2   Internal supplies

Internal mains that are correctly located and well maintained provide the following advantages:

— reduce hose lengths

— speed of operation

— keep stairways clear

— reduce the chance of water damage.

The equipment requirements for firefighting from the landing valve on an internal main are the same whether the main is wet or dry. The floor area that is used as a guide to the installation of an internal main is not significant; it is the travel distance and whether it is necessary to attack the fire from more than one direction that are important. Accordingly, the maximum distances from a landing valve to all parts of a floor area and the access requirements should be independent of the type of internal main.

The prescriptive recommendations for access within multi-storey buildings distances and rising mains should be discounted for building specific pre-planning.

There are no legislative requirements for the testing and maintenance of internal mains. In many existing installations landing valves on dry rising mains have been stolen or vandalised or are inoperative due to poor maintenance. In buildings where the above problems are common, rising mains become a liability instead of an asset. Landing valves that are left open or are missing mean that not only does the water flood all the lower floors but the water does not reach the floor where it is needed. These problems do not usually occur with wet mains.

Fire brigades have developed several techniques for transporting water to high places (roofs, chemical plant etc.) where there are no rising mains. These techniques are also used in buildings where the quality of the rising mains cannot be trusted. There are three basic techniques used:

— The first, and least efficient, is to run-out hose lines up staircases.

— The most common is for firefighters to access the floor below the fire floor and to lower a line (rope) to the ground. A hose line is run out at ground level and attached to the pump. The branch and hose is then hauled up the outside of the building. This technique is usually used with delivery hose, however, with continuous hose reel tubing of 60 m

(not 20 m lengths joined by couplings); it is also being used for hose reel attack on fires in upper floors.

— A variation on hauling aloft is for firefighters to access the floor below the fire floor taking with them a length of hose in addition to that carried in the high-rise pack. The lugs on the female coupling are held out of a window and the hose unwound to ground level. It is possible to do this with a maximum of two lengths of hose (40 m from ground level to window-cill height).

It will be realised that the latter two techniques fulfil all of the advantages of a dry rising main. Before planning to install a dry rising main, the fire brigade should be consulted as to the preferred method of providing water at high level and the probability of a dry rising main being fully functional throughout the life of the building.

Note: there is no alternative to a rising main if the base of a tower block is a podium.

If it is decided to install a dry or wet rising main, consideration needs to be given to the siting of the landing valves. The general recommendation in Approved Document B[26] is for the outlets from each main to be sited in the firefighting lobby giving access to the accommodation. If it is the practice of the local fire brigade to attack a fire from the lobby of the affected floor, the lobby is the preferred location for the landing valves. However, it is standard operating procedure in some fire brigades to attack the fire from the floor below, i.e. run hose from the floor below to the fire floor. If that is the way the local fire brigade operates, the preferred location for the landing valves is on the stairway.

It might be that the standard operating procedure of the local fire brigade is dependent on the layout of the floor areas of each building. Where there is an open floor area beyond the lobby doors, the attack is mounted from the floor below. Where the floor area is subdivided off a 'protected' corridor the attack is mounted from the lobby of the fire floor.

The fire brigade should be consulted as to their standard operating procedures to ensure that landing valves are located in the optimum positions.

9.13.8   Arrival protocol and entry preparation time

The arrival protocol and entry preparation time are dependent on whether the premises are occupied or closed and secured.

If the premises are occupied, the system of fire safety management should ensure that the first attending pumps are met at the main entrance for details of the fire and its location to be passed on to the officer in charge of the predetermined attendance.

If the premises are unoccupied, the location of the fire should be available from the fire alarm indicator board but the time taken to interrogate the panel and break into the premises could extend the entry time considerably.

Once the location of the fire is known, the officer in charge will determine the action to be taken having regard to the risk involved.

The entry preparation time includes the period which must be allowed, after the arrival of the predetermined attendance, for crews to make an entry and deploy equipment. It is probable that the initial attack team of two firefighters will have donned breathing apparatus whilst en-route to the incident. However, the equipment necessary for the attack could vary from a hose reel to one or more main jets.

If it is known that the fire is relatively small or contained and access is immediately available, the entry will be very quick (typically within 90 seconds of arrival) and it would be reasonable to assume a maximum entry time of two minutes for most fires. If a large part of the building is smoke-logged or there are other features of the fire or the structure that give cause for concern, the entry time will be extended. Whether an immediate entry is possible or an extended entry time, the time to run out a single length of hose from the pump to the entrance to the building or the collecting breeching of a riser inlet should be no more than 10 seconds.

It will be realised from the above that the objectives of a fire attack must be closely aligned to the layout of the building and its contents and must be matched to the installation of fire protection measures to assist fire-fighting.

9.13.9   Travel time within buildings

The prescriptive recommendations that specify a maximum distance for hose lines of 60 metres are considered to be appropriate for planning purposes. However, that distance needs to be translated into travel time in order to prepare a time line for fire attack. For planning purposes, it is necessary to calculate travel time from entry points to fire attack zones.

As noted in 9.9.5, all firefighters can be assumed to have a similar general standard of fitness. The speeds at which

they are able to traverse a given distance in clear visibility are dependent on the level of personal protective equipment (PPE) being worn and the weight of equipment carried or hose being run-out. For planning travel time within buildings it should be assumed that firefighters will be wearing full fire kit and breathing apparatus.

Timings for running out hose from a fire pump in good visibility are as shown in Figure 9.4.

For example, from Figure 9.4, it would take two firefighters 50 seconds to run out a line of hose with a total length of 60 m, 60 seconds to run out a total length of 80 m etc.

The timings shown in Figure 9.4 can be applied to all circumstances where it is possible for the firefighters to see the route that they are taking. These timings can, therefore, be applied to buildings where the fire is detected in its incipient stages and an immediate call made to the fire brigade, and:

—   the contents of the building (materials that are non-combustible or are of limited combustibility) are such that the fire will not have developed beyond the capacity of the first attending pump crews, or:

—   the structure of the building (small compartments such as in hotels etc.) is such that the fire will be contained until after the arrival of the first attending pump crews, or:

—   active fire protection systems (sprinklers etc.) will limit the fire growth until after the arrival of the first attending pump crews.

When using the timings it is necessary to calculate the time for each line of hose separately and then to sum the results. For example, if it is necessary to run two lengths between a pump and a riser inlet and a further four lengths between a riser outlet and the point of attack, the total time will be 20 seconds (for two lengths) plus 60 seconds (for four lengths), a total of 80 seconds (i.e. not 140 seconds for six lengths).

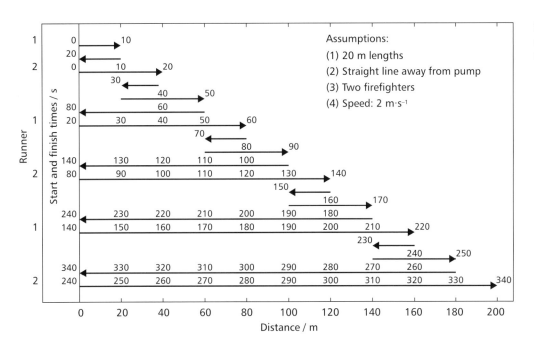

Figure 9.4 Timings for running out hose from a fire pump in good visibility

Table 9.8 Time allowance for firefighters ascending by staircase

Floor	Basic allowance / seconds	Additional allowance for floors above floor 1 / seconds	Total allowance / seconds
1	30	—	30
2	60	15	75
3	90	30	120
4	120	45	165
5	150	60	210
6	180	75	255

If the attack team are accessing an upper floor by means of a firefighting lift a time of one minute should be added.

If ascending via staircase a time of 30 seconds per floor, plus an additional 15 seconds for each floor above the first floor, should be used for the calculations, see Table 9.8.

If the final layout of the building is not known at planning stage (e.g. as with a distribution building that is to have different mezzanine and deck levels) the travel time within the building should be assumed to be 50 seconds plus an element for each level of mezzanine or deck, based on the time line to floor.

It is not appropriate to use the above calculations if it is anticipated that the building will be smoke logged by the time the first attending fire pumps arrive, as travel time within the building would be subject to too many variables.

Equally, if the point of origin of the fire was in the perimeter roof or it had spread into the main roof (sometimes from an external fire such as a waste skip), the difficulties of accessing the roof, so that water could be applied onto the roof structure from the inside, would considerably increase the 'entry preparation time'. There are too many variables associated with roof fires to produce a meaningful time line for fire brigade attack. It should also be noted that experience has shown that an automatic sprinkler system, with a traditional configuration, will not prevent the spread of fire through a roof and that external fire attack on a roof fire is ineffective.

In all cases, practical timings from similar buildings in the area should be used if they are available.

9.13.10   'Fire safe' access routes

The concept of phased evacuation, and the fire protection elements on which it is based, is valid for access for rescue and firefighting. In the same way that fire resisting construction and fire resisting self closing doors separate those escaping from the compartment in which the fire has occurred, so those same elements protect the firefighters when they are approaching the fire.

In buildings constructed to modern fire safety standards, the means of escape and other provisions designed for health and safety (including life safety) should be such that people can make their escape by their own unaided efforts. As such it is considered to be unlikely that rescue and firefighting external to buildings, other than large compartment single storey buildings, would ever be necessary for such buildings.

Fighting a fire in a building would be undertaken by the use of breathing apparatus teams using hoses fed from a fire service pumping appliance. For both rescue and firefighting, the fastest, easiest and safest means of access and egress from a building would be via one or more of the staircases.

9.13.10.1   Location

If the exit routes and travel distances comply with the relevant codes for means of escape, they should also be appropriate for access for fire attack.

If, because of the size of the building, it is necessary to construct firefighting shafts these should be located solely on the basis of hose run distance and travel time within floors and not on the area of the floors.

In a building with more than one staircase, it may be necessary to construct more than one firefighting shaft, even though the hose run distance and travel time is within accepted norms for the type of construction and occupancy. This situation would typically arise where there was a perceived danger of a fire being 'driven' towards a critical staircase by an attack from a firefighting lobby.

Travel distances from the entry point to the foot of a firefighting shaft (or any other staircase that would probably be used for firefighting access) should not be based on prescriptive distances but on a calculation of time line for fire brigade attack. It is clearly incompatible to require a fixed maximum distance for an access corridor to the foot of a firefighting shaft depending on whether the rising main is dry or wet. It is also incompatible to require a fixed maximum distance for an access corridor to the foot of a firefighting shaft when the firefighters who are to use that corridor may arrive between two minutes and twenty minutes of the call being received.

The planned access routes for firefighting should be based on an assessment of the assumed growth rate of a fire (dependent on the limiting factors noted earlier, the actual speed and 'weight' of fire brigade attendance, arrival protocol and entry preparation time and travel time within the building from entry points to fire attack zone.

9.13.10.2   Protection

All elements of construction that are required to be fire resisting for ensuring the safety of means of escape routes, will form part of the protection necessary to safeguard firefighters accessing the building for rescue and firefighting purposes. The standard of fire resistance required within a floor should be the same as that required for means of escape purposes. The standard of fire resistance required for firefighting shafts etc. should be based on the prescriptive standards contained in current codes with the exception that there is no need to protect the route from a building entry point to the foot of a firefighting shaft to a greater standard than that required for means of escape purposes.

9.13.10.3 Firefighting lifts

The number, location and protection of firefighting lifts should be in accordance with the prescriptive standards contained in current codes[39].

9.13.10.4 Ventilation

As noted in 9.10, the prescriptive measures for all applications of smoke and heat exhaust ventilation for firefighting are inconsistent within themselves, conflict with other standards, do not take account of the fire load in a building or the installed fire protection systems and do not address the practical requirements for firefighting.

The recommendations for natural ventilation of staircases and lobbies for firefighting access vary depending on whether the evacuation of the building is planned to be single-stage or phased. The assumed build-up of smoke and heat in basements and the stated increased difficulties for firefighting do not relate to the realities of modern construction.

With mechanical ventilation systems, the limiting temperatures for individual units vary between 300 °C and 800 °C.

None of the prescriptive measures take account of the commodities within the buildings and the potential for the production of smoke. Equally, no account is taken of the installation of automatic fire suppression systems and the effect such systems would have on limiting the quantity and the buoyancy of smoke produced from a fire.

When considering smoke and heat exhaust ventilation systems (SHEVS) from a building it is important to define the objectives of providing the ventilation, as this will have a marked effect on the system chosen and therefore the cost of installation and continued maintenance.

In the case of multi-storey buildings, the question of whether to ventilate the firefighting staircases and lobbies, and if so by what means, should be based on an assessment of the potential for smoke production in all floor areas, the extent of compartmentation between the possible seats of fire and the lobby, and the effects on smoke production and smoke flow as a result of any automatic fire attack systems.

The necessity to ventilate large compartment single storey buildings for firefighting access is dependent on the objectives of firefighting, the nature of the goods within the premises, the rate of smoke production, the size of the smoke reservoir created by the volume of the building, and the time line for fire brigade attack.

If is considered necessary to ventilate spaces in large buildings, underground car parks, basements and fire-fighting shafts, three processes should be undertaken:

— determine functional ventilation requirements for the spaces/shafts

— establish height of clear layers and smoke temperatures as a function of time

— calculate the circumstances that will fulfil the requirements.

Table 9.9 Example time line for fire attack

Action	Time
Initiation to detection (generic)	2 min
Actuation of detector to transmission of alarm (generic)	10 s
Processing by central monitoring station (generic)	1 min
Receipt of call by fire service mobilising control (generic)	10 s
Transmission to fire station and response (from wholetime-staffed fire station) (generic)	1 min
Travelling time	Variable
Arrival protocol and entry preparation time (generic)	2 min
Travel time within building	Variable
Subtotal (generic time line for fire attack)	6 min 20 s
Subtotal (variable time line for fire attack)	Variable
Total time line for fire attack	Variable

9.13.11 Time line for fire brigade attack

In order to develop a time line for fire brigade attack that would be considered to be reasonable in most cases, the following inputs should be used in the calculation:

— average detection time of an automatic fire detection system

— average transmission time from building to central monitoring station

— average time from receipt by central monitoring station to transmission of alarm to fire brigade mobilising control

— average time for fire brigade mobilising control to obtain address and operate turnout system at fire station(s)

— actual average attendance time of first pumps

— arrival protocol

— entry preparation time

— travel time within buildings from entry points to fire attack zone.

Some figures can be considered to be generic (i.e. statistics show that the times for all events are similar). However, even those figures identified as generic in the example shown in Table 9.9 could be determined more accurately for individual buildings. The generic figures and the variable figures should be tabulated so that each aspect of the time line is understood.

References

1   BS 5588: *Fire precautions in the design construction and use of buildings*; Part 0: 1996: *Guide to fire safety codes of practice for particular premises/applications*; Part 1: 1990: *Code of practice for residential buildings*; Part 4: 1998: *Code of practice for smoke control using pressure differentials*; Part 5: 1991: *Code of practice for firefighting stairs and lifts*; Part 6: 1991: *Code of practice for places of assembly*; Part 7: 1997: *Code of practice for the incorporation of atria in buildings*; Part 8: 1999: *Code of practice for means of escape for disabled people*; Part 9: 1999: *Code of practice for ventilation and air conditioning ductwork*; Part 10: 1991: *Code of practice for*

shopping complexes; Part 11: 1997: *Code of practice for shops, offices, industrial, storage and other similar buildings* (London: British Standards Institution) (dates as indicated)

2   *Out of the line of fire — modernising the standards of fire cover* Central Fire Brigades Advisory Council (CFBAC) (London: Home Office) (1998).

3   The Fire Services Act 1947 (London: HMSO) (1947)

4   Building and Buildings England and Wales. The Building Regulations 2000 Statutory Instrument 2000 No. 2531 (London: The Stationery Office) (2000)

5   Building and Buildings. The Building Standards (Scotland) Amendment Regulations 2001 Scottish Statutory Instrument 2001 No. 320 (Edinburgh: Scottish Executive) (2001)

6   The Fire Precautions Act 1971 (as amendmended) (London: HMSO) (1971)

7   The Fire Precautions (Workplace) (Amendment) Regulations 1999 Statutory Instrument 1999 No. 1877 (London: The Stationery Office) (1999)

8   The Management of Health and Safety at Work Regulations 1999 Statutory Instrument 1999 No. 3242 (London: The Stationery Office) (1999)

9   *Management of Health and Safety at Work — Management of Health and Safety at Work Regulations 1999* HSC Approved Code of Practice and Guidance L21 (London: The Stationery Office) (2000)

10   The Personal Protective Equipment Regulations 2002 Statutory Instrument 2002 No. 1144 (London: The Stationery Office) (2002)

11   *Personal Protective Equipment at Work — Personal Protective Equipment at Work Regulations 1992 — Guidance on Regulations* HSC Legislation Series L25 (London: HSE Books) (1994)

12   *Fire Service Guide: Volume 1: Guide for Senior Officers* (ISBN 0 11 341218 5); *Fire Service Guide: Volume 2: Guide for Managers* (ISBN 0 11 341218 5); *Fire Service Guide: Volume 3: Guide to Operational Risk Assessment* (ISBN 0 11 341218 5) HM Fire Service Inspectorate (London: The Stationery Office) (1998)

13   *Fire Service Guide: Dynamic Management of Risk at Operational Incidents* (ISBN 0 11 34122 1) HM Fire Service Inspectorate (London: The Stationery Office) (1998)

14   BS 5306: *Fire extinguishing installations and equipment on premises*: Part 8: 2000: *Selection and installation of portable fire extinguishers. Code of practice* (London: British Standards Institution) (2000)

15   BS EN 3: *Portable fire extinguishers*: Part 1: 1996: *Description, duration of operation, class A and B fire test*; Part 2: 1996: *Tightness, dielectric test, tamping test, special provisions*; Part 3: *Construction, resistance to pressure, mechanical tests*; Part 4: *Charges, minimum required fire*; Part 5: *Specification and supplementary tests*; Part 6: *Provisions for the attestation of conformity of portable fire extinguishers in accordance with EN 3 Part 1 to Part 5* (London: British Standards Institution) (dates as indicated)

16   *Fire Safety in Section 20 Buildings* LDSA Guide No. 1 (London: London District Surveyors Association) (1990)

17   BS 5306: *Fire extinguishing installations and equipment on premises*: Part 1: 1976 (1988): *Hydrant systems, hose reels and foam inlets* (London: British Standards Institution) (1988)

18   BS 5274: 1985: *Specification for fire hose reels (water) for fixed installations and foam inlets* (London: British Standards Institution) (1985)

19   BS 3169: 1986: *Specification for first aid reel hoses for firefighting purposes* (London: British Standards Institution) (1985)

20   BS 1010: *Specification for draw-off taps and stopvalves for water services (screw-down pattern)*: Part 2: 1973: *Draw-off taps and above-ground stopvalves* (London: British Standards Institution) (1973)

21   BS 5154: 1991: *Specification for copper alloy globe, globe stop and check, check and gate valves* (London: British Standards Institution) (1991)

22   *Report of the Joint Committee on Standards of Fire Cover* Home Office Fire Service Circular 4/1985 (London: Home Office) (1985)

23   *Standards recommended in the Fire Service Circulars of 1947 and supported by the Report of the Joint Committee on Standards of Fire Cover* Central Fire Brigades Advisory Council (CFBAC) (London: Home Office) (1958)

24   *Report of the Joint Committee on Standards of Fire Cover, May 1958* Central Fire Brigades Advisory Council (CFBAC) (London: Home Office) (1958)

25   BS 5041: *Fire hydrant systems equipment*: Part 1: 1987: *Specification for landing valves for wet risers*; Part 2: 1987: *Specification for landing valves for dry risers*; Part 3: 1975 (1987): *Specification for inlet breechings for dry riser inlets*; Part 4: 1975: (1987): *Specification for boxes for landing valves for dry risers*; Part 5: 1974 (1987): *Specification for boxes for foam inlets and dry riser inlets* (London: British Standards Institution) (dates as indicated)

26   *Fire safety* Building Regulations 2000 Approved Document B (London: The Stationery Office) (2003)

27   BS EN 81-1: 1998: *Safety rules for the construction and installation of electric lifts* (London: British Standards Institution) (1998)

28   BS EN 81-2: 1998: *Safety rules for the construction and installation of hydraulic lifts* (London: British Standards Institution) (1998)

29   BS 9999: (draft): Code of practice for fire safety in the design, construction and use of buildings (London: British Standards Institution) (to be published)

30   *Manual of Firemanship: Practical Firemanship I: Book 11* (London: HMSO) (1995)

31   *Ventilation* chapter 10 in *Manual of Firemanship: Book 12: Practical Firemanship 11: Part 3* (London: HMSO) (1992)

32   *Fire Service Operations — Compartment Fires and Tactical Ventilation* HM Fire Service Inspectorate Fire Service Manual Vol. 2 (London: The Stationery Office) (1997)

33   BS 7346: *Components for smoke and heat control systems*: Part 4: (draft): *Code of practice on functional recommendations and calculation methods for smoke and heat exhaust ventilation systems, employing steady-state design fires* (London: British Standards Institution) (to be published)

34   *ESFR sprinkler protection* LPC Technical Bulletin TB25 (Borehamwood: Loss Prevention Council) (2001)

35   Health Technical Memorandum HTM 81 (London: HMSO) (1996)

36   *Fire Precautions Act 1971. Guide to fire precautions in existing Places of work that require a fire certificate* (London: HMSO) (1993)

37   *Fire Statistics United Kingdom* Home Office Statistical Bulletin (London: Home Office) (annual)

38   Report of the Joint Committee of the CFBAC on the Audit Commission Report *In the Line of Fire — A management handbook on value for money in the fire service* ISBN 0 11 886406 8 (London: HMSO) (1995)

39   BS EN 81: *Safety rules for the construction and installation of lifts. Particular applications for passenger and goods lifts*: Part 72: 2003: *Firefighters lifts* (London: British Standards Institution) (2003)

10   Fire dynamics

10.1   Introduction

10.1.1   General

Fire dynamics describes the complex subject of fire behaviour and encompasses chemistry, physics, heat transfer and fluid dynamics. With a knowledge of fire dynamics, a more fundamental approach to fire safety engineering can be applied at the design stage rather than in response to the occurrence of an incident which has highlighted a fire hazard.

Fire is a chemical reaction between combustible species and oxygen from the air which produces heat, the mode of burning depending more upon the physical state and distribution of the fuel and its environment than on the chemistry. An example often quoted is that a wooden log is difficult to ignite but thin sticks can be ignited easily and will burn fiercely when piled together.

This section aims to present a basic understanding of the processes which govern fire development and to guide the reader in the available techniques for calculating the important parameters. It is not exhaustive and much use will be made of references to more detailed publications which should be consulted for further information. The most important of these is *An Introduction to Fire Dynamics*[1] by Dougal Drysdale.

Most of the equations presented in this section are drawn from CIBSE TM19: *Relationships for smoke control calculations*[2].

It should be noted that most fire safety engineering calculations are based upon experiment and testing. Therefore the validity of such calculations will be limited and extrapolation beyond these limits may not be appropriate.

10.1.2   Symbols and definitions

A_f Floor area of room (m²)

A_{net} Internal surface area of room minus area of openings (i.e. $(A_t - A_o)$) (m²)

A_o Area of opening (window or doorway) of a room (m²)

A_s Plan area of fire source (m²)

A_t Internal surface area of room (walls, floor, ceiling) (m²)

A_{vi} Area of ventilation inlet (m²)

A_{vo} Area of ventilation outlet (m²)

a Constant (relating to growing fires) (kW·s⁻²)

b Depth of balcony (i.e. horizontal distance between edge of balcony and plane of opening below) (m)

C_d Discharge coefficient for ventilator (—)

c_p Specific heat capacity of air (kJ·kg⁻¹·K⁻¹)

c_w Specific heat capacity of wall material (kJ·kg⁻¹·K⁻¹)

d Depth of room behind opening (m)

d_l Depth of smoke layer flowing under a ceiling (m)

d_s Diameter of circular source or longer side of rectangular source (m)

f_m Mass fraction in ceiling layer (—)

g Acceleration due to gravity (m·s⁻²)

H_c Heat of combustion (kJ·kg⁻¹)

h Floor-to-ceiling height of room or height of ceiling above base of fire (m)

h_b Height of balcony above base of opening (m)

h_o Height of opening (window or doorway) (m)

I_r Intensity of radiation (kW·m⁻²)

K Extinction coefficient (m⁻¹)

L Fire load in equivalent weight of wood (kg)

l_c Separation of channelling screens (m)

l_s Length of line source (m)

M Mass flow of entrained air (kg·s⁻¹)

M_c Mass flow at height z_c (kg·s⁻¹)

M_o Horizontal mass flow from opening of a room containing a fire (kg·s⁻¹)

M_{out} Mass flow of vented (extracted) smoke (kg·s⁻¹)

m_{CO} Mass rate of generation of carbon monoxide (kg·s⁻¹)

m_s Mass concentration of smoke aerosol (kg·m⁻³)

p Perimeter of plan area of source (m)

Q Rate of heat release (kW)

Q_{ave} Average rate of heat input (kW)

Q_f Rate of heat release to cause flashover (kW)

Q_p Convective portion of heat release rate (kW)

Q_p' Convective portion of heat release rate per unit length of line source (i.e. Q_p / l_s) (kW·m⁻¹)

Q_u Heat release rate per unit area (kW·m⁻²)

Q^* $Q_p / [\rho_o T_o c_p (g h)^{1/2} h^2]$ (—)

q Fire load (MJ·m⁻²)

R Rate of burning (kg·s⁻¹)

r Horizontal distance from fire axis (m)

S Visibility (m)

T (Absolute) temperature of smoke (K)

T_c (Absolute) axial temperature of Gaussian plume (K)

T_f (Absolute) flame temperature (K)

T_m Average (absolute) temperature of plume (K)

T_o (Absolute) temperature of ambient air (K)

T_s Average (absolute) temperature of smoke layer (K)

t Time after effective ignition (s)

t_c Characteristic burn time (s)

t_g Characteristic growth time (s)

u Velocity of smoke layer or jet under ceiling or airflow (m·s⁻¹)

V_s Volume of smoke (m³)

v Volume flow of smoke or air (m³·s⁻¹)

w Width of wall containing an opening (window or doorway) (m)

w_c Width of channel under a ceiling or a corridor width (m)

w_o Width of opening (window or doorway) (m)

Y_{CO}	Mass yield of carbon monoxide per unit mass of fuel decomposed ($kg \cdot kg^{-1}$)
Y_{HCl}	Mass yield of hydrogen chloride per unit mass of fuel decomposed ($kg \cdot kg^{-1}$)
Y_{HCN}	Mass yield of hydrogen cyanide per unit mass of fuel decomposed ($kg \cdot kg^{-1}$)
Y_{smoke}	Mass yield of smoke particles per unit mass of fuel decomposed ($kg \cdot kg^{-1}$)
Z	Ratio of height above base of fire to floor-to-ceiling height (z / h) (—)
z	Height above base of fire (inside room containing fire) or height above top of opening (outside room containing fire) (m)
z_b	Height above balcony (m)
z_c	Critical height of clear layer (m)
z_f	Flame height (m)
z_{fo}	Flame height above top of opening (outside room containing fire) (m)
z_l	Limiting height (intermittent flames) (m)
z_m	Maximum height of smoke rise above base of fire (stratification) (m)
z_o	Height of virtual source above base of fire (m)
α	Numerical factor (—)
α_k	Effective heat transfer coefficient ($kW \cdot m^{-2} \cdot K^{-1}$)
β	Numerical factor related to number of extract points (—)
ε_f	Emissivity of flame (—)
ε_s	Emissivity of smoke layer (—)
λ_w	Thermal conductivity of wall material ($kW \cdot m^{-1} \cdot K^{-1}$)
ρ	Density of smoke at temperature T ($kg \cdot m^{-3}$)
ρ_o	Density of ambient air ($kg \cdot m^{-3}$)
ρ_s	Average density of smoke layer ($kg \cdot m^{-3}$)
ρ_w	Density of wall material ($kg \cdot m^{-3}$)
σ	Stefan–Boltzmann constant ($kW \cdot m^{-2} \cdot K^{-4}$)
ϕ	proportionality constant (—)

10.2   Ignition

Ignition is the process whereby a material passes from a relatively inert state to one where a vigorous reaction takes place producing temperatures greatly in excess of ambient.

Ignition of most materials requires the application of an external source of heat, the incident heat flux causing the surface temperature of the fuel to rise. In the case of flammable liquids this liberates vapour; solid materials decompose to release flammable volatiles. Combustion takes place in the gas phase above the fuel surface.

Whether or not ignition occurs, and whether the reaction then becomes self-propagating, depends on a complex heat balance between the incident heat flux, the convective and radiative heat gains by the fuel, and the heat losses to the surroundings. However, it has been found by experiment that the critical radiant heat flux for ignition where there is already a flame present (i.e. pilot ignition) is in the range 10–30 $kW \cdot m^{-2}$ depending on the fuel. For spontaneous ignition, where there is no flame present, critical heat fluxes are higher at about 40 $kW \cdot m^{-2}$.

10.3   Fire growth

For sustained combustion to occur oxygen, heat and a fuel source must all be present. The removal of any one of these will terminate the reaction. The burning process in fires involves pyrolysis or thermal decomposition of fresh fuel. This pyrolysis will produce volatiles from the surface of the fuel and these gases will join the flames, generating combustion products and releasing heat. If there are no control measures present, and both air and fuel are available, it must be assumed that the fire will continue to grow in a manner which may be predictable, based on experimental or other evidence. However, the calculation of flame spread or fire growth rates from first principles is not easy. Characteristic fire growth rates are given in section 10.5.3.1.

10.4   Compartment fires

10.4.1   General

A distinction may be made between fires arising in the open, where radiated heat is lost to the surroundings, and fires which occur in confined spaces or compartments. In the latter, heat is transferred to the compartment walls by radiation from the fire and also by convection from the hot gases which accumulate within the compartment. Re-radiation from these hot boundaries can significantly increase the heating of combustibles in the room.

If there are openings to the compartment to permit the inflow of air and if there is sufficient fuel, the fire will continue to grow and the temperature of the hot gas layer at ceiling level will rise. Ultimately the point may be reached where the downward radiation from this layer is so intense that all of the remaining fuel in the compartment becomes involved. This occurs at layer temperatures of 500–600 °C, see section 10.10.4. The transition from growing to fully developed fire happens very rapidly and the event is often referred to as 'flashover'.

Following flashover the rate of heat release of the fire increases rapidly and the oxygen content decreases and anyone remaining in a compartment which has undergone flashover is unlikely to survive. The risk of fire spread from the compartment to adjacent areas increases greatly and the structure becomes heated.

Because radiation from the smoke layer is the driving force in initiating flashover, any factors which promote loss of heat from the layer will tend to reduce the risk of its occurrence. In particular, in compartments which are high or wide and where there is limited material to burn, the smoke will be unlikely to reach temperatures which would result in flashover. Flashover will not occur where sprinklers are operating.

A useful way of showing the development of a compartment fire is shown in Figure 10.1. The stages are:

—   *Initiation*: the fire will grow only slowly as a result of flame spread over the item first ignited.

—   *Growth*: the fire will grow more quickly and begin to spread to other items, but remain effectively local.

— *Fully developed steady-state* or *post-flashover*: all the combustibles are involved and flames appear to fill the entire volume, average temperature very high.

— *Decay*: at this stage the average temperature of the fire has fallen to 80% of its peak value.

10.4.2 Limiting fire development

Once flashover has occurred, the development of the fire in a compartment will be limited by lack of air (i.e. ventilation controlled fires) or combustible material (i.e. fuel bed controlled fires), or by firefighting.

Ventilation controlled fires have their combustion and heat output controlled by the amount of air reaching the fire which is governed by the openings to the fire compartment. A ventilation controlled fire usually means that the whole compartment is involved and flashover has occurred. Flames may project from the openings of the compartment and significant combustion may take place outside.

Flashover is unlikely to occur in large or tall compartments with small fire loads such as airport concourses, multi-storey malls and atria or multi-storey malls and atria protected from fire in an adjacent enclosure. However, given sufficiently high fire loads, high bay warehouses, for example, may reach flashover conditions. Fuel bed controlled fires have excess air available and their combustion rate, heat output and growth are limited by the fuel being burnt. All the burning takes place within the fire compartment.

10.5 Calculation of fire parameters

10.5.1 General

This Guide seeks to bring together the results of recent developments in fire engineering. The expressions given in the following sections have previously been published in the technical literature of the fire safety industry. They are the result of experiment and observation and there-fore each has its limitations. Some of the calculation procedures given may be superseded by better or more accurate relationships as a result of continuing research worldwide.

10.5.2 Design fires

The design fire is characterised by the variation of heat output with time. In the initial stages of fire growth it is assumed that the fire is well ventilated, its rate of burning being characterised by the type, amount and configuration of the fuel. The fire is assumed to be confined initially to a single object or group of objects.

If unchecked, the fire may spread to adjacent objects and, once flames reach the ceiling, flashover may occur and the whole room or compartment becomes involved in a fully developed fire. After flashover, the rate of smoke production can be so great that smoke control becomes impracticable. However, if there is a post-flashover fire in a small room it may be possible to design a smoke control system which protects an adjacent large volume space, such as an atrium, when smoke emerges from a window or doorway of the room. Types of smoke control system and their practical application are considered in section 7: *Fire and smoke ventilation*.

The parameter which governs most strongly the way in which a fire and its products behave is its rate of heat release, commonly termed 'fire size'. (The physical dimensions of fires are considered in sections 10.8.2 and 10.8.5.) In order to carry out a fire engineering design it is essential to define at the outset a series of design fires which represent the worst fire situations likely to arise in the building under consideration. Information is available, both experimental and theoretical, which may be used by the designer in selecting suitable design fires. Pre-flashover fires are considered in section 10.5.3; post-flashover fires are dealt with in section 10.5.4.

10.5.3 Pre-flashover fires

The design fire size will depend on the characteristics of the type and arrangement of the fuel and may be categorised for design purposes as one of the following:

— a growing fire

— a fire having a fixed size for a finite time

— a steady-state fire.

Fixed size or steady-state fires will usually have grown to some limit, further extension being restricted by one or more of the following:

— fire control activities such as automatic (or manual) fire suppression

— sufficient space separation to neighbouring combustibles

— for hydrocarbon fires, the leakage versus burning rate or, if bunded, the extent of the bund.

A fixed design fire size applicable to all situations is not feasible, especially when designing for means of escape or estimating the activation time of automatic detectors. However, fixed design fire sizes are often quoted in the

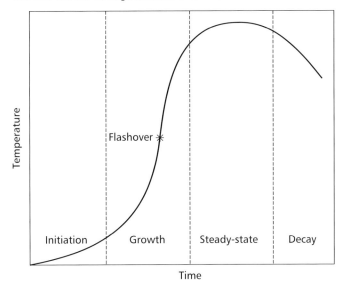

Figure 10.1 Stages of development of a fire

UK. The specification of a fixed fire size must be considered carefully since design fires are usually based on limited statistical analysis and some design fires are unsupported by data. In some cases, where naturally ventilated smoke control systems are employed, the design fire size is not critical but in mechanical systems the performance may be particularly sensitive to fire size. In general, the use of a fixed fire size will result in a conservative solution.

A great deal of experimental work has been carried out on rates of heat release from different materials when burned in fire tests. Much of this information is summarised in the *SFPE Handbook of Fire Protection Engineering*[3]. Many of the measurements relate to heat release rates from goods such as those which might be stored in warehouses. There is also a significant body of data on foam-filled furniture[4].

As a result of measurements, it has been found possible to characterise fire growth rates in different ways:

— *t*-squared fires (USA)

— standard fires, types 1, 2 and 3 (Japan)

— growing fires (Australia)

This *Guide* concentrates on the method of determining fire growth rates used in the USA. Fire growth rates for various types of fire have been compared by Bukowski[5], see Figure 10.2.

10.5.3.1 Fire growth rate

Much experimental work has been carried out in the USA on heat release rates in fires as a function of time. Some of the results are summarised in NFPA 92B[6].

Additional data on real fires are available from the National Institute for Standards and Technology* (NIST), see Figure 10.3[7], and BRE FRS†. These large scale tests show fire growth and decay for a series of objects and groups of objects. The data show that fire curves are closer to spikes with rapid growth and rapid decay of time. The fact that heat release rate peaks may be very high but last for a limited time should be taken into account when designing fire systems and allowing for appropriate safety factors.

It has been found that after an initial incubation period, the heat release rate grows approximately as the square of the time, i.e:

$$Q = a\,t^2 \qquad (10.1)$$

where Q is the heat release rate of the fire (kW), a is a constant (kW·s^{-2}) and t is time (s).

Figure 10.4 illustrates *t*-squared fire growth. The growth parameter for a *t*-squared fire is defined by the time taken for the heat output to reach 1055 kW (i.e. approximately 1 MW). This is known as the characteristic growth time. It has been suggested that fires may be conveniently classi-

---

* US Department of Commerce, National Institute for Standards and Technology, Centre for Fire Research, Gaithersburg, Maryland MD 20899, USA (www.nist.gov)

† Fire Research Station, BRE, Garston, Watford WD25 9XX, UK (www.bre.co.uk)

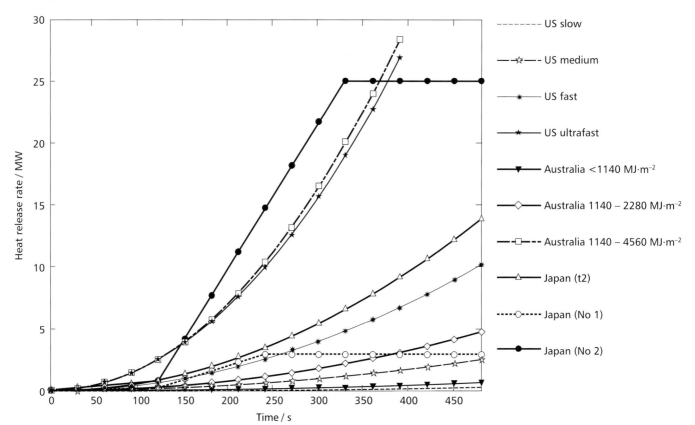

Figure 10.2 Bukowski's comparison of idealised fire growth curves[5]

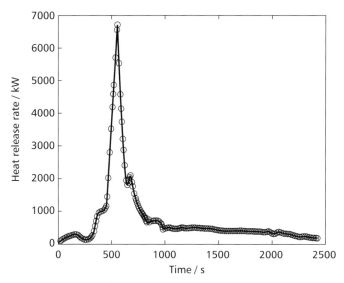

Figure 10.3 Example fire growth rate for 3-panel workstation (from NIST[7])

Table 10.1 Characteristic growth time for various classes of fire

Fire class	Characteristic growth time, t_g / s	Constant a / kW·s^{-2}
Ultra-fast	75	0.1876
Fast	150	0.0469
Medium	300	0.0117
Slow	600	0.0029

the occupants or by an automatic detector, if adjacent to the source.

Fire growth depends on the type of fuel and its arrangement but some growth rates are suggested in Table 10.2, based on the experimental evidence available[8,9].

Research[10] suggests that for a high rack warehouse (fire in the flue) the growth rate can be modelled as a 't-cubed' fire, given by:

$$Q = 0.045 \, t^3 \tag{10.2}$$

For this rapid fire growth, the incipient stage is significant and the curve is valid up to 10 MW for a 10 m high rack. (There are no data for fires greater than 10 MW.) For a fire in the racking flue, the amount of entrainment of fresh air in the rack plume is restricted, compared to that for a fire on the face of the rack. For a typical cellulosic fire, racking flue entrainment can be estimated as:

$$m_{\text{flue}} = (1.08 \times 10^{-4}) \, t^3 \tag{10.3}$$

where m_{flue} is the mass flow of smoke produced (kg·s^{-1}).

See Appendix 10.A1 for derivation of equation 10.3. Equations 10.2 and 10.3 are to be used together.

fied as 'slow', 'medium', 'fast' and 'ultrafast', depending on the characteristic growth time.

Table 10.1 gives the characteristic growth time, t_g, and the corresponding values of constant a for the various classes of fire.

The fastest burning upholstered sofas and plastic goods stacked to a height of about 4.5 m give 'ultrafast' growth rates while other upholstered furniture and lower piles of plastic goods give 'fast' rates. Tightly rolled paper produces a 'slow' growth rate. Experiments on burning computer workstations suggest 'medium' to 'fast' growth rates.

The incubation period (see Figure 10.4) is of indeterminate length and is ignored for design purposes although the fire may be detected during this period by

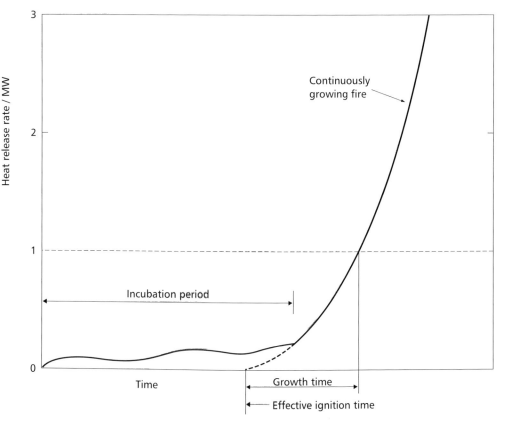

Figure 10.4 Illustration of t-squared fire growth (reprinted with permission from NFPA 92B-2000: *Smoke Management Systems in Mall, Atria and Large Areas*[6], copyright ©2000, National Fire Protection Association, Quincy, MA 02269. This reprinted material is not the complete and official position of the NFPA on the referenced subject, which is represented only by the standard in its entirety)

Table 10.2 Growth rates for growing fires

Building area providing fuel	Growth rate
Dwelling	Medium
Office	Medium
Shop	Fast
Warehouse	Ultrafast†
Hotel bedroom	Medium
Hotel reception	Medium
Assembly hall seating	Medium–fast
Picture gallery	Slow
Display area	Slow–medium

† depends on fire load

10.5.3.2   Unit heat release rate

Estimates of heat release rates per unit floor area or per unit fuel area for various commodities and materials can be gained from the *SFPE Handbook*[3] and NFPA 92B[6]. Survey data from actual occupancies in use have also been published[11]. Measured survey loads, q, are given in MJ per m^2 of floor area. By assuming a conservative burn-out time of 20 minutes (i.e. 1200 s) the unit heat release rate can be estimated for well-ventilated compartment fires, thus:

$$Q_U = q / 1200 \tag{10.4}$$

where Q_U is the unit heat release rate ($kW \cdot m^{-2}$) and q is the measured survey load ($kJ \cdot m^{-2}$).

Note: the measured survey load is usually given in $MJ \cdot m^{-2}$ and must be converted to $kJ \cdot m^{-2}$ for use with equation 10.4.

Some commonly used values of heat release rate are shown in Table 10.3.

Table 10.3 Commonly used values of heat release rate[6]

Occupancy	Unit heat release rate, $Q_U / kW \cdot m^{-2}$
Offices	290
Shops	550
Industrial	260
Hotel rooms	249

10.5.3.3   Steady-state fires — not sprinklered

Once the fire has spread from item to item until all the available fuel is burning, the heat output will reach a steady value, eventually declining as the fuel decays. The estimation of the steady value is given in section 10.5.4.

10.5.3.4   Steady-state fires — sprinklered

For design purposes the value of Q may be assumed as steady after operation of the first sprinkler, i.e. no further items of fuel ignite, and the value of mass flow in the plume is calculated accordingly. After operation it may be assumed that the sprinklers cool most of the smoke layer

to a temperature less than the operating temperature of the sprinklers. For calculation purposes, an average smoke layer temperature of 100 °C may be assumed with conventional sprinkler heads, while the sprinklers are operating.

10.5.3.5   Transient fires

To simplify calculations of smoke-filling during the transient phase (see section 10.9) an average value of Q may be used:

$$Q_{ave} = \frac{\int_0^t Q \, dt}{t} \tag{10.5}$$

where Q_{ave} is the average heat output of the fire and t is time (s).

For t-squared fires:

$$Q_{ave} = 333 \, (t / t_g)^2 \tag{10.6}$$

where t_g is the characteristic growth time (s). Values of t_g are given in Table 10.1.

10.5.4   Post-flashover fires

10.5.4.1   Condition for flashover

For design purposes, it may be assumed that flashover does not occur if the smoke layer at ceiling level is at a temperature of less than 600 °C. Methods for calculating this temperature are given in section 10.8.7. *Note that in the plume above a fire the temperature at the tip of intermittent flames is about 350 °C and at the tip of sustained flames is about 550 °C.*

If sprinklers operate it may be assumed that flashover will not occur since sprinklers are designed to operate while the smoke layer is at a temperature much lower than 600 °C.

Because flashover is such a serious event, a great deal of research effort has been invested in methods to predict the conditions which give rise to it. A presentation and comparison of the different correlations which are available are given in chapter 2-2 of the *SFPE Handbook*[3]. The simplest of these relates the heat release rate required for flashover, Q_f, to what has become known as the ventilation factor ($A_{vo} \sqrt{h_o}$), such that:

$$Q_f = 600 \, A_{vo} \sqrt{h_o} \tag{10.7}$$

where Q_f is the heat release rate required for flashover (kW), A_{vo} is the area of the opening to the compartment (m^2) and h_o is the height of the opening (m).

The heat release rate is given by:

$$Q = H_c \times R \tag{10.8}$$

where H_c is the heat of combustion ($kJ \cdot kg^{-1}$) and R is the mass rate of burning ($kg \cdot s^{-1}$). (The heat of combustion, H_c, is discussed in section 10.7.7 and values for various materials are given in Table 10.7.) The rate of burning, R, is considered in sections 10.5.4.2 and 10.5.4.3.

10.5.4.2 Ventilation controlled fires

The mass rate of burning is given by:

$$R = 0.02 \, [A_o \, h_o^{1/2} \, (A_t - A_o) \, (w / d)]^{1/2} \qquad (10.9)$$

where R is the mass rate of burning (kg·s^{-1}), A_o is the area of ventilation opening (door, window etc.) (m^2), h_o is the height of ventilation opening (m), A_t is the area of room surface (wall, floor, ceiling) (m^2), w is the width of wall containing the opening (m) and d is the depth of room behind the opening (m).

Effective values for these parameters for rooms with more than one opening can be derived using the procedures given in Appendix 1 of CIBSE TM19[2].

Equation 10.9 has been derived from experiments with wood cribs and can be used for most types of fire load found in houses, offices and shops. Conventionally fire load may be expressed in terms of the equivalent weight of wood. If expressed in MJ or MJ·m^{-2}, the fire load may be converted to kg or kg·m^{-2} of wood by dividing by 18 MJ·kg^{-1}, e.g. 360 MJ·m^{-2} is equivalent to 20 kg·m^{-2} of wood.

10.5.4.3 Fuel bed controlled fires

For low values of fire load, equation 10.9 overestimates the mass rate of burning by a factor of 2 or 3.

With the furnishings typically found in houses, offices and shops, an effective fire duration of 20 minutes may be assumed and R is given by:

$$R = L / 1200 \qquad (10.10)$$

where L is the total fire load (kg), or:

$$L = (L / A_f) \times A_f \qquad (10.11)$$

where A_f is the floor area (m^2).

Values of (L / A_f) (kg·m^{-2}) are derived from surveys or design data. Where such data are expressed in MJ·m^{-2} they may be converted by dividing by 18, see section 10.5.4.2.

For design purposes, R should be calculated from equations 10.9 and 10.10 and the lower value adopted.

10.6 Effect of sprinklers

The following paragraphs deal with the effect of sprinklers on fire growth. Sprinkler design is considered in detail in section 8: *Fire suppression*.

10.6.1 General principles

The plume of hot smoky gases from a fire rises as a result of its buoyancy. When it hits the ceiling the plume turns and spreads laterally where it may interact with sprinklers,

eventually causing them to operate. The time to sprinkler operation depends on:

— fire growth rate

— sprinkler location

— sprinkler sensitivity.

10.6.2 Sprinkler location

As the smoke plume rises from a fire, it draws in air from the surroundings which causes it to cool. Therefore, the higher the ceiling, the lower will be the temperature of the smoke which reaches the sprinklers. Additional cooling then occurs as the smoke spreads laterally. Clearly, the hotter the smoke, the more rapidly the sprinkler will operate. Equations have been developed to predict smoke temperatures at different ceiling positions above a fire which are summarised in NFPA 92B[6].

10.6.3 Sprinkler and smoke detector sensitivity

In order to operate and release water onto a fire, a sprinkler must be heated to its operating temperature, usually about 70 °C, at which point a temperature-sensitive element is designed to fail, e.g. a solder link melts or a glass bulb breaks. The rate at which the element heats up when exposed to hot smoke depends on its shape and mass. A heavy, short bulb will take longer to reach a given temperature than a light, slim bulb. The parameter used to describe sprinkler sensitivity is known as the response time index or RTI, see section 8.1.5.6. Sprinklers with RTI values below 50 m$^{1/2}$·s$^{1/2}$ are described by the Loss Prevention Council[11] as having a quick response whilst values up to 200 m$^{1/2}$·s$^{1/2}$ are regarded as having a standard response.

Note: a smoke detector can be considered as an equivalent heat detector having an RTI of 0.5 m$^{1/2}$·s$^{1/2}$ and a fixed temperature rise of 13 °C[13].

A computer program which combines the above effects of fire growth, sprinkler location and sprinkler sensitivity has been developed by the (American) National Institute for Standards and Technology (NIST)*. This program, known as DETACT, is used to predict sprinkler response times and corresponding fire sizes at sprinkler operation.

10.6.4 Effect on fire size

Real fire tests are rarely performed. However, should a series of tests be carried out on the intended typical layout (i.e. room dimensions, fuel type etc.) and if these tests show that a fire will be quickly suppressed with the installed sprinkler system, then it seems reasonable to assume that combustion ceases when the sprinklers operate.

In a room equipped with sprinklers, a fire may grow until the heat in the plume sets off the first sprinkler heads; the effect of the sprinklers on the design fire size can be taken

---

* US Department of Commerce, National Institute for Standards and Technology, Centre for Fire Research, Gaithersburg, Maryland MD 20899, USA (www.nist.gov)

into account by assuming that the fire stops growing when the sprinklers are activated. The design fire is then estimated as the size the fire has grown to at the moment of sprinkler actuation unless there is reason to suspect that fire will continue to spread after the sprinklers have been actuated. Since the sprinklers will cool most of the smoke layer to below 100°C, flashover is not likely to occur where they are installed. It can then be assumed conservatively that the fire will have a constant rate of heat release (see Figure 10.5).

The sprinkler spray will cool the hot gases to the actuation temperature of the sprinkler or less. Alternatively it could be assumed that after sprinkler activation the heat output will slowly decrease. American experiments in small compartments[14] have suggested that fire heat release rates will fall by 50% over a period of a few minutes although in some circumstances it may be assumed that the fire continues to grow but at a slower rate. Whether or not such an assumption is made, the fire will continue to burn until all the fuel is consumed.

10.7   Smoke control: essential requirements

10.7.1   General

This section considers the engineering relationships which can be used as part of the overall fire safety design of buildings where people may be exposed to smoke, toxic atmospheres and hot gases. The need for smoke control depends on many aspects of the building design and use, including the combustibility of the contents, mobility of the occupants and ease of escape. The smoke control measures needed, if any, may be simply achieved, perhaps exploiting the normal ventilation system, or they may require extra equipment and controls.

Smoke control may be a requirement for means of escape purposes, see section 4: *Means of escape*. The purpose of smoke control in these circumstances may be to retard the descent of the smoke layer, see Figure 10.6, or to dilute the smoke, see Figure 10.7. The required amount of extract

can be calculated by setting up a mass balance based on the entrainment equations given below. Methods of containment and extraction are considered in section 7: *Fire and smoke ventilation*.

10.7.2   Hazards of smoke

The toxic products of fires consist of irritant and narcotic components, which can cause disorientation, incapacitation or death, the effect depending upon the concentration and length of exposure. The predominant irritant components are organic smoke products and acid gases such as hydrogen chloride (HCl). The immediate effects of irritants are related to the concentration, consisting of pain to the eyes and lungs accompanied by difficulties in breathing. The predominant narcotic component in pre-flashover fires is carbon monoxide, hydrogen cyanide also being important in pre-flashover fires. Narcotic effects, disorientation and collapse occur only when a certain dose (i.e. the product of exposure concentration and exposure time) has been inhaled over a period.

The temperature of smoke is significant since it can cause burns by convection (to exposed skin and lungs) and by radiation. With long exposure times there is also the risk of hyperthermia.

Smoke particles and irritant products can reduce visibility. While loss of visibility is not directly life threatening, it can prevent or delay escape and thus expose people to the risk of being overtaken by fire.

If a tenability limit for visibility for escape purposes is set at 8 m (for light reflecting surfaces) then, for most fire types, it is likely that smoke at this concentration will cause some eye irritation but it is unlikely to contain irritants at concentrations high enough to seriously inhibit escape or cause collapse. A visibility distance of 2 m is likely to represent the safe toxic limit, although escape under these conditions is unrealistic. Neither well ventilated pre-flashover fires, nor post-flashover fires at smoke densities up to this limit are likely to contain sufficient narcotic gases to cause disorientation or collapse within a 5 minute exposure period, although such effects may become a hazard over longer time scales. Therefore it

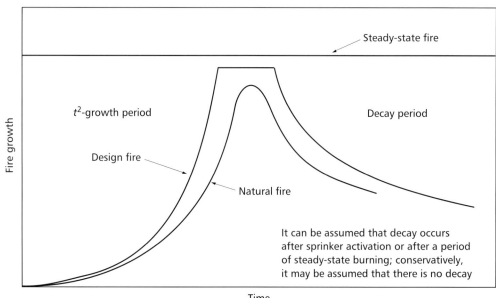

Figure 10.5 Typical fire model

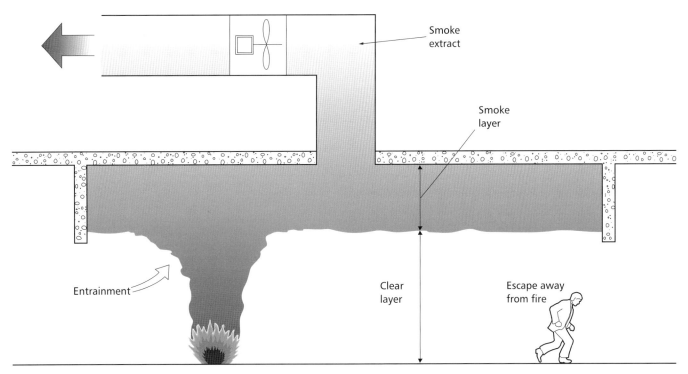

Figure 10.6 Smoke control concept

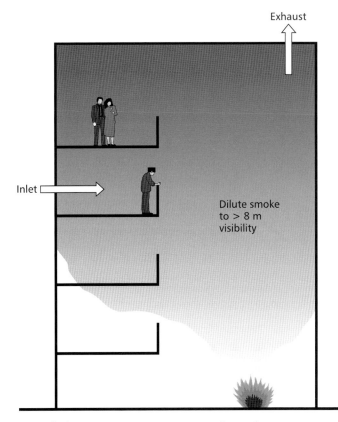

Note: Dilution systems may or may not require smoke extract depending upon the design fire size and the geometry of the space in which the smoke collects

Figure 10.7 Dilution smoke management

may be convenient to define critical conditions for short exposures in terms of visibility only. However, hot smoke layers above head height can still pose a radiation hazard and the concentration of toxic smoke to which people may be exposed can increase very rapidly.

Table 10.4 shows the criteria for the various hazards associated with fire[15].

Table 10.4 Tenability criteria given in NFPA 130[15]

Hazard	Criterion for stated exposure	
	Few seconds	6 minutes
Temperature	60 °C	50 °C
Carbon monoxide	2000 ppm	1500 ppm
Noise	115 dBa	92 dBa
Radiation	6.3 kW·m^{-2}	1.5 kW·m^{-2}
Air velocity	Up to 12 m·s^{-1}	Up to 12 m·s^{-1}

For the purposes of this section, it is assumed that the fires are flaming and well ventilated since these are the types of fire which are of interest to the designers of smoke control systems, see section 10.5.2.

10.7.3 Critical conditions for toxicity — design values

Table 10.5 enables the designer to estimate whether there is likely to be a toxic threat to the occupants of a building. For this purpose, the effects of these common toxic products may be considered as approximately additive. For example, incapacitation would result after 5 minutes for a dose of 4000 ppm CO plus 50 ppm HCN (i.e. two thirds of stated CO dose plus one third of stated HCN dose). More detailed studies of toxic effects would also consider other aspects such as oxygen deficiency and increase in carbon dioxide.

For well ventilated pre-flashover fires the contribution from low oxygen and HCN may be considered relatively minor.

The estimation of toxic concentrations in smoke is described in section 10.7.7 and of smoke extinction coefficients in section 10.7.8.

Table 10.5 Exposure to common toxic products of combustion

Chemical product	Exposure time			
	5 minutes		30 minutes	
	Incapacity	Death	Incapacity	Death
Carbon monoxide CO (ppm)	6000	12 000	1000	2500
Hydrogen cyanide HCN (ppm)	150	250	90	170
Hydrogen chloride HCl (ppm)	500	16 000	200	<12%
Smoke organic irritants (K†)	1.2	7	1.2	1.2

† expressed in terms of smoke extinction coefficient

10.7.4 Critical conditions for temperature — design values

Table 10.6 identifies the critical temperature for different exposure conditions and the resulting effects on people. The temperature attained by smoke is described in section 10.8.7.

10.7.5 Critical visibility — design value

For the purposes of escape, visibility should be at least 8 m. The estimation of visibility in smoke is described in 10.7.8.

10.7.6 Firefighting

Firefighters wearing breathing apparatus can feel their way through thick smoke provided that the smoke temperature does not exceed the values given in Table 10.6.

10.7.7 Fire products

The combustion of material vapours in fires is not complete and the heat of combustion (H_c) is always less than the net heat of complete combustion. Suggested

Table 10.6 Critical temperature for different exposure conditions

Type and period of exposure	Effect	Temperature /°C
Radiation	Severe skin pain	185†
Conduction (metal) (1 second)	Skin burns	60
Convection (30 minutes)	Hyperthermia	100
Convection (< 5 minutes)	Skin/lungs burns by hot gases	120
Convection (< 1 minute)	Skin/lungs burns by hot gases	190

† black-body: 2.5 kW·m⁻²

values of H_c for flaming fires are given in Table 10.7 in units of heat produced per mass burnt (kJ·kg⁻¹). The convective portion is about 65% for wood fires and 50–60% for commonly found plastics. Some values of yield of carbon monoxide Y_{CO} for flaming fires in units of mass of CO per mass burnt (kg·kg⁻¹) are also given in Table 10.7. The table also gives values of Y_{HCN} and Y_{HCl} and some values of the yield of smoke particles, Y_{smoke}, for flaming fires in units of mass of smoke per mass burnt (kg·kg⁻¹).

For individual materials, the yields of smoke particulates and toxic products vary considerably with the decomposition conditions, being at a minimum for the early stages of well ventilated fires. Therefore the figures given in Table 10.7 are 'best case' values for toxic product yields and can be applied only to pre-flashover situations where there is no restriction on ventilation for the fire and no significant reduction in oxygen concentration in the fire compartment. Under vitiated post-flashover conditions the yields of CO are much higher at approximately 0.25 kg·kg⁻¹ for most fuels. HCN yields from flexible and rigid polyurethanes are much higher at approximately 0.01–0.05 kg·kg⁻¹. Smoke yields are also higher under vitiated combustion conditions by a factor of up to 10.

10.7.8 Smoke visibility

Visibility in smoke is defined in terms of the furthest distance at which an object can be perceived, S (m), and an extinction coefficient, K (m⁻¹).

Light emitting objects such as electric lights are more easily perceived than objects which receive ambient illumination:

—   for light emitting signs: $K \times S = 8$

—   for light reflecting signs: $K \times S = 3$

For flaming combustion of wood or plastics:

$$K \approx 7.6 \times 10^3 \, m_s \qquad (10.12)$$

Table 10.7 Fire products with flaming combustion

Material	H_c / kJ·kg⁻¹	Y_{CO} / kg·kg⁻¹	Y_{HCN} or Y_{HCl} / kg·kg⁻¹	Y_{smoke} / kg·kg⁻¹
Timber	13.0×10^3	0.020	0	< 0.01–0.025
Polyvinyl chloride	5.7×10^3	0.063	0.25–0.5†	0.12–0.17
Polyurethane (flexible)	19.0×10^3	0.042	0.001	< 0.01–0.23
Polyurethane (rigid)	17.9×10^3	0.180	0.011	0.09–0.11
Polystyrene	27.0×10^3	0.060	0	0.15–0.17
Polypropylene	38.6×10^3	0.050	0	0.016–0.10

† HCl yield depending upon formulation, i.e. plasticised or rigid

where K is the extinction coefficient (m^{-1}) and m_s is the mass concentration of smoke aerosol (kg·m^{-3}).

For a fire burning at rate R (kg·s^{-1}) for a duration t (s), m_s is given by:

$$m_s = Y_{smoke} R t / V_s \qquad (10.13)$$

where Y_{smoke} is the yield of smoke particles (kg·kg^{-1}) and V_s is the volume of smoke (m^3).

Hence, for light emitting signs:

$$S = 8 V_s / (7.6 \times 10^3 Y_{smoke} R t) \qquad (10.14)$$

and for light reflecting signs:

$$S = 3 V_s / (7.6 \times 10^3 Y_{smoke} R t) \qquad (10.15)$$

For fires of predominantly wood-based fuel (e.g. timber, paper, cotton etc.) $Y_{smoke} = 0.025$ (from Table 10.7). Therefore, substituting for R from equation 10.8, the furthest distance at which a sign can be seen, S (m), is given by the following equations.

For light emitting signs:

$$S = 545 V_s / Q t \qquad (10.16)$$

where Q is the heat release rate (kW).

For light reflecting signs:

$$S = 205 V_s / Q t \qquad (10.17)$$

Mulholland[3] also gives a technique for calculating the obscuration based on the mass concentration m_s (kg·m^{-3}) of particles in the smoke and shows that the visibility is given by:

$$S = 3 / K m_s \qquad (10.18)$$

where S is the visibility (m), K is the smoke extinction coefficient and m_s is the mass concentration (kg·m^{-3}).

10.8   Smoke plumes

10.8.1   Entrainment

In this section it is assumed that the amount of smoky gases produced in a fire is the same as the amount of air entrained into the plume. The concentration of smoke particles and toxic products depends on the type of fuel being burnt and the ventilation rate.

Relationships are given for the mass flow and temperature of the ambient air when it is entrained into fire plumes. These are based on both theoretical and experimental data. Except where stated otherwise, the mass flow of fuel is negligible and is not taken into account.

At a given height, entrainment depends on the heat output and, at small plume heights, on the geometry of the source. The geometry is characterised here as a point, circle, rectangle or line. At large plume heights, entrain-

ment is equivalent to that above a point source. The plume itself may be in the room of fire origin (directly above the source) or it may be outside the room, having emerged from an open door or window. For the purposes of smoke control design, the zone of interest is above the luminous part of the plume.

10.8.2   Point source — axisymmetric plume

An axisymmetric plume is expected for a fire originating on the floor away from the walls, see Figure 10.8. It has a virtual point source. Air is entrained from all sides and along the entire height of the plume until the plume becomes submerged in the smoke layer beneath the ceiling.

The height of luminous zone above the base of the fire is given by:

$$z_1 = 0.20 Q_p^{2/5} \qquad (10.19)$$

where z_1 is the limiting height for use of the entrainment equation (10.20) and Q_p is the convective heat output of fire (kW), see equation 10.43.

Estimates of the value of the coefficient in equation 10.19 vary from 0.17 to 0.23. The equation may be used for sources in which the diameter or larger dimension, d_s, is less than $0.072 Q_p^{2/5}$; see section 10.8.3 for sources of greater dimensions.

For $z > z_1$:

$$M = 0.071 Q_p^{1/3} (z - z_0)^{5/3} \qquad (10.20)$$

where M is the mass flow by entrainment (kg·s^{-1}), z is the height above the base of the fire (m) and z_0 is the height of the virtual source above the base of the fire (m).

The location of the point source has been determined for pool-type fires only. For most solid fuels found in buildings the value of z_0 is likely to be small and for design purposes it may be taken as zero, i.e. the source is at the base of the fire.

Entrainment in the far field of a fire against a wall can be considered as being approximately half that for an axisymmetric point source plume and, using equation 10.20:

$$M = 0.044 Q_p^{1/3} z^{5/3} \qquad (10.21)$$

Entrainment for a point source fire in a corner can be considered as being approximately one quarter of that for

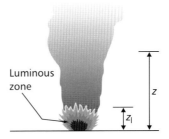

Figure 10.8 Axisymmetric plume

Luminous zone

an axisymmetric point source plume and, using equation 10.20:

$$M = 0.028 \, Q_p^{1/3} \, z^{5/3} \tag{10.22}$$

10.8.3 Finite area source — circle or rectangle

For a circular source of diameter d_s or a square source with side of length d_s, originating on the floor away from the walls, the height of the luminous zone is given by:

$$z_1 = 0.035 \, Q_p^{2/3} / (d_s + 0.074 \, Q_p^{2/5})^{2/3} \tag{10.23}$$

For $z > z_1$:

$$M = 0.071 \, Q_p^{1/3} \, z^{5/3} \tag{10.24}$$

The coefficient in equation 10.23 is believed to represent the upper limit.

When d_s is small in relation to z_1, equation 10.23 reduces to that for the axisymmetric plume (equation 10.19). When d_s is large, equation 10.23 gives the same answer as early work using square-based fires of wood cribs.

Equations 10.23 and 10.24 may also be used for rectangular sources where d_s, the greater dimension, does not exceed three times the length of shorter side.

Note: equation 10.24 is the same as equation 10.20.

An alternative equation for M based on the perimeter of the source, p (m), and its plan area, A_s, may be used for circular or square sources as follows.

For $z < 2.5 \, p$ and $200 < Q_p / A_s < 750$:

$$M = 0.188 \, p \, z^{3/2} \tag{10.25}$$

where p is the perimeter of the source (m).

Equation 10.25 is justified theoretically for $z \approx z_1$. For larger values of z it is justified only empirically, within the limits stated.

10.8.4 Line source

A line source is defined here as a rectangular source where d_s, the longer side, is greater than three times the length of the shorter side. For a line source originating on the floor

away from the walls the height of the luminous zone is given by:

$$z_1 = 0.035 \, Q_p^{2/3} / (d_s + 0.074 \, Q_p^{2/5})^{2/3} \tag{10.26}$$

Note: equation 10.26 is the same as equation 10.23.

For $z_1 < z < 5 \, d_s$:

$$M = 0.21 \, Q_p^{1/3} \, d_s^{2/3} \, z \tag{10.27}$$

For $z > 5 \, d_s$

$$M = 0.071 \, Q_p^{1/3} \, z^{5/3} \tag{10.28}$$

The coefficient in equation 10.27 is based on the Lee and Emmons[16] theory and is believed to be an upper limit.

Equation 10.28 is the same as equation 10.20 for the axisymmetric plume.

10.8.5 Flow from an opening

Flow from an opening is a controversial subject. Equation 10.25 is commonly used, with the mass of smoke from the fire conservatively 'doubled' due to lack of detailed information. This Guide recommends that the equations below be used to calculate flow from an opening.

The horizontal mass flow from an opening of a room containing a fire, see Figure 10.9, is given by:

$$M_o = 0.09 \, (Q_p \, w_o^2)^{1/3} \, h_o \tag{10.29}$$

where M_o is the horizontal mass flow by entrainment (kg·s^{-1}), Q_p is the convective heat output of fire (kW), w_o is the width of the opening (m), h_o is the height of the opening.

Entrainment in the vertical plume above the opening is given by:

$$M = 0.23 \, Q_p^{1/3} \, w_o^{2/3} \, (z_o + h_o) \tag{10.30}$$

where z_o is the plume height above the top of the opening (m).

Where there is a balcony above the opening, see Figure 10.10, the entrainment in the vertical plume above the balcony is given by:

$$M = 0.36 \, Q_p^{1/3} \, l_c^{2/3} \, (z_b + 0.25 \, h_b) \tag{10.31}$$

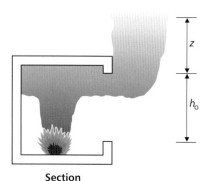

Section

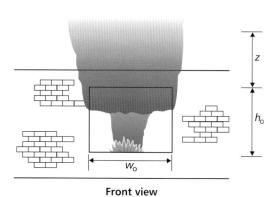

Front view

Figure 10.9 Plume from an opening

where l_c is the separation of the channelling screens (m), h_b is the height of the balcony above the base of the opening (m) and z_b is the plume height above the balcony (m).

Where there are no channelling screens beneath the balcony the entrainment in the vertical plume is given by:

$$M = 0.36\, Q_p^{1/3}\, (w_o + b)^{2/3}\, (z_b + 0.25\, h_b) \qquad (10.32)$$

where b is the depth of the balcony (m).

These equations may be used whether or not there is a wall above the opening or balcony.

Equations 10.29, 10.30, 10.31 and 10.32 are empirical and therefore do not necessarily coincide at the extremes. Data for equations 10.29 and 10.30 were obtained from pre-flashover and post-flashover fires.

At large heights the plume can be considered as axisymmetric and it is suggested that for $z_o > 5\, w_o$ or $z_b > 5\, l_c$, the entrainment is calculated using equation 10.20 with z_o taken as zero if this gives a more conservative solution. If the critical condition is smoke temperature or smoke concentration, then the lower value of M gives a conservative solution. If the critical condition is smoke volume, then the higher value of M gives a conservative solution.

10.8.6 Ceiling flow

The velocity of a flowing layer beneath a ceiling along a channel of width w_c is given by:

$$u = 0.7\, (g\, Q_p\, T / \rho_o\, c_p\, T_o^2\, w_c)^{1/3} \qquad (10.33)$$

where u is the velocity of the layer (m·s⁻¹), g is the acceleration due to gravity (m·s⁻²), T is the (absolute) smoke temperature (K), ρ_o is the ambient air density (kg·m⁻³), T_o is the (absolute) ambient air temperature (K) and w_c is the width of the channel.

Assuming conservation of heat:

$$d_1 = \{M\, T / [38\, w_c\, (T - T_o)^{1/2}]\}^{2/3} \qquad (10.34)$$

where d_1 is the depth of layer (m) and M is the mass flow entering the layer (kg·s⁻¹).

T may be calculated as the average temperature of the smoke plume as it enters the layer.

10.8.7 Plume temperature

The average temperature of the plume is given by:

$$T_m - T_o = Q_p / (M\, c_p) \qquad (10.35)$$

where T_m is the (absolute) average plume temperature (K), T_o is the (absolute) ambient air temperature (K), Q_p is the convective heat output of fire (kW), M is the mass flow entering the layer (kg·s⁻¹) and c_p is the specific heat of air (kJ·kg⁻¹·K⁻¹).

For an assumed Gaussian temperature distribution across the plume, taking $c_p \approx 1$, the axial temperature is given by:

$$T_c - T_o = 2\, (T_m - T_o) \qquad (10.36)$$

where T_c is the (absolute) axial temperature (K).

Note: temperatures in excess of 1200 °C are unlikely to occur in fires in buildings. Higher temperatures are possible with fires in tunnels or in hydrocarbon fires.

10.8.8 Volume flow rate

The volume flow rate is given by:

$$v = M / \rho = M\, T_m / \rho_o\, T_o \qquad (10.37)$$

where v is the volume flow rate (m³·s⁻¹), ρ is the smoke density (kg·m⁻³) and ρ_o is the ambient air density (kg·m⁻³).

Substituting from equation 10.35:

$$v = M / \rho_o + Q_p / \rho_o\, T_o\, c_p \qquad (10.38)$$

10.8.9 Ceiling jet

When the plume above a fire reaches a ceiling, a horizontal jet is formed. Section 10.6.3 considers the performance of ceiling-mounted detectors. The following relationships are valid for a steady heat release rate but can be modified to take into account t-squared fires[17].

For an axisymmetric plume below an unconfined ceiling (no accumulated warm upper layer) the ceiling jet has the following properties when the distance between the walls and the source is at least 1.8 times the ceiling height.

For $r / h \le 0.18$:

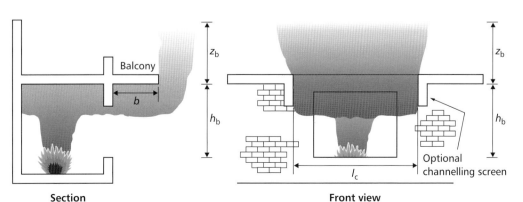

Figure 10.10 Plume from an opening with balcony above

Section   Front view

$$T - T_o = 16.9\, Q^{2/3} / h^{5/3} \qquad (10.39)$$

For $r / h > 0.18$:

$$T - T_o = 5.38\, Q^{2/3} / h \qquad (10.40)$$

where r is the horizontal distance from fire axis (m), h is the height of ceiling above base of fire (m), T is the temperature of jet (K), T_o is the (absolute) ambient air temperature (K) and Q is the total heat release rate (kW).

For $r / h \le 0.15$:

$$u = 0.96\, (Q / h)^{1/3} \qquad (10.41)$$

For $r / h > 0.15$:

$$u = 0.195\, Q^{1/3}\, h^{1/2} / r^{5/6} \qquad (10.42)$$

where u is the velocity of the jet (m·s⁻¹).

10.8.10   Convective heat release

The proportion of the total heat release rate which is in the plume varies with the type of combustible material and the characteristics of the compartment (for flow out of an opening). For the purposes of design the following may be assumed:

$$Q_p = Q / 1.5 \qquad (10.43)$$

where Q_p is the convective heat output of fire (kW) (i.e. heat into the plume) and Q is the total heat release rate (kW).

10.9   Accumulated ceiling layer

10.9.1   General

The simplest zone model postulates that smoke rises to form a smoke layer of uniform depth and temperature with a substantially smoke-free layer below it. Smoke control systems are frequently required to maintain a minimum height for the smoke-free layer for a specified time, see section 7: *Fire and smoke ventilation.*

10.9.2   Smoke filling times

For steady-state smoke control design the entrainment equations may be used to calculate the extract required. However, in some large spaces the volume of the smoke reservoir is so large that the size itself is a form of smoke control since any smoke reservoir will take a finite time to become full. This time may be calculated by a number of methods, as follows:

(a)   by using a computer program to integrate calculated smoke volumes produced at small time intervals (e.g. the 'available safe egress time' (ASET) model)

(b)   by integrating various relationships mathematically, using simplifying assumptions, to derive a formula (see below).

The latter method is more approximate but will usually produce a conservative figure.

Calculation routines for simple smoke filling can easily be written. A specified growth curve (e.g. fast, medium or slow) is subdivided into time elements and the entrainment equations are applied to each successive element. The layer depth in the reservoir at the end of each time element can then be taken as the starting point for the next element. The smoke layer will therefore consist of a number of elemental thin layers. In addition to adding elemental layers, elemental smoke extract may be subtracted, depending on what type of smoke control (if any) is applied. The output of the program can show, as a function of time, the following:

—   clear layer position

—   average temperatures

—   average visibilities.

10.9.3   Smoke filling — rooms with low-level ventilation openings

In such rooms there is no smoke flow out of the low-level opening in the wall, see Figure 10.11. Heat loss to the room surfaces is neglected, which is conservative.

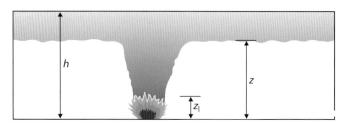

Figure 10.11 Smoke-filling a room with a low-level opening

10.9.3.1   Axisymmetric plume

The elapsed time at which the smoke-free layer is at a height z (m) is obtained by solving the differential equation:

$$\rho_o\, A_f\, \frac{dz}{dt} + M + \frac{Q_p}{T_o\, c_p} = 0 \qquad (10.44)$$

where A_f is the floor area (m²).

The variation of M with z is described in section 10.8.

Solutions to equation 10.44 are given in Figure 10.12 for an axisymmetric plume (equation 10.20) and constant Q_p, using dimensionless parameters as follows:

$$Z = z / h$$

$$Q^* = Q_p / [\rho_o\, T_o\, c_p\, (g\, h)^{1/2}\, h^2] = Q / (1100\, h^{5/2})$$

$$\tau = t\, (g / h)^{1/2}\, (h^2 / A_f) = (3.13\, t\, h^{3/2}) / A_f$$

Figure 10.12 solves the following integral:

$$\tau = \int_z^1 \frac{dZ}{0.195\, (Q^*)^{1/3}\, Z^{5/3} + Q^*} \qquad (10.45)$$

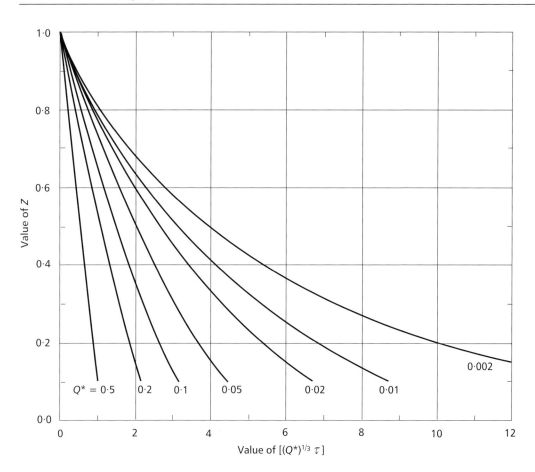

Figure 10.12 Solutions of equation 10.45 for an axisymmetric plume

Where the ceiling area and the smoke base area are both equal to A_f, the average density of the smoke layer is given by:

$$\rho_s / \rho_o = 1 - Q^* \tau / (1 - Z) \qquad (10.46)$$

The average temperature of the smoke layer T_s (K) is given by:

$$(T_s - T_o) / T_o = 1 / [1 - Q^* \tau / (1 - Z)] \qquad (10.47)$$

Where an impurity such as carbon monoxide can be related to Q by the following expression:

$$m_{CO} = C (Q / c_p T_o) \qquad (10.48)$$

the mass fraction in the ceiling layer is given by:

$$f_m = C Q^* \tau / (1 - z) \qquad (10.49)$$

where f_m is the mass fraction in the ceiling layer and C is given by equation 10.51.

Note:

$$m_{CO} = Y_{CO} R = Y_{CO} Q / H_c \qquad (10.50)$$

$$C = Y_{CO} c_p T_o / H_c \qquad (10.51)$$

where H_c is the heat of combustion (kJ·kg^{-1}).

10.9.3.2   Line plume

For a plume from a line source, such as given by equation 10.27, 10.30, 10.31 or 10.32, i.e:

$$M = \alpha Q^{1/3} l_s^{2/3} z \qquad (10.52)$$

where α is a numerical factor and l_s is the length of the line source (m), the differential equation is:

$$\rho_o A_f \frac{dz}{dt} + \alpha Q_p^{1/3} l_s^{2/3} z + \frac{Q_p}{T_o c_p} = 0 \qquad (10.53)$$

The solution to this equation, with constant Q_p, is:

$$(Q^*)^{1/3} \tau = \frac{1}{\alpha_2} \ln \left(\frac{\alpha_2 + (Q^*)^{2/3}}{\alpha_2 Z + (Q^*)^{2/3}} \right) \qquad (10.54)$$

where:

$$Q^* = Q_p / [\rho_o T_o c_p (g h)^{1/2} (h l_s)] = Q / (1100 h^{3/2} l_s)$$

$$\tau = t (g / h)^{1/2} (h l_s / A_f) = 3.13 t h^{1/2} l_s / A_f$$

$$\alpha_2 = \alpha (T_o c_p / \rho_o^2)^{1/3} = 2.72 \alpha$$

$$Z = z / h$$

$$(Q^*)^{1/3} \tau = 0.303 (Q l_s^2)^{1/3} t / A_f$$

Equations 10.47, 10.48 and 10.49 can be used to calculate average temperature, density and mass fraction by inserting the above values.

This solution can be used where smoke flows from a communicating space into a large volume space such, as a shopping mall or atrium, by entering equation 10.30, 10.31 or 10.32 and the dimensions A_f and h of the large volume.

10.9.3.3 Room filling with smoke extract from layer

A critical height of the smoke layer may be dictated by the need to keep it above eye level, inside a reservoir or, if otherwise too hot, well above head level. The 'clear layer' position should be based on maintaining a tenable environment, rather than by selecting an arbitrary figure, such as 2.5, 3 or 3.5 m, as has generally been customary, see section 10.7.

If the critical clear layer height z_c (m) would be reached before the occupants have escaped, then extract from the smoke layer can be provided, under steady-state conditions, as follows:

$$M_{out} = M_c \qquad (10.55)$$

where M_{out} is the mass flow rate of the vented smoke (kg·s^{-1}) and M_c is mass flow rate in the plume (kg·s^{-1}) at height z_c (m).

The temperature of the vented smoke, T_s (K), under steady-state conditions will be given by:

$$T_s - T_o = Q_p / (M_{out} c_p) \qquad (10.56)$$

and the volume flow rate, v (m^3 s^{-1}), by:

$$v = (M_{out} / \rho_o) + Q_p / (\rho_o T_o c_p) \qquad (10.57)$$

With natural ventilation, the mass flow rate of the vented smoke is given by:

$$M_{out} = \frac{C_d A_{vo} \rho_o [2 g (h-z) (T_s - T_o) T_o]^{1/2}}{T_s^{1/2} [T_s + (A_{vo}/A_{vi})^2 T_o]^{1/2}} \qquad (10.58)$$

where A_{vo} is the outlet ventilation area (m^2), A_{vi} is the ventilation inlet area (m^2) and C_d is the discharge coefficient.

Value for discharge coefficients (between 0.6 and 0.9) are provided by the vent manufacturers.

10.9.4 Smoke filling — open rooms approaching flashover

The calculations given in 10.9.3 are not suitable where flames are approaching ceiling height or where smoke flows out of the wall opening. Under these circumstances the following equation may be used:

$$T_s - T_o = 9.15 [(Q_p^2 / (A_o h_o^{1/2} \alpha_k A_t)]^{1/3} \qquad (10.59)$$

where Q_p is the convective heat output of fire (kW), A_o is the area of ventilation opening (door, window etc.) (m^2), h_o is the height of the ventilation opening (m), α_k is the effective heat transfer coefficient (kW·m^{-2}·K^{-1}) and A_t is the area of the room surface (wall, floor, ceiling) (m^2).

Equation 10.59 was derived for $A_t / (A_o h_o^{1/2}) = 16$ to 530 m$^{-1/2}$.

By substituting $(T_s - T_o) = 580$ K in equation 10.59 the value of Q_p at flashover is given by:

$$Q_f = 505 (A_o h_o^{1/2} \alpha_k A_t)^{1/2} \qquad (10.60)$$

where Q_f is the convective heat output of fire at flashover (kW).

For $[A_{net} / (A_{vo} h_o^{1/2})] < 10$ m$^{-1/2}$, the following value for Q_p is recommended:

$$Q_f = 5.2 A_{net} + 252 A_o h_o^{1/2} \qquad (10.61)$$

where:

$$A_{net} = A_t - A_o \qquad (10.62)$$

The effective heat transfer coefficient is derived from the following:

$$\alpha_k = (\lambda_w \rho_w c_w / t_c)^{1/2} \qquad (10.63)$$

where λ_w is the thermal conductivity of the wall material (kW·m^{-1}·K^{-1}), ρ_w is the density of the wall material (kg·m^{-3}), c_w is the specific heat capacity of the wall material (kJ·kg^{-1}·K^{-1}) and t_c is the characteristic burn time (s).

Table 10.8 gives values of α_k for a characteristic burn time of 900 s.

Table 10.8 Effective heat transfer coefficient to surfaces of room or compartment

Material of surface	$\alpha_k / $ kW·m^{-2}·K^{-1}
Concrete	55×10^{-3}
Brick	36×10^{-3}
Plaster	21×10^{-3}
Plasterboard	13×10^{-3}
Fibre insulating board	5.2×10^{-3}

Flashover is not expected until there are sustained flames at ceiling level. For axisymmetric sources of base dimension less than the ceiling height, the minimum condition for flashover is given by:

$$h < 0.094 Q_p^{2/5} \qquad (10.64)$$

where h is the height of the ceiling above base of fire (m).

For extended area sources, the minimum condition for flashover is given by:

$$h < 0.035 Q_p^{2/3} / (d_s + 0.074 Q_p^{2/5})^{2/3} \qquad (10.65)$$

where d_s is the longer dimension of the source.

Equation 10.65 is conservative because it uses equation 10.26 for intermittent flames.

10.9.5 Heat transfer to building surfaces

In the simple room filling model considered in 10.9.3, heat transfer to the ceiling and wall surfaces is neglected. This is a conservative assumption in that the volume of smoke is overestimated. However, if low temperature smoke is filling a large reservoir, then cooling may lead to loss of buoyancy which should be taken into account. In the absence of experimental data it is suggested that cooling effects should be allowed for, using computational fluid dynamics (CFD), where the area of the reservoir is greater than 2000 m², and/or the average layer temperature is less than 10 K above ambient when calculated by neglecting cooling.

10.9.6 Heat transfer from smoke layer by radiation

The radiation emitted from a hot smoke layer is given by:

$$I_r = \varepsilon_s \, \sigma \, T_s^4 \qquad (10.66)$$

where I_r is the intensity of the emitted radiation (kW·m⁻²), ε_s is the emissivity of the smoke layer, σ is the Stefan-Boltzmann constant (5.67×10^{-11}) (kW·m⁻²·K⁻⁴) and T_s is the average (absolute) smoke layer temperature (K).

As a conservative assumption ε_s may be taken as unity. Alternatively it may be estimated for a ceiling layer from:

$$\varepsilon_s = 1 - \exp[-(0.33 + 470\,m_s)(h - z)] \qquad (10.67)$$

where h is the height of the ceiling (m), z is the height of the layer interface (m) and m_s is the mass concentration of smoke aerosol (kg·m⁻³) (see section 10.7.8).

10.9.7 Stratification

When the ambient temperature at ceiling level is significantly higher than at the level where the fire starts, the upward movement of the smoke plume may cease, due to lack of buoyancy, and stratification may occur.

The maximum height of rise of an axisymmetric plume is given by:

$$z_m = 5.54 \, Q_p^{1/4} \, (\mathrm{d}T / \mathrm{d}z)^{-3/8} \qquad (10.68)$$

where z_m is the maximum height of smoke rise above base of fire (m), Q_p is the convective heat release rate (kW) and $\mathrm{d}T / \mathrm{d}z$ is the rate of change of ambient temperature with respect to height (assumed to be linear) (K·m⁻¹).

The maximum height of rise of a line plume of length l_s at source is given by:

$$z_m = 4.81 \, (Q_p')^{1/3} \, (\mathrm{d}T/\mathrm{d}z)^{-1/2} \qquad (10.69)$$

where:

$$Q_p' = Q_p / l_s \qquad (10.70)$$

10.9.8 Number of extract points

When the smoke layer is relatively shallow, a high extract rate at any point may lead to 'plug-holing', whereby some air is extracted along with the smoke. Accordingly, more than one extract point may be needed with an extract rate from one point not exceeding M (kg·s⁻¹) given by:

$$M = \beta \, [g \, (h - z)^5 \, (T_s - T_0) \, T_0]^{1/2} / T_s \qquad (10.71)$$

where g is the acceleration due to gravity (9.81 m·s⁻²) and β is a numerical factor which takes the value 2.0 where the extract point is near a wall and 2.8 where the extract point is distant from a wall. (These estimates are based on limited experimental data.)

If two points are close together, the flow around them will basically be the same as if they were one point. NFPA 92B[6] provides guidance for the minimum separation between extract points.

10.9.9 Loss of buoyancy in large reservoirs

10.9.9.1 Limits on size of smoke reservoirs

Some codes and design guides limit the size of a smoke reservoir to, for example, 60 m or 2000 m². These limits are based either on travel distances under a smoke layer or on concerns over excessive smoke cooling. As detailed in section 7, these limits need not apply to all buildings and detailed analysis may be undertaken to demonstrate the actual limits for smoke cooling. The extent to which stratification of smoke does occur and the effect that it will have on the means of escape strategy, for example, can also be assessed. Such assessment may be undertaken using CFD models, for example, that take into account building volume, fire size and boundary conditions[18].

10.9.9.2 Mixed use systems

The use of natural and mechanical smoke control systems in the same smoke control reservoir may be possible provided that it can be demonstrated that the systems will perform the design duties under all wind conditions.

10.10 Flame calculations

10.10.1 General

Various methods are available to calculate flame heights for both hydrocarbon and cellulosic, and post-flashover fires. This is mainly used to estimate radiant heating or radiant and convective heating of combustible materials and elements of the structure, although it may be necessary to assess radiant effects on personnel such as firefighters. Calculating flame height can show where flame impingement is likely to occur. For example, if it can be shown that a steel member is not engulfed in flame, it may be possible to use materials having shorter fire resistance periods.

10.10.2 Heat flux calculation

By assuming flame heights and areas of burning, it is possible to calculate the radiation due to a fire which impinges on a separate fuel package.

In areas not equipped with sprinklers fires will tend to grow until limited by lack of fuel or air. In compartments where items of fuel are very widely spaced, it is possible to predict whether fire spread will occur from item to item. This is done by calculating the radiative heat flux originating from the fire and which falls on the target item[3]:

$$I_r = \phi \, \varepsilon_f \, \sigma \, T_f^4 \qquad (10.72)$$

where I_r is the radiative heat flux (kW·m^{-2}), ϕ is a configuration factor (see below), ε_f is the flame emissivity, σ is the Stefan–Boltzmann constant (5.67 × 10^{-11} kW·m^{-2}·K^{-4}) and T_f is the flame temperature (K).

The configuration factor, ϕ, represents the geometrical relationship between the source and target.

The above is a very general method for calculating radiative heat flux. A more detailed treatment, including techniques for calculating ϕ, are given in the *SFPE Handbook*[3].

The heat flux impinging on combustible material will cause it to heat up. Whether this heating results in ignition depends on the intensity of the incident flux. Experimental work by Babrauskas[19] suggests that for very thin materials such as curtains, the heat flux required for ignition could be relatively low at around 10 kW·m^{-2}. For thick materials the value may be higher, i.e. about 40 kW·m^{-2}. It is suggested that a value of 20 kW·m^{-2} be taken as appropriate for most materials. This figure is the same as that found by Thomas[20] as the critical heat flux for flashover in a room.

10.10.3   Calculation of flame height

Clearly the larger the flame or the surface which is radiating heat, the larger will be the total heat which is emitted. This implies that larger flames give larger values of ϕ. Therefore the estimation of flame heights is a crucial part of the calculation process.

For flames arising from fuels which are relatively compact, and without much in-depth burning, equation 10.73 has been shown to be applicable over a very wide range of heat release rates. Figure 10.13 summarises relationships drawn

from various sources[21-23] for fuels which are burning over an extensive area.

On occasions it may be necessary to calculate the flame projection from openings in a compartment which is involved in a fully developed fire. The extent of flame projection can be calculated from equations given by Law and O'Brien[24], see equation 10.74.

The flame height z_f is given by:

$$z_f = 0.235 \, Q^{2/5} - 1.02 \, d_s \qquad (10.73)$$

where z_f is the flame height (m), Q is the heat output of fire (kW) and d_s is the fire diameter (m).

If unknown, the fire diameter may be estimated from the heat output by assuming an average fire load density and then calculating the area of burning.

The above relationship does not apply to hydrocarbon fires. The calculation of such fires is complex and attention is drawn to chapter 2-4 of the *SFPE Handbook*[3]. Hydrocarbon fires in the open are likely to be influenced strongly by the wind, and this should be taken into account.

10.10.4   Flame projection (post-flashover)

Flame projection from the windows or doors in a compartment can be estimated from the work of Law and O'Brien, as contained in Eurocode 1[24]. The height of the flame above the top of the opening, z_{fo}, is given by:

$$z_{fo} + h = 12.8 \, (R / w)^{2/3} \qquad (10.74)$$

where z_{fo} is the flame height above the top of the opening (m), h is the height of the opening (m), R is the rate of fuel combustion (kg·s^{-1}) and w is the width of compartment openings (m).

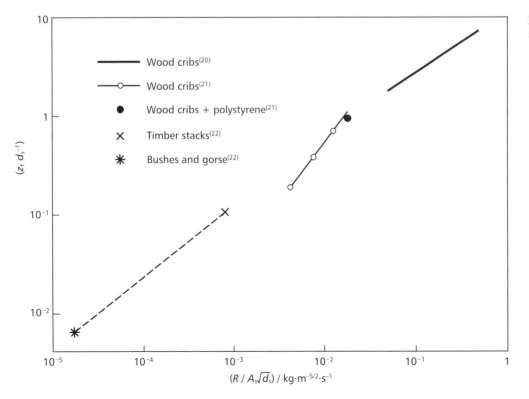

Figure 10.13 Flame heights for a range of fire sizes

For cellulosic fires, the ventilation-controlled rate of burning, R, may be calculated from Thomas' correlation[25] as follows:

$$R = 0.02 \left[(A_t - A_o)(A_o \sqrt{h_o})(w / d) \right]^{1/2} \qquad (10.75)$$

where R is the rate of fuel combustion ($kg \cdot s^{-1}$), A_t is the area of enclosing walls (m^2), A_o is the area of the window (m^2), h_o is the height of the opening (m), w is the width of the wall containing an opening (m) and d is the depth of the room behind an opening (m).

The heat output of the fire is given earlier by equation 10.8.

10.10.5   Fire resistance assessment

The regulatory fire resistance is based on a furnace test specified in BS 476: Part 20[26] and a real fire may be shown to be less severe, see Figure 10.14, in which case the fire resistance period may be reduced[27]. In Figure 10.14, curves $60(\frac{1}{4})$ and $60(\frac{1}{2})$ are typical of shop fires ($60 \ kg \cdot m^{-2}$), and curves $30(\frac{1}{4})$ and $30(\frac{1}{2})$ are typical of office fires (20–$30 \ kg \cdot m^{-2}$).

Methods for calculating compartment temperatures are beyond the scope of this section. However, the calculation of compartment temperatures and equivalent fire resistance periods is considered in section 5: *Compartmentation and spread of flame* and detailed calculation procedures are given by Law and O'Brien in Eurocode 1[24], Walton and Thomas in the *SFPE Handbook*[3] and Thomas[11].

10.11   Fire and smoke modelling

10.11.1   General

In recent years there have been major developments in the application of computer fire models to some of the problems discussed in this section. Most models are concerned with predicting the behaviour of smoke and some also attempt to incorporate fire spread, flashover and structural response. Whilst it is not possible to review individual models and their performance, it is useful to mention the principal types of model.

10.11.2   Zone models

Experiment shows that within a compartment smoke from a fire rises to ceiling level and accumulates as a layer. Smoke rises in a plume from the fire into the upper layer. If there are openings in the compartment such as doors, vents or broken windows, smoke will flow to the outside and fresh air will be drawn in. Zone fire models recognise that, to a first approximation, the smoke layer can be characterised by a temperature and depth and this may be defined as one zone; the relatively clear air below is another. The plume, whereby heat and mass are transferred from the lower layer to the upper, is treated as a third zone.

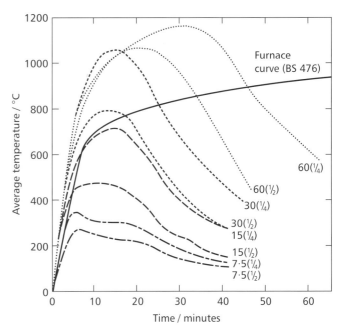

Note: $60(\frac{1}{2})$ means fire load $60 \ kg \cdot m^{-2}$ of floor area and ventilation 50% of one wall

Figure 10.14 Effect on fire temperature of fire load and ventilation[27] (reproduced from *Designing for fire safety* by E G Butcher and A C Parnell, by permission of David Fulton Publishers Ltd.)

Depending on the sophistication of the zone model used, calculation of the development of the smoke layer can be carried out with respect to:

—   time

—   the mass inflow and outflow associated with openings

—   the temperatures of the compartment walls.

Generally the fire has to be specified as a heat release rate (or a mass loss rate) as a function of time. However, some zone models can predict fire spread rates. Zone models are generally reasonably quick to use and are useful in analysing simple geometries. Zone models are available from the (USA) National Institute for Standards and Technology (NIST)* free of charge, these models have been validated and are widely used and accepted by the majority of fire professionals.

10.11.3   Field models (CFD)

It should normally be possible to use the information given in section 10 without resort to computational fluid dynamics (CFD) or physical modelling, although these are valuable tools which can be used to obtain detailed predictions of smoke flow in complex geometries. In field models involving CFD, the space to be analysed is divided into many thousands or even tens of thousands of cells. The conservation equations for energy, mass and momentum are then solved simultaneously for all cells at a series of time steps. It is possible to obtain very detailed predictions of flows of hot gases rising from the fire over a period of time. CFD models differ in the techniques they use to deal with turbulent flow and in their ability to predict the combustion process. Many rely, as do zone models, on a description of the fire represented by a heat release rate as a function of time.

* US Department of Commerce, National Institute for Standards and Technology, Centre for Fire Research, Gaithersburg, Maryland MD 20899, USA (www.nist.gov)

Due to the complex nature of CFD analysis, it is difficult, both for the engineer and fire authorities, to check the results obtained and, ideally, CFD models are used only to confirm what has already been predicted by simpler modelling techniques.

With powerful computers now widely available to practictioners, CFD models are less costly to run and are therefore becoming more commonplace.

10.11.4 Points to consider when using CFD modelling

Since computational fluid dynamics is a particularly complex undertaking, its practitioners tend to be specialists in that subject with little experience in its application to fire science and fire engineering. Therefore, when applying CFD to fire problems, it is particularly important that the project be supervised by a multi-disciplinary team in order to ensure that the problem is properly posed and that the results produced are sensible.

The responsibilities of the fire engineer and CFD prac-titioner can be summarised as follows:

The fire engineer must:

— have an idea of the answer beforehand; CFD should confirm the simple model results

— insert a fire load case into the converged environmental model, as normal environmental flows within a building may affect the movement of smoke to a greater or lesser degree

— be aware that the model may predict unusual fire effects that may be perfectly valid or, more commonly, show an error in the analysis that needs to be checked

— simplify the problem to its essentials; the presence of design features may influence some aspects of a problem but not others, e.g. structural beams which may significantly affect detection times but not smoke filling times

— specify the way that the fire source is to be treated (e.g. constant or growing fire) and decide in discussion with the CFD practitioner whether the fire is to be treated simply as a heat source of known volume/area or whether a combustion sub-model is required.

The CFD practitioner must:

— decide on the placement and refinement of the grid mesh, and the time step size, in discussion with fire safety engineer (to determine where steep property gradients are expected etc.)

— demonstrate convergence, energy and mass balance information

— provide a statement on the degree to which grid-insensitive solutions have been obtained

— set down the assumptions on which any 'secondary' variables are based.

10.11.5 Physical or scale modelling (Froude modelling)

Probably the most useful form of scale modelling for smoke movement and smoke control applications is Froude modelling. Froude modelling can be useful both as a design tool and to demonstrate system effectiveness as part of acceptance testing.

A scaled down fire is built in air at atmospheric pressure in the model, and the modelling is conducted so that the 'Froude number' is the same for all locations in both the model and the full scale facility.

The Froude number is given by:

$$Fr = \frac{U}{\sqrt{g\, l}} \tag{10.76}$$

where Fr is the Froude number, U is velocity (m·s⁻¹), g is the acceleration due to gravity (m·s⁻²) and l is length (m).

For buildings of normal construction, the model can be made of gypsum board, glass or similar materials. The heat release rate for the scaled down fire is:

$$Q_{model} = Q_{full}\,(S)^{5/2} \tag{10.77}$$

where Q_{model} is the rate of heat release in the model (kW), Q_{full} is the rate of heat release in the full size facility (kW) and S is the scale of the model.

The temperatures from the scale model are the same as for corresponding places in the full size facility. Any fan-powered flow rates are scaled as:

$$V_{model} = V_{full}\,(S)^{5/2} \tag{10.78}$$

where V_{model} is the volumetric flow rate in the model (m³·s⁻¹) and V_{full} is the volumetric flow rate in the full scale facility (m³·s⁻¹).

Measurements from the scale model of smoke location at various times are adjusted to full scale by:

$$t_{full} = \frac{t_{model}}{\sqrt{S}} \tag{10.79}$$

where t_{model} is the time in the model (s) and t_{full} is the volumetric flow rate in the full scale facility (s).

Froude modelling is not appropriate for spaces of high temperature such as flames, but it is appropriate for smoke flow away from flames. The scale of the model needs to be chosen such that the flow becomes fully turbulent. The general rule is that the smallest length that can support such turbulent flow is about 0.3 m. If in a particular application the smallest length where realistic modelling is desired is a 3 m high balcony, then a scale for the model would be $S = (0.3 / 3) = 0.1$.

Consider a smoke reservoir in a 0.1 scale model that takes 7 minutes to fill. From equation 10.79, the time to fill the full scale smoke reservoir would be 22 minutes.

For further details of Froude and other types of modelling, see *Principles of Smoke Management Design*[28] by J Klote.

References

1   Drysdale D D *An introduction to fire dynamics* (Chichester: Wiley) (2001)

2   *Relationships for smoke control calculations* CIBSE TM19 (London: Chartered Institution of Building Services Engineers) (1995)

3   *SFPE Handbook of Fire Protection Engineering* (Boston, Mass. USA: Society of Fire Protection Engineers/Quincey, Mass. USA: National Fire Protection Association) (2002)

4   Babrauskas V   Free burning fires *Fire Safety J.* **11** 33–51 (1986)

5   Bukowski R W A review of international fire risk prediction methods *Proc. 6th Inter. Fire Conf. (Interflam 93)* (Oxford: Interscience Communications) (1993)

6   *Smoke Management Systems in Mall, Atria and Large Areas* NFPA 92B-2000 (Quincey, MA: National Fire Protection Association) (2000)

7   *Fire scenario for three-panel workstation* (Gaithersburg, MD: National Institute for Standards and Technology) (1991) (www.fire.nist.gov/fire/fires/work3/work3.html)

8   Nelson H Fire modelling assessment of areas of refuge intended to provide safety for persons with mobility limitations *Proc. 6th Inter. Fire Conf. (Interflam 93)* (Oxford: Interscience Communications) (1993)

9   Residential sprinklers *Fire Technol.* **29** (3) 203–226 (1993)

10   *Fire experiments in a two-dimensional rack storage* (Brandforsk project 701-917) SP Report 1993:56 (Borås, Sweden: Swedish National Testing and Research Institute (SP)) (1993)

11   Thomas P H   Design Guide — Structural Fire Safety (CIB W14 Workshop) *Fire Safety J.* **10**(2) (1986)

12   *The selection of sprinkler heads* LPC Technical Bulletin TB20 (London: Loss Prevention Council) (1994)

13   Evans D D and Stroup D W *Methods to calculate the response of heat and smoke detectors installed below large unobstructed ceilings* NBSIR 85-3167 (Washington DC: National Bureau of Standards) (1985)

14   Madrzykowski D and Vettori R L   *A sprinklered fire suppression algorithm for the GSA Engineering Fire Assessment System* (Gaithersburg, MD: National Institute for Standards and Technology) (1991)

15   *Standard for fixed guideway transit and `passenger rail systems* NFPA 130 (Quincey, MA: National Fire Protection Association) (2000)

16   Lee S L and Emmons H W A study of natural convection above a line fire *J. Fluid Mech.* **11** (21) (1961)

17   McCaffrey B J, Quintiere J G and Harkleroad M F Estimating room temperatures and the likelihood of flashover using fire test data correlations *Fire Technology* **17** 98–119 and **18** 122 (1981)

18   Keeley M Fire safety for the Millenium Dome *Proc. CIBSE Nat. Conf., Harrogate, 4–5 October 1999* (London: Cartered Institution of Building Services Engineers) (1999)

19   Babrauskas V *Will the second item ignite?* Report NBSIR 81-2271 (Gaithersburg, MD: National Institute for Standards and Technology) (1981)

20   Thomas P H and Bullen M L On the role of $K\rho C$ of room limiting materials in the growth of room fires *Fire and Materials* **3** (2) (1979)

21   Thomas P H et al. Some experiments on bouyant diffusion flames *Combustion and Flame* **5** (4) (December 1961)

22   Kruppa J and Lamboley G *Contribution a l'etude des incendies dans les batiments de grand volume realises en construction metallique* Service 'Incendie' Document No. 1016-5 (Puteaux, France: Centre Technique Industriel de la Construction Métallique (CTICM)) (1983)

23   Thomas P H *The size of flames from two very large fires* Fire Research Note 481 (Borehamwood: Fire Research Station) (1961)

24   Eurocode 1: *Basis of design and actions on structure*: Part 2.7: *Actions on structure exposed to fire* Annex C CEN/TC250/SC1 (Brussels: Comité Européen de Normalisation) (1993)

25   Thomas P H *Behavior of fires in enclosures — some recent progress* (Pittsburgh PA: Combustion Institute) (1973)

26   BS 476: *Fire tests on building materials and structures*: Part 20: 1987: *Method for determination of the fire resistance of elements of construction (general principles)* (London: British Standards Institution) (1987)

27   Butcher E G and Parnell A C *Designing for fire safety* (London: David Fulton Publishers) (1983)

28   Klote J H and Milke J A *Principles of Smoke Management Design* (Atlanta GA; ASHRAE) (2002)

Appendix 10.A1: Rack storage *t*-cubed fire

10.A1.1   General

Some fundamental research on rack storage fires has been undertaken at the SP Boras Swedish National Testing and Research Institute[A1-1]. The results of this research are summarised below.

A dynamic fire model is more appropriate when considering escape from a building, since steady state conditions are unlikely to be achieved during the relatively short escape period.

10.A1.2   Smoke production from flue fires

The Boras experiments concluded the following:

—   The width of the vertical flue is found to be the predominant geometrical parameter controlling the flue flow.

—   Variations in horizontal flue heights had negligible effects on vertical flue flow.

—   For a certain vertical flue width, the mass flow is found to be nearly constant, independent of heat output.

—   The ratio of entrained air to stoichiometric air requirements at the flame tip was found to be 7.5. A flue fire is different from an open fire for two reasons: (*a*) the air is entrained stepwise (through horizontal flues) and (*b*) the flow is bounded by solid boundaries (walls).

The amount of air entrained is given by:

$$m \propto m_f \, r \qquad \qquad (A1.1)$$

where m is the total mass entrainment rate (kg·s^{-1}), m_f is the pyrolysis or mass burning rate (kg·s^{-1}) and r is the stoichiometric mass ratio (air to volatiles) (—).

Therefore:

$$m = \phi \, m_f \, r \qquad \qquad (A1.2)$$

where ϕ is the proportionality constant and m_f is given by:

$$m_f = Q / H_c \qquad \qquad (A1.3)$$

where Q is the total heat release rate (kW) and H_c is the heat of combustion per unit mass of fuel (kJ·kg^{-1}).

Combining equations A1.2 and A1.3 gives:

$$m = \phi \, Q \, r / H_c \qquad \qquad (A1.4)$$

The proportionality constant f has been determined from the Borås experiments as 7.5. As most of the fire load will be cellulosic in nature the following values have been used:

— H_c (cellulose) = 16.09 kJ·g^{-1} or 16.09 × 10^3 kJ·kg^{-1}

—   stoichiometric ratio; r = 5.1

Substituting these values into equation A1.4 gives:

$$m = \frac{7.5 \times Q \times 5.1}{16.09 \times 10^3} = (2.4 \times 10^{-3}) \, Q \qquad (A1.5)$$

Note: for propane, as used in the Borås experiments, the equation would be $m = (2.5 \times 10^{-3}) \, Q$.

Q varies over time according to the following relationship:

$$Q = 0.045 \, (t^\star)^3 \qquad \qquad (A1.6)$$

where $t^\star$ is given by:

$$t^\star = t - t_0 \qquad \qquad (A1.7)$$

where t is time from start/ignition of fire and t_0 is the incipient time of fire growth (s).

The mass of smoke produced prior to sprinkler operation can be calculated by combining equations A1.5 and A1.6, hence:

$$m = 1.08 \times 10^{-4} \, (t^\star)^3 \qquad \qquad (A1.8)$$

Reference (Appendix 10.A1)

A1-1   *Fire experiments in a two-dimensional rack storage* (Brandforsk-project 701-917) SP Report 1993:56 (Borås, Sweden: Swedish National Testing and Research Institute (SP)) (1993)

Appendix 10.A2: Background to equations

Note: references additional to those listed at the end of the main text are identified by the prefix 'A3' and are given at the end of this appendix.

Section:

10.5.3   Equation 10.2 from Brandforsk project[10].

Table 10.1: characteristic growth times from NFPA 92B[6].

Transient fire calculation: use of average value from Zukoski[A2-1].

10.5.4   Based on work by McCaffrey et al.[A2-2] and discussion in Drysdale[1].

Equation 10.9: from Thomas[12].

Equation 10.10: from Law[A2-3].

10.7.3   From *SFPE Handbook* (Chapter 1-14)[3] and comments by Fire Research Station.

10.7.4   From *SFPE Handbook* (Chapter 1-14)[3].

10.7.7   Table 10.7 from *SFPE Handbook* (Chapters 1-13 and 1-25)[3] and comments by Fire Research Station.

10.7.8   Equations 10.12–10.15: from *SFPE Handbook* (Chapter 1-25)[3].

10.8.2   Equation 10.19: the coefficient for $Q^{2/5}$ is given as 0.166 by NFPA 92B[6], as 0.2 by McCaffrey[A2-4] and Cox and Chitty[A2-5] and as 0.23 by Heskestad[A2-6]. A mid value of 0.2 has been chosen.

Equation 10.20: estimates of the coefficient 0.056 by Rouse, Yih and Humphreys[A2-7], 0.063 by Yokoi[A2-8], 0.077 by Zukoski et al.[A2-9], 0.082 by Cox and Chitty[A2-5], 0.071 by NFPA 92B[5]. It is suggested that there is no reason to change from NFPA 92B value of 0.071.

Equation 10.21: from Zukoski et al.[A2-9];

$$M = 0.5 \times 0.071 \, (2 \, Q_p)^{1/3} \, z^{5/3} = 0.044 \, Q_p^{1/3} \, z^{5/3}.$$

Equation 10.22: see explanation for equation 10.21.

10.8.3   Equation 10.23 uses data from Hasemi and Nishihata[A2-10] as interpreted by Thomas[A2-11].

Equation 10.25: from Thomas et al.[A2-12]; limits for applicability from Hinkley[A2-13].

10.8.4   Equation 10.27: from Thomas[A2-14], Lee and Emmons[16]; range of applicability from Hasemi and Nishihata[A2-10].

10.8.5   Equation 10.29: based on various data collected by Law[A2-15] and recent data from Hansell et al.[A2-16]; see review by Thomas[A2-17].

Equation 10.30: based on data from Hansell et al.[A2-16] and Porter[A2-18]; attached plume[A2-16] increased by 50%.

Equation 10.31: based on Law[A2-19] and data from Hansell et al.[A2-16].

Equation 10.2: based on recent data from Hansell et al.[A2-16] as interpreted by Law[A2-20].

10.8.6   Equation 10.33: from Hinkley[A2-21].

10.8.9   Equations 10.39–10.42: from Alpert[A2-22], *SFPE Handbook* (Chapter 1-9)[3].

10.8.10 Equation 10.43: based on *SFPE Handbook* (Chapter 1-13)[3].

10.9.3   Equation 10.58: from Thomas et al.[A2-12].

10.9.4   Equation 10.59: from McCaffrey et al.[A2-2]; their equation has been modified using Q_p where $Q_p = Q/1.5$.

Equation 10.61: from Thomas[A2-23] with $Q_p = Q/1.5$.

Equation 10.63 and Table 10.7: from Drysdale[1].

Equation 10.64: uses measurements of Cox and Chitty[A2-5] for the continuous region.

10.9.6   Equation 10.67: from *SFPE Handbook* (Chapter 2-19)[3].

10.9.7   Equation 10.68: from NFPA 92B[6], based on Morton, Taylor and Turner[A2-24].

Equation 10.69: derived by Thomas (private communication) using Morton, Taylor and Turner approach; a paper has been prepared for publication[A2-25].

10.9.8   Equation 10.71: derived from Fire Research Note 1001[A2-26] (as amended 1976) and Fire Research Note 954[A2-27] and takes into account data not considered in BR 186[A2-28].

References (Appendix 10.A2)

A2-1   Zukoski E E *Development of Stratified Ceiling Layer in Early Stages of a Closed-room Fire* Fire and Materials **2** (2) 54–62 (1978)

A2-2   McCaffrey B J Quintiere J G and Harkleroad M F Estimating room temperatures and the likelihood of flashover using fire test data correlations *Fire Technol* **17** 98–119 and **18** 122 (1981)

A2-3   Law M Fire safety of external building elements — the design approach *Engineering J.* (New York: American Institute of Steel Construction) (1978)

A2-4   McCaffrey B J *Purely buoyant diffusion flames: some experimental results* NBSIR 79-1910 (Washington DC: National Bureau of Standards) (1979)

A2-5   Cox G and Chitty R A study of the deterministic properties of unbound fire plumes *Combustion and Flame* **39** 191 (1980)

A2-6   Heskestad G Peak gas velocities and flame heights of buoyancy-controlled turbulent diffusion flames *Proc. 18th Inter. Symp. on Combustion* (Pittsburg, USA: The Combustion Institute) (1981)

A2-7   Rouse H, Yih C S and Humphreys H W Gravitational convection from a buoyancy source *Tellus* **4** (3) 201–210 (1952)

A2-8   Yokoi S *Study on the prevention of fire spread caused by hot upward current* Report No 34 (Tokyo: Japanese Ministry of Construction Building Research Institute) (November 1960)

A2-9   Zukoski E E, Kubota Toshi and Cetegen Baki Entrainment in Fire Plumes *Fire Safety J.* **3** 107–121 (1980/81)

A2-10   Hasemi Yuji and Nishihata Mitsuru Fuel Shape Effect on the Deterministic Properties of Turbulent Diffusion Flames *Proc. 2nd Inter. Symp. on Fire Safety Science* (Boston, MA: International Association for Fire Safety Science/Hemispheres Publications) (1989)

A2-11   Thomas P H *On flames and plumes from rectilinear sources* Committe Paper 47 (private communication)

A2-12   Thomas P H, Hinkley P L, Theobald C R and Simms D L *Investigations into the flow of hot gases in roof venting* Fire Research Technical Paper No 7 (London: HMSO) (1963)

A2-13   Hinkley P L Rates of Production of Hot Gases in Roof Venting Experiments *Fire Safety J.* **10** 57–65 (1986)

A2-14   Thomas P H On the upward movement of smoke and related shopping mall problems *Fire Safety J.* **12** 191–203 (1987)

A2-15   Law M Design formulae for hot gases from narrow openings — points for consideration *Technical Seminar: Flow of smoke through openings, Fire Research Station, Borehamwood* (Garston: Building Research Establishment Fire Research Group) (June 1989)

A2-16   Hansell G O, Morgan H P and Marshall N R *Smoke flow experiments in a model atrium* BRE Occasional Paper (Garston: Building Research Establishment) (July 1993)

A2-17   Thomas P H Two-dimensional Smoke Flows from Fires in Compartments: Some Engineering Relationships *Fire Safety J.* **18** 125–137 (1992)

A2-18   Porter A M Large scale tests to evaluate mass flow of smoke in line plume *Technical Seminar: Flow of smoke through openings, Fire Research Station, Borehamwood* (Garston: Building Research Establishment Fire Research Group) (June 1989)

A2-19   Law M A note on smoke plumes from fires in multi-level shopping malls *Fire Safety J.* **10** 197–202 (1986)

A2-20   Law M Measurements of Balcony Smoke Flow *Fire Safety J.* **24** 189–195 (1995)

A2-21   Hinkley P L *The flow of hot gases along an enclosed shopping mall — A tentative theory* Fire Research Note 807 (Garston: Building Research Establishment Fire Research Group) (1970)

A2-22   Alpert R L Calculation of response time of ceiling-mounted detectors *Fire Technol.* **8** 181 (1972)

A2-23   Thomas P H Testing products and materials for their contribution to flashover in rooms *Fire and Materials* **5** 103 (1981)

A2-24   Morton B R, Taylor Sir Geoffrey and Turner J S Turbulent Gravitational Convection from Maintained and Instantaneous Sources *Proc. Royal Society* **A234** 1–23 (1956)

A2-25   Thomas P H On the stratification of line plumes (to be published)

A2-26   Heselden A J M and Spratt D *Efficient extraction of smoke from a thin layer under a ceiling* Fire Research Note 1001 (Garston: Building Research Establishment Fire Research Group) (1974)

A2-27   Heselden A J M, Wraight H G H and Watts P R *Fire problems of pedestrian precincts — Part 2: Large-scale experiments with a shaft vent* Fire Research Note **954** (Garston: Building Research Establishment Fire Research Group) (1972)

A2-28   Morgan H P and Gardner J P *Design principles for smoke ventilation in enclosed shopping centres* BRE Report BR186 (Garston: Building Research Establishment) (1990)

11 Fire safety management

11.1 Introduction

The importance of fire safety management should not be underestimated. Even with the most comprehensive fire safety provisions that modern technology can provide, it is essential that there is adequate management of fire safety to ensure that the occupants of a building reach a place of safety in the event of fire and to avert disaster. In many multi-fatality disasters poor fire safety management has been seen to be a significant contributing factor.

Fire safety management here encompasses the whole of the management of fire safety. It is the management activities that ensure that the incidence of fire in a building is minimised, but that when a fire does occur, all of the passive, active and procedural fire safety systems are in place and operating properly.

Fire safety management primarily concerns the life safety of building occupants and firefighters but can also concern the protection of property, heritage and environment.

Fire safety management is a process covering the life cycle of the building, i.e. from design to construction, hand-over, occupation, changes of use etc., through to demolition, see Figure 11.1. It is primarily about building occupation. It is not only about maintenance of fire safety systems.

The fire safety manager(s) is/are the person(s) that carries/carry out the job of fire safety management within the building. In a small building, this task might only be a small part of the manager's job. In a large, complex building, this task may be a full time job with a team of staff.

The designer needs to ensure that the overall design of a building assists and enhances the job of the fire safety manager. Also, the fire safety manager needs to be aware of the fire safety provisions designed into the building.

There is currently no comprehensive published guidance on fire safety management. Detailed guidance is contained in draft British Standard BS 5588: Part 12[1]. Some

- • Pre-planning
- • Design
- • Construction
- • Fitting-out
- • Approvals and certification
- • Commissioning and handover
- • Building in use:
  - — 'normal' running (e.g. planning, trainging, maintenance and house keeping
  - — changes in use (extensions, alterations, refurbishment)
  - — units in disuse and areas decommissioned
- • Building in disuse or decommissioned
- • Building being demolished

Figure 11.1 Life cycle of a building

information on fire safety management can be found in various other parts of BS 5588[2].

This section covers the following aspects of fire safety management:

- — legal obligations and statutory duties
- — the management input to the design brief
- — designing so that the building can be managed
- — the fire safety manual
- — the role of fire safety management in fire prevention and fire protection
- — planning for and managing an emergency.

11.2 Legal obligations and statutory duties

The senior management of the building needs to identify and meet legal requirements and statutory duties imposed upon them by various Regulations and Acts which impact on the management of fire safety. These include the Building Regulations, Health and Safety at Work (etc.) Act, Fire Precautions (Workplace) Regulations, Fire Precautions Act, Construction (Design and Management) (CDM) Regulations, Disabled Persons Act, Disability Discrimination Act, local acts, environmental acts, and in some premises, Petroleum (Consolidation) Act. They have to be aware of the statutory requirements in connection with certificated premises concerning the maintenance of the means of escape, fire warning systems, portable fire extinguishers, escape lighting, fire safety instructions to staff, etc.

There is a legal requirement to consult the local building and fire authorities prior to the implementation of extensions or alterations within the building and for necessary approvals under planning acts which control external elevations of buildings.

The management need to be aware of the interim duty imposed on occupiers in between applying for and obtaining a fire certificate and the statutory duties imposed on occupiers of premises granted exemption from the requirement to have a fire certificate.

11.3 Designing for a manageable building

11.3.1 Pre-planning

Although the formal responsibilities of the designer and the fire safety engineer largely end once the building is completed and occupation and/or use has commenced, many, if not all, of the systems included will impose management responsibilities. The job of the fire safety manager will be made more difficult if the fire safety design conflicts with the normal, everyday, use of the building, e.g. by placing fire doors across through routes, or fails to take account of real behaviour during an incident, such as counter-flows in escape routes as parents search for their children.

In practice, therefore, the fire safety engineer can assist the work of the fire safety manager by ensuring that the:

— active fire safety systems are able to be properly maintained and tested

— passive fire safety systems are not likely to be made ineffective

— design assumptions regarding the use and management of the building are sound, e.g. that they correctly anticipate the type of occupancy or the fire load.

Therefore, wherever possible, the key management issues relating to any new project should be identified at the earliest stage, ideally the concept stage, and properly taken into account. It is important at this early stage to initiate liaison with other agencies, such as building control officers, fire safety officers, health and safety inspectors, and insurers.

The designer should become familiar with the responsibilities and tasks of the fire safety manager so that these issues might reasonably be taken into account in the design, see section 11.4.

11.3.2   Management input at the design stage

It is a principle of good fire safety design that buildings should be designed and equipped so that in an emergency the occupants of the building make their way easily to a place of safety. This requires the designers to take account of human behaviour, in particular in emergency situations, and seek to use this behaviour to lead people to safety, rather than design a complex system which requires a rapid learning process by the occupants at a time of stress.

There is therefore a need for the fire safety systems to be appropriate for what people actually do, not what the designer would like them to do.

A clear statement of the design requirements for the management of the complex has to be developed and conveyed to the design team (architect, designer and fire safety engineer), otherwise, there is a danger that the new building will need extensive modifications to cater for conditions that were not anticipated by the designers.

A design that does not fulfil the management brief can adversely affect running costs, staffing levels and the general safety and efficiency of the building.

Fire safety systems need to be considered as an inherent part of the basic design, and not as supplementary to other matters such as services or finishes. Where there are

conflicts of interest, compromises may be necessary. In any case, a flexible approach is essential if novel problems are to be solved. It needs to be recognised that there can be conflicts between the fire safety requirements and the normal use of the building or with building services or with other safety systems.

An important aspect of design team management is the co-ordination of the specialists designing systems, which will have to interact. Wherever possible checks should be carried out to ensure that the systems are compatible and that, when changes are made, any consequential effects are accommodated and that the overall objectives will still be satisfied.

Where the project is speculative build, without a particular occupier, or even a particular use, in mind then it may be appropriate to design with minimal management requirements.

Other aspects to consider will be the management of environmental issues and the long-term implications of the proposed design for management over the life of the building.

11.3.3   Designing for the management of fire prevention

By careful and considered design or location, the designer or fire engineer can provide the building with facilities and equipment which can assist the fire safety manager in carrying out their duties in fire prevention, see section 11.8. In particular, the designer can assist the fire safety manager with the housekeeping in the building, see section 11.8.1.

A significant way of preventing fire incidents is to maintain non-fire equipment that might start a fire and control the storage and use of materials that might allow a fire to develop and spread. The designer should therefore consider the needs of the manager to inspect and maintain the following items:

— potential sources of ignition such as gas, oil and electrical heating installations

— electrical and gas installations

— other heat dissipating equipment

— furniture, furnishings, decor and equipment

— floor coverings, furniture, furnishings, scenery, props, curtains and drapes

— other equipment which have particular fire risks.

The designer can assist the manager in a number of ways to reduce the likelihood of arson and to mitigate the effects if it does occur, see section 11.8.3. One way is that the designer can provide for good security arrangements in the building to reduce the risk of arson. However, the designer will need to be aware of the possible conflict between security and means of escape, see section 11.8.3.

11.3.4 Designing for the management of fire protection

By careful and considered design or planning, the designer or fire engineer can provide the building with facilities and equipment which can assist the fire safety manager. This includes ensuring that the fire protection systems are working and organising effective evacuation.

11.3.5 The provision of safety systems

All safety equipment should be available, reliable, testable, resilient and maintainable. Fire safety systems requiring inspection, maintenance and testing, or inspection and repair are detailed in section 11.9.2.

11.3.6 Designing for change of use

The designer needs to consider whether the building is being designed to meet a specific occupancy with a defined management regime. The designer may wish to provide a greater level of designed-in safety with the least possible dependence on management so as to allow for maximum flexibility in the future use of the building.

11.4 Construction to handover

11.4.1 Construction

Many fires occur during construction, often in the latter part of a project nearing completion, partly due to work being carried out, often including hot work, partly due to the necessarily complex management regime and partly due to the level of fire protection measures, which although fitted, may not be operable. Fire safety on construction sites, including fire safety management is covered in detail in section 12.

11.4.2 Fitting-out and speculative build

Management during fitting-out will need to consider most of the same issues as for construction, although different processes may be employed, since fire safety systems may still not be in place or be operational. Again, particular care is needed during any hot work, and to avoid blocking escape routes.

Some buildings will be speculative and have no known occupier at the time of construction. Such buildings must either be well equipped with fire safety provisions and require the minimum of fire safety management from the eventual occupiers, or the management assumptions or implications must be stated in the fire safety manual as a limitation on the eventual use of the building.

11.4.3 Approvals and certification

All documentation relating to approvals and certification must be made available to the fire safety manager and included in the fire safety manual.

11.4.4 Commissioning and handover

Before accepting the building for occupation it is essential that the safety of the staff, public and construction personnel, if the building is being completed in phases, is assured.

The design and construction of the building and the systems installed in it needs to be recorded in the fire safety manual.

Guidance on the commissioning and hand-over of fire safety systems is given in appropriate British Standards and other guidance documents. On completion of the fire safety system, the complete installation needs to be checked for conformity with the approved drawings and system design. The handover procedure should include operation of the system.

All the fire safety systems need to be individually tested to establish that the final installation complies with the specified design, is functioning properly and is ready for acceptance testing. It needs to be documented in writing that the installation of each system component is complete and that the component is functional.

Acceptance testing needs to demonstrate that the final integrated system installed complies with the specified design and is functioning correctly. The details and findings of acceptance tests should be recorded and verified. The extent and form of any acceptance tests should be agreed with the enforcing authority at the design stage.

Arrangements for standby power supplies need to be checked.

The appropriate members of the management need to be available during the handover period to ensure that an understanding of every aspect of the building is passed on. (Note that the fire safety engineer will not normally be present at handover and resposibility for conveying an understanding of the fire safety aspects will be the responsibility of the architect.)

All installed safety systems need to be operational before the building (or part of the building) is accepted and any units are handed over to tenants in mixed user developments and premises in different occupation.

All installed safety systems need to be commissioned and, where essential, tested by full commissioning tests involving fire and/or smoke, with the appropriate members of the management present. Such tests have the following purposes:

(a)   to demonstrate that the safety system design objectives are achieved

(b)   to identify any problems of detail not considered in the design

(c)   to demonstrate that the design has been properly implemented

(d)   to identify any problems with interactions, or failures to interact

(e)   to provide management with the opportunity to operate the systems

(f) to give confidence to the users of the building

(g) and to give confidence, and training, to the fire service.

The fire safety management need to be provided with the information on all installed active and passive fire safety systems incorporated into the building, in the fire safety manual, including:

(a) documentation from contractors and manufacturers (including any instructions, guarantees and test certificates) and spare parts;

(b) as-built drawings and specifications and equipment operating parameters and record drawings;

(c) instructions on its use, planned maintenance and testing;

(d) the results of acceptance tests (which may involve the regulatory authorities and insurance company representatives).

All components of any installed safety system for which the tenant is responsible need to be operational and compatible with the systems common to the complex before the tenant occupies their unit.

The design and construction of the building and the systems installed in it need to be fully documented for hand-over to the management on completion.

The fire safety manual needs to be prepared.

11.5 Fire safety manual

11.5.1 Purpose and contents of the fire safety manual

The designer of a large or complex buildings has the responsibility to document and communicate the design for the benefit of the management of those premises. All this relevant information needs to be included in the fire safety manual. This will enable a better understanding of the responsibility for ensuring that a high standard of safety is maintained. It should be available for inspection or tests by auditors and regulators. The fire safety manual should provide:

— a permanent means of communication between the designer and successive fire safety managers

— a full description of the assumptions and philosophies that led to the fire safety design, including explicit assumptions regarding the management of the building, housekeeping and other management functions

— a full description of the active and passive protection systems in the building

— a full description of all the other design aspects which have a direct bearing on the fire safety management

— an 'operators manual', containing inspection, maintenance and repair manuals for the fire safety systems

— interactions with security, building management, other safety systems, etc.

— information required under the CDM Regulations for the Safety Plan

— information relating to any fire certificates or licensing

— continuing control and audit plans

— a 'log book' of all events that occur over the life of the building that relate to fire safety.

The fire safety manual should contain the following items:

(a) Part 1: Design information

— fire safety policy statement endorsed by the highest level of management

— fire safety specification for the building supported by layout plans

— which computer models have been used to derive the safety design

— assumptions, inputs and outputs to any computer models used to derive the safety design

— any quantitative or qualitative risk assessments and sensitivity analyses

— a description of the active and passive fire safety measures

— integration of active and passive fire safety measures

— any identified fire risks, and particular hazards for firefighters

— planned inspection, maintenance and testing schedules

— control systems utilised throughout the building

— critical transportation routes for buildings' services

— the site plans

— escape routes

— assembly points and/or muster stations

— exterior and interior access for the fire service

— pre-planned procedures agreed with the fire service

— pre-planned procedures for salvage

— fire-fighting equipment

— communication systems

— fire prevention and security and arson prevention

— any IT system used to manage the manual (e.g. maintenance schedules, record keeping);

— CDM Regulations information

—   information relating to the Fire Precautions Act

—   information relating to certification

—   information relating to licensing

—   information relating to the Fire Precautions (Workplace) Regulations

—   copies of all certificates and licences

—   other information etc. relating to other reasons for protecting the building (property, contents, fabric, heritage, environment)

—   proposed testing regime for the manual.

(b)   Part 2: Operational records

—   changes to management structure

—   the testing of fire safety systems including acceptance tests

—   the results of monitored fire drills

—   training and education records

—   maintenance records (of all heat-dissipating equipment and fire safety equipment)

—   issuing of 'hot work' permits

—   a log of the contractor's and/or worker's attendance

—   changes to building structure

—   changes to building systems

—   information relating to regulatory requirements (e.g. Fire Prevention Certificate, Building Regulations approvals)

—   feedback from staff, occupants or other users of the building

—   any fire incidents

—   any 'near-miss' events

—   false alarm and evacuations

—   records of any appeals or prosecutions

—   results and changes following reviews and testing of the manual

—   inventories of flammable materials

—   details of any operations that have a high fire hazard.

11.5.2   Location, access and maintenance of the fire safety manual

The fire safety manual should be kept in a secure and fireproof container on the premises. It should be readily accessible to fire officers attending an incident. At least one duplicate maintained identical copy should be retained in a separate stated location away from the premises.

It should be available for inspection by the fire enforcement authority or other relevant enforcing authority on request. However, they may not necessarily accept the fire safety manual in lieu of the 'log book' required as a part of the certification provisions of the Fire Precautions Act.

The fire safety manual should be kept up to date by the fire safety manager or a competent person nominated for the task, so that the information is included within one week of any event. It should be updated, as appropriate, to record feedback from staff and other users of the building. Records of reliability problems with particular equipment should be kept.

11.5.3   Review and testing of fire safety manual

The fire safety manual needs to be reviewed and its procedures tested annually, or whenever alterations are made to the building, in accordance with a documented procedure.

Most of the testing should be a matter of routine activity for the management to ensure that prescribed activities are being properly carried out. The testing should be monitored by senior management to ensure that prescribed activities are being properly carried out.

Records of the reviews should be kept and of the changes made. If an IT system is used to manage the manual then there should be regular checks that the requirements are being met.

Inspection routines should make provision for all fire safety systems installed in the building, including systems installed in units and other occupancies.

There should be a major, monitored building evacuation drill at least once a year to test all of the systems and procedures in the manual. Such evacuations should always be carried out shortly before and after the first full occupation of a new building. If the interval between these is more than about twelve months, consideration should be given to conducting a monitored evacuation in the interim period. The purpose of any test exercise or drill should be clearly defined by management, and explained to the staff, so that it can be assessed afterwards. The records of fire drills etc. should be made available for scrutiny by the fire authority.

11.6   Authority and responsibilities of the fire safety manager

The fire safety manager is or are the person or persons in overall control of the premises whilst people are present, or the person or people with direct responsibility for fire safety. The fire safety manager may exercise this responsibility in their own right, e.g. as the owner, or it may be delegated. Whatever the building size, there should be no doubt as to the person or persons with whom the responsibility lies.

The fire safety manager needs to be provided with sufficient authority and powers of sanction to ensure that standards of fire safety in the complex are adequately maintained. These powers may need to include closing the building to the public, restricting its use, or shutting down normal operations. The appointed manager needs to be provided with sufficient resources to ensure that essential repairs or maintenance are carried out.

The fire safety manager has responsibility for the following:

— Being aware of all of the fire safety features provided and their purpose.

— Being aware of any particular risks on the premises.

— Being thoroughly conversant with all legal duties, codes or regulations that apply and all terms, conditions and restrictions imposed by any licence and be aware of all of the fire safety features provided and their purpose.

— Being in attendance on the premises, or some other competent person delegated in writing, whenever the public are present or when the building is occupied.

— Liaising with, and where necessary seek the advice of, the fire authority and the licensing authority.

— Having powers to deal with individuals who sabotage or tamper with safety systems which are inconvenient, who ignore any smoking policy, or who block exits.

— Being responsible for the Fire Risk Assessment required under the Fire Precautions (Workplace) Regulations.

Other responsibilities of the fire safety manager include:

— routine maintenance and testing of fire safety equipment

— maintaining documentation for the fire safety manual, training records, drill records, "near miss" events

— developing a fire strategy appropriate for the particular risk

— ensuring compliance with appropriate codes, regulations, terms or conditions

— responding to any rare or unexpected events that could increase the risk of fire or affect the evacuation procedures, e.g. by limiting the number of people permitted on the premises

— notifying the authorities of any changes that will affect the fire precautions in the building, e.g. structural alterations, extensions, alterations to internal arrangements or the start of keeping explosives or highly flammable materials.

In addition, for larger buildings and complexes, the fire safety manager is responsible for:

— appointment of fire marshals/fire wardens

— appointment or delegated appointment of members of any site fire team

— development of the training policy for the building

— ensuring that staff have the necessary competencies

— organising training and maintaining training records

— organising audits by an independent third party

— organising periodic internal audits to review current fire safety management procedures and the effect of changes in personnel, usage of the building

— ensuring the effectiveness of automatic fire safety systems, even after a change in building use

— consideration of and, if appropriate, preparation of disaster plans, where a fire incident could affect the local community.

The management of all individual units and other occupancies need to understand that their own fire safety responsibilities are in no way diminished by the existence of a further tier of management with a wider span of control. In particular, it is necessary that a clear understanding exists on the subject of emergency procedures so as to ensure that no element of these procedures is neglected, and no element unreasonably duplicated.

Where the fire safety management is outsourced, e.g. as part of facilities management, then the final responsibility should reside within the main organisation.

The everyday tasks of the fire safety manager can be divided into four main areas:

(a)   fire prevention

(b)   ensuring systems respond properly in an emergency

(c)   planning for a fire emergency and

(d)   actions in the event of a fire.

These four tasks can be further divided into sub-tasks, see sections 11.8 to 11.11.

11.7   Communication

Good communication is the key to successful management. Large, crowded, complex buildings represent a significant potential for loss of life in fire and therefore demand the highest standards of management to ensure that risks are anticipated and covered by the best possible systems for life safety and property protection.

It is the responsibility of the fire safety manager to ensure that all necessary and appropriate communication systems are in place to deal with any fire incident. This includes both equipment and chains-of-command, especially if it is intended to investigate first alarms before sounding warnings, or if control room staff are taking decisions based on many channels of information. It must include contingency planning, e.g. for abnormal occupancy loads, or for absent staff or for equipment failure. Such systems should be tested as part of the testing of the overall fire safety procedures and audited.

Other issues that need to be considered are:

— the communications structure, in particular where there is a cascade decision process involving a number of levels of management

— maintenance and routine testing of systems

— testing of 'emergency conditions

— selection of languages to use in voice messages

— special provisions for people with sensory disabilities

— contingency planning.

11.8   Fire prevention

The task of fire prevention is to attempt to avoid fire occurring and to work to create an environment in which fires are preventing from starting. The fire prevention tasks of the fire safety manager include:

— monitoring the behaviour of occupants

— monitoring any smoking policy

— housekeeping

— routines for the disposal of waste

— minimising hazards of combustible contents, furnishings and surface finishes

— minimising hazards of materials, components and elements of construction

— establishing purchasing standards for furniture, furnishings and fittings

— seeking to avoid conditions leading to gas and dust explosion hazards

— maintenance of furniture, furnishings, decor and equipment

— reviewing and appraising the risks; how a fire might start, spread and its consequences

— routine checks, inspections, tests and monitoring the maintenance of equipment that could cause fires (especially heat generating equipment), chaffing of cables, self-heating and fuel supplies

— maintaining integration with other systems (e.g. ventilation)

— assessing the risks from new equipment, new business processes or changing or new technologies

— issuing work permits

— training and education

— establishing and maintaining out-of-hours inspection and security procedures

— security.

The task requires vigilance and, in larger buildings and complexes, may need separate teams to cover all of the possible areas of hazard. Regular inspections should be carried out and logged in the fire safety manual, and any problems and remedial action stated.

It is probable that surreptitious smoking presents the greatest risk, especially by members of the staff in back rooms and other areas not in continuous view of supervisory staff. The best recommendation that can be made is that smoking be prohibited other than in designated smoking areas and that fire-safe ashtrays and bins are provided.

Outside contractors can pose a greater fire risk than a firm's own employees. They are not as familiar with the premises as the people permanently employed by the firm. Therefore, they cannot be expected to know the fire risks, necessary precautions and correct action in the event of fire. Yet, these contractors may have to carry out operations which are much more hazardous than those normally occurring on the premises, e.g. hot work. Effort should be made to make contractors and sub-contractors aware of the risks involved in their work. All activities of outside contractors should be strictly supervised and controlled, and management should ensure that all necessary precautions against fire are taken.

11.8.1   Housekeeping

Good housekeeping will reduce the chances of fire starting or developing. It is vital that all employees are aware of the particular risks associated with hazardous substances and practices that may be encountered in factories and warehouses.

Where additional risks are introduced anywhere in the building, e.g. the introduction of car displays and grottoes inside shops, advice as to their protection needs to be obtained from the appropriate authority.

Housekeeping measures include:

— keeping combustible materials separate from possible ignition sources

— storing flammable liquids, paints and polishes in appropriate containers

— recognition of potential hazards

— monitoring proper waste control

— cleaning, including build-up of dust on machinery, extract ducts

— checks on electrical machinery overload

— clearing waste from the outside of the building

— checking 'dark' areas (e.g. cinemas, darkrooms)

— out-of-hours checks, or after closing

— other routine precautions.

11.8.2   Training and education

An essential task of the fire safety manager is the training of all staff, including part-time, security and cleaning staff, in fire prevention. This training aims to ensure that each member of staff takes the appropriate actions to minimise the likelihood of a fire starting. In a complex, the training should include the tenants of every unit and other occupancy in the complex.

All staff need to be trained in basic fire prevention, risk awareness, smoking policy, process shutdown, good housekeeping and reporting procedures. Fire safety training needs to commence on the first day of appointment of new staff and continue in the form of regular refresher training.

11.8.3   Security

Arson fires can start with a rapid burning material such as petrol and the arsonist can start fires in several places simultaneously so that the alternative escape routes normally provided in a building are blocked. Building management can reduce the risk of serious fires by arson by using a number of management methods to reduce the likelihood of arson and to mitigate the effects if it does occur. These include:

— management awareness of vulnerability to arson

— security against intruders

— intruder detection

— control of ignition sources/easily ignitable materials

— fire detection throughout building

— fire suppression control throughout building

— segregation of risks

— effective staff training.

Good security arrangements will reduce the risk of arson. However, the fire safety manager needs to be aware of the possible conflict between security and means of escape and needs to ensure that the security arrangements do not prevent occupants from egress to reach a place of safety or hinder the entry of the fire service into the building to fight the fire or effect the rescue of occupants. In certain premises, the need to restrict the occupants from leaving the premises must be integrated with adequate and manageable emergency egress.

11.9   Ensuring systems respond properly in a fire emergency

Another task of the fire safety manager is to ensure that all of the safety systems respond properly in a fire emergency. This task includes:

— housekeeping

— ensuring compliance with appropriate codes or regulations

— maintenance of structural/passive safety systems

— routine inspection, maintenance and testing of active systems

— testing under simulated 'emergency' conditions

— safety audits and inspections

— recording and taking appropriate remedial action to false alarms

— learning from drills, false alarms and near miss events

— using false alarms and near miss events as data

— revising safety plans and fire safety manual.

In addition, for larger buildings and complexes, this task includes:

— ensuring that systems mesh properly with the emergency procedures

— integration of the fire safety systems

— maintaining integration with other systems (e.g. ventilation).

11.9.1   Good housekeeping

To reduce the chances of fire and smoke spreading and escape routes being blocked, good housekeeping is essential and measures needs to include:

— ensure that escape routes are kept clear and are available for use at all times the building is occupied

— ensure that fire doors that should be kept closed are kept closed and are not obstructed

— ensure that fire doors on hold-open devices are operable, are not obstructed and are closed at night

— prevent warning signs or way guidance lighting from becoming obscured

— general inspection of all the fire safety equipment.

Management procedures should ensure that control is exercised over the parking of commercial vehicles on service roadways also used for fire service access, so that fire appliances are not obstructed in an emergency and are able to proceed to within the required distance of any fire main, foam or other inlets. In the interest of security, it may also be considered necessary to restrict unauthorised entry via such roadways, and should be agreed with the fire authority.

11.9.2   Fire safety maintenance and testing

It is essential for the safety of the occupants of a building that all fire safety equipment is checked frequently. Planned inspection, maintenance and testing procedures need to be established and used to ensure that all fire protection systems can operate effectively when required. Maintenance needs to be carried out in accordance with the relevant British Standards or manufacturer's instructions at the recommended time intervals and the testing and inspection of these systems should be carried out by competent persons.

Fire safety equipment needing checking includes the following:

— fire detection and alarm systems (see section 6)

— fire suppression systems (see section 8)

— smoke control systems (see section 7)

— means of escape systems (see section 4)

— structural/passive elements

— firefighters' systems (see section 9)

— control systems and power supplies, including emergency power arrangements

— access to the building and its surroundings (see section 9)

— communications systems.

In addition to being responsible for daily checks on the premises prior to the admission of the public, it is also the fire safety manager's responsibility to ensure that all fire safety equipment is adequately and routinely maintained and tested. Failure to maintain any one of the fire safety provisions in effective working order could negate the whole fire safety strategy.

All fire safety installations need to be tested individually, but interdependent fire safety installations need to be tested collectively to demonstrate satisfactory interfacing/interlinking, etc.

Alterations or modifications to an existing installation should not be carried out without consultation with the enforcing authority and, where possible, the original system designer or installer or other qualified persons. This is particularly important where systems are combined and depend upon a sequence of control events.

The manager needs to be aware that safety equipment can itself be a hazard, e.g. poorly maintained fire doors can cause injury. Where necessary, equipment may need to be replaced, but without reducing the safety of the building. Similarly, equipment that is not reliable, or is regularly vandalised or abused due to poor or inappropriate design, may need to be replaced.

When repairs or alterations are made to the building structure it should be ensured that compartment walls or other passive fire protection systems are reinstated if damaged.

Any alterations, additions, repairs or modifications to services and equipment needs to be carried out only by competent persons.

Contingency plans need to be prepared to cope with equipment failures or other problems, such as a failure in the water supplies for the sprinkler system.

The maintenance of furniture, furnishings, decor and equipment is as important for the safety of occupants as is the maintenance of the fire safety equipment. Contents and equipment affect the likelihood of fire occurring, its development and subsequent events. Diligent attention to detail can minimise the risk of fire. Floor coverings, furniture, furnishings, scenery, props, curtains and drapes should be maintained to the appropriate standards of fire retardancy and in a condition that does not reduce overall fire safety, as well maintained floor coverings reduce the risk of persons tripping during any emergency evacuation.

A record of all tests and checks, and any defects remedied, needs to be recorded in the fire safety manual.

11.10 Planning for a fire emergency

The task of the fire safety manager in planning for a fire emergency is to seek to ensure in the event of a fire that all occupants escape to a place of safety quickly, without injury or distress. This requires that occupants react promptly to any alarm, and also that they exit the building by the most efficient route. In a complex building, this will usually require that trained staff assist other occupants who may be unfamiliar with the building or fire safety systems. This task includes:

— staff training and fire drills, including full evacuations

— review all plant and equipment interface controls, to ensure that they properly mesh with the procedures

— continuous inspections and testing of system and emergency procedures including major incident simulations

— testing under simulated emergency conditions

— carrying out safety audits and inspections

— responding to false alarms

— learning from and recording drills, false alarms, near miss events and minor incidents

— review of all staff duties and training procedures

— checks of the record as-built drawings and specifications for all fire protection measures

— feedback from, and to, participants, from staff, other occupants etc. from drills

— managing site fire team

— liaison with external fire brigade, and, if appropriate, provision of an 'emergency pack', prepared in collaboration with the fire authority containing essential information for firefighting, and indicating escape routes and special hazards.

— monitoring and recording in the fire safety manual, revising safety plans.

Specific plans include:

— developing and maintaining emergency plan(s) including evacuation plans, victim help and emergency accommodation plans

— planning for bad weather including evacuation into hostile weather conditions

— plans for the mitigation of potential environmental impact of fire

— risk management, contingency planning, re-start planning

— contingency plans for salvage and damage control.

11.10.1 Training and education

An essential sub-task of the fire safety manager is the training and education of all staff to ensure that in a fire emergency, they each take appropriate actions to safeguard occupants and facilitate safe escape. This training is in addition to training in fire prevention, see section 11.8, and should include:

— the fire routine

— the action to be taken upon discovering a fire

— exits and exit routes

— raising the alarm, including the location of alarm indicator panels

— the action to be taken upon hearing the fire alarm

— the arrangements for calling the fire service

— the location, selection and use of fire-fighting equipment

— knowledge of the escape routes, refuges and exits, especially those not in regular use

— appreciation of the importance of fire doors and of the need to close all doors at the time of a fire and on hearing the fire alarm

— process shutdown and shutting down non-essential equipment, stopping machines and processes and isolating power supplies, where appropriate

— evacuation procedures

— evacuation of the building (this will include reassuring any members of the public, escorting them to exits, and encouraging them to get well clear of the building).

Details of all training and instruction given and received should be recorded in the fire safety manual, e.g. date of instruction or exercise, duration; the name of the trainer/instructor, name of person receiving the training/instruction and the nature of the instruction, training or drill.

The basis of fire safety is the fire routine. Staff needs to know how to act on discovery of fire or on the raising of the alarm. It is essential that the management draws up an effective routine which covers all situations, from a false alarm, to a major incident. The fire routine needs to take into account the types of activities which take place in the premises, the fire precautions that are provided and, above all, the fire warning and communications systems that are available and the emergency actions that will be required.

The core of the fire routine will be the actions in the event of fire. The fire routine should be developed that keeps the procedures as simple as possible and minimises the decisions needed to cope with a particular incident.

A fire routine should be carefully devised for each building, taking into account the uses to which the premises are put and, in particular, the means of giving warning and the means of communication. This fire routine should take account of the relationship between the trained staff and other occupants, the familiarity of occupants with the building, the availability of fire marshals or a site fire team. The planning of the fire routine should take account of the needs of all occupants, including the needs of disabled people and proper arrangements for their assistance.

All staff should be familiar with the fire routine and evacuation procedures and prominent 'fire instruction'

notices should be displayed in all staff areas. These should state the essentials of the action to be taken upon discovering a fire and on hearing the fire alarm and be placed in conspicuous positions in all parts of the building.

Key members of staff should have specific roles relevant to the fire routine.

Designated staff who require master keys to assist in an evacuation should carry them at all times.

The fire authority and licensing authority should be consulted regarding the fire routine.

A key issue for training and the fire routine will be how to decide if the fire service should be called in from outside. Many minor fires will not appear to be (and will not be) life threatening and might be successfully extinguished with portable first-aid fire-fighting equipment. However, nearly all large fires start off as small fires, and if this initial judgement is faulty then disaster can follow.

11.10.2 Evacuation management

Fire alarms in most smaller buildings are best operated in a 'single stage' mode in which the actuation of a call point or detector gives an instantaneous warning from all fire alarm sounders for an immediate evacuation.

In large or complex buildings, a staged evacuation procedure may be adopted, in which the operation of a call point or detector gives an evacuation signal on the storey or zone affected, and an 'alert' warning signal sounds in all other parts of the premises. The decision to evacuate the remainder of the occupants then rests with the management and/or the fire service. It is essential that adequate means of communication between storeys or zones is provided. A public address system or voice alarm is the most suitable way to control the evacuation process instead of fire alarm sounders.

The evacuation process can be phased evacuation in which different parts of the building are evacuated in a controlled sequences of phases, the original fire affected storey or zone, then the remainder of the building in various phases. A phased evacuation will normally require at least a two-stage alarm system to give 'alert' or 'evacuate' signals, or 'staff alarm' and 'evacuate' signals. The escape stairs in the building will have been designed specifically for phased evacuation and the evacuation will normally be co-ordinated from a fire control centre, having directive public address announcements aided, where appropriate, by colour closed-circuit television.

In general, evacuation procedures would not be intended to cope with extreme events which may require simultaneous evacuation.

The sophistication of the fire alarm system and public address arrangements are major factors when considering evacuation procedures in large or complex buildings.

Directive messages provide the occupants with the clear, prompt and accurate information they will need to move safely without delay. The use of public address systems should not be restricted to coded staff messages.

Members of the public may need to be guided to a suitable exit as, otherwise, they tend to follow the same route they used to enter the building, or they may be disorientated or unaware of the location of exits. If they arrived by car they are likely to try to return to it. Parents and children who have been separated will tend to seek each other so as to leave together. People will often attempt to carry out normal activities when faced with an unexpected situation.

Careful attention needs to be given to the wording and delivery of both live and pre-recorded messages, not only to provide reassurance and relevant information, but also to convey the sense of urgency necessary to motivate people to move promptly in the safest direction when required.

11.11 Management of a fire emergency

The actions in the event of fire for which fire routine planning is appropriate include:

— action on discovery

— warning and evacuation signals

— calling the fire service, providing information and advising them

— initiation of evacuation

— fighting the fire and other staff activities

— evacuation procedures

— meeting the fire service, providing information and advising them

— completion of evacuation.

Other issues to consider include: environmental protection; security/salvage and damage control, protecting the building contents, protecting the building fabric and recording lessons learned.

The following procedure provides the basis for any plans that are developed for a specific building:

(a) operate the fire alarm system and alert employees, or selected employees, and any control room, to the emergency

(b) call the fire service

(c) establish the location and apparent extent of the fire and assess the situation

(d) organise and effect the movement and/or evacuation of the public and staff as determined by item (c)

(e) take steps consistent with the safety of individuals to fight the fire or contain it

(f) ensure that everyone assembles at a place of safety and is accounted for, so that if anyone is missing the fire service can be informed on their arrival. Ensure that people do not re-enter the building

(g) ensure that, on the arrival of the fire service, every assistance is given to enable them to attack the fire effectively, and in particular inform the fire service

of the situation as regards the safety and where-abouts of the occupants of the building

(h) implement any pre-planned procedures with respect to care for evacuees, salvage, environmental protection, etc.

(i) initiate the pre-planned recovery process.

11.12 Other planning issues

Other planning issues may involve plans for limiting loss and damage to building structure, contents, the environment and business operations. Plans may involve actions for both during and after the fire emergency.

The fire safety manager may wish to consider plans for the post-fire operation of the business or the function of the building. This could include arrangements to keep duplicates of business records off-site. This may only involve preparing a list of contacts but may include prior arrangements for alternative premises. For other types of occupancy or businesses more detailed planning may be appropriate. Re-start planning for the business may form part of the overall risk management.

The fire safety manager may also wish to consider plans for the protection of building structure, contents, and the environment. Building fabric and property protection will be a particular issue for heritage buildings. It needs to be recognised that while it is often the case that protecting occupants will also protect contents etc., there may be conflicts of interest and in such cases life safety must take precedence.

11.13 Changes to a building

Changes to a building include: extensions, alterations, refurbishment, change of use, disuse, or decommissioning and demolition.

11.13.1 Extensions, alterations, refurbishment

Experience has demonstrated that fires are more likely to occur when general maintenance work or alterations are being carried out to a building, most notably when work is being carried out by external contractors. All external contractors activities should be strictly supervised and controlled, and management should ensure that all necessary precautions against fire are taken. It is therefore particularly important that guidance is given to both general maintenance staff and external contractors on:

(a) the fire safety arrangements within the building, to ensure that they are not adversely affected by maintenance work or alterations, and

(b) procedures to avoid fire occurring, particularly in relation to 'hot work' such as welding or cutting.

During maintenance work, and particularly when alterations are being carried out in buildings which remain occupied, appropriate arrangements should be made to ensure the safety of escape routes and operation of all fire protection facilities.

Approval should be obtained from the local building and fire authorities where appropriate before the implementation of extensions or alterations within the building[3].

Management should ensure that arrangements are made for the instruction and supervision of contractors/workers in maintaining fire safety, in particular, good safety practices, the actions to be taken in case of fire and are made familiar with appropriate escape routes.

There is a need for documentation in many cases, and a permit system for contractors carrying out any kind of structural work. Any form of hot work should be the subject of specific approval and insistence on appropriate safeguards.

Before any hot work is carried out, a thorough safety check should be made in the area and adjacent areas where the work is to be undertaken, to see that flammable materials are either removed to safety or protected. Suitable portable fire extinguishers should be provided adjacent to the hot work area. A further check should be carried out immediately after work has finished for the day to ensure that the area is safe.

No hot work should be allowed in or near the building unless a hot work permit has been issued. The permit will be issued only if the fire safety manager is satisfied that the contractor understands and can carry out their responsibilities on the following issues:

— no satisfactory alternative method is feasible

— preparation of the place of work

— care and attention during work

— leaving the work place clean and safe

— the need for a check after the job is completed and for a final check at a later time

— training in the operation of available fire extinguishers

— availability of a safety officer (if appropriate)

— particular precautions needed where there are special risks in the premises.

A log of the contractors' attendance should be maintained so that, at any time, the number and location of all personnel can be determined.

11.13.2   Change of use

Any occupiers of a building will be subject to the management requirements specified at the design stage and recorded in the fire safety manual. Where there is a change of use of the building, or where the scale of the operation within the building changes, then the fire safety management requirements specified will have to be carefully re-examined and assessed for the new use. The management assumptions and the level of management specified must then either be appropriate for the new use, or else some changes will be needed. These changes could

be either to the management structure, or be additional facilities or equipment, retro-fitted to the building.

As a change of use, the building will be subject to review by various regulatory bodies and they will need to be assured that an appropriate level of fire safety has been reinstated in the building.

11.13.3   Units in disuse and areas decommissioned

For units in disuse and decommissioned areas, routine inspection by staff should be intensified to prevent careless practice and to ensure that fire protection systems remain fully operative. These units/areas should be physically separated from the rest of the building or either have an operational sprinkler system or be separated from the rest of the building by appropriate fire-resisting construction.

11.13.4   Buildings in disuse or decommissioning

Building in disuse or decommissioned do not present a very great risk to life. Any fire safety management of such a building should focus on the prevention of fire starting and include:

— ensuring that all power supplies are disabled

— removing any material that might self-heat

— removing any material that might be subject to an arson attack

— maintaining security to prevent arson attacks.

11.13.5   Buildings being demolished

The management of fire safety in buildings being demolished will be very similar to that during construction, see chapter 12. There will be significant risks of ignition in a building where many or most of the fire protection systems will be disabled or missing.

References

1   BS 5588: *Fire Precautions in the design, construction and use of buildings*: Part 12: (draft): *Managing fire safety* (London: British Standards Institution) (to be published)

2   BS 5588: *Fire precautions in the design, construction and use of buildings*: Part 0: 1996: *Guide to fire safety codes of practice for particular premises/applications*; Part 1: *Code of practice for residential buildings*; Part 4: 1998: *Code of practice for smoke control using pressure differentials*; Part 5: 1991: *Code of practice for firefighting stairs and lifts*; Part 6: 1991: *Code of practice for places of assembly*; Part 7: 1997: *Code of practice for the incorporation of atria in buildings*; Part 8: 1999: *Code of practice for means of escape for disabled people*; Part 9: 1999: *Code of practice for ventilation and air conditioning ductwork*; Part 10: 1991: *Code of practice for shopping complexes*; Part 11: 1997: *Code of practice for shops, offices, industrial, storage and other similar buildings* (London: British Standards Institution) (dates as indicated)

3   *Building regulations and fire safety procedural guidance* (London: The Stationery Office) (2001)

12 Fire safety on construction sites

12.1 Introduction

It has been reported[1] that the fires at London's Minster Court and Broadgate Phase 8 accounted for £138.5 million of the £143 million total for fire losses on construction sites between 1984 and 1991. More recently, three large site fires have resulted in losses totalling some £250 million. In response to these losses, the Loss Prevention Council, in conjunction with various other bodies, has produced a code of practice, *Fire Prevention on Construction Sites — The Joint Code of Practice on the Protection from Fire of Construction Sites and Buildings Undergoing Renovation*[2], for fire prevention on construction sites. In addition, the HSE, which has powers over fire precautions on construction sites, has published guidance[3] on managing fire safety during construction, pointing out the respective responsibilities for all those concerned. The application of either may be required for insurance risks in the future. However, it is the opinion of some professionals that the application of the LPC's *Joint Code* would not have avoided at least one of the major incidents which resulted in its production. The *Joint Code* highlights issues already covered by guidance which existed at the time of the incidents. Since these issues were not being addressed then, there is no assurance that they are being addressed now.

As with completed buildings, there is a conflict between the building user and the regulatory controls designed to limit the incidence of fire. The designer, contractor and building user do not really believe that the building will ever be involved in a fire whereas the regulating authorities assume that a fire will occur and require the building to be designed accordingly. There is a conflict between the two views. After a fire, however, everyone involved is surprised at the extent and cost of fire damage and the resulting disruption, both to the construction process and to the commercial consequences of delayed handover of the finished building. Therefore, it is important to clarify the problems of site fires and to emphasise where attention should be placed.

12.2 Long-term objectives

12.2.1 Assimilation of fire precautions into routine site practice

The long-term objective of effective site fire precautions should be a reduction in site fires and a reduction in losses and insurance claims. In reaching this objective, it is important not to make the construction process more onerous — indeed, the more onerous the fire prevention measures, the more likely they are to be ignored or overridden. The objectives should include the assimilation of site fire precautions in the most unobtrusive manner such that they become effective commensurate with the risk. They should be as effective during construction, when the risk is highest, as they will be in the completed building.

12.2.2 Improved fire awareness

The petrochemical and other hazardous industries have considerable experience in assessing the risks associated with their processes and plant and ensuring that their staff are made fully aware of such risks. These principles should also be applied to the construction industry. It is likely that this would lead to a contractual condition either that site operatives are qualified in fire awareness and first aid firefighting or that they be accompanied by persons who are so qualified.

12.3 Implications of site fires

There are environmental issues associated with site fires, apart from pollution, such as the wastage of materials and workmanship which will often be regarded as unacceptable. However, in financial terms, there need be little cause for concern provided that the insurance industry continues to cover the losses. Furthermore, the workforce may continue to be employed on a site affected by fire and materials suppliers may similarly continue to benefit. There is little risk of loss of life. Hence the emotive dimension present in fires in dwellings is absent from construction site fires. Therefore the incentive for improving construction site fire safety lies mainly with the insurance industry which meets the costs of reinstatement and with the client who is interested in seeing the project completed, ready for occupation. Substantial losses are incurred by not being able to conduct business at the expected time.

12.4 Legislation

In England and Wales the construction of new buildings and the alteration of existing buildings is controlled by the Building Regulations[4] and to some extent by Local Acts. Similar legislation applies in Scotland[5] and Northern Ireland[6], see section 3.3. The principal legislation relevant to existing buildings is the Fire Precautions Act 1972[7] which, if applicable, becomes operative when the building is occupied. In the course of construction, the Health and Safety at Work etc. Act 1974[8], the Construction (Health Safety and Welfare) Regulations 1996[9] (regulation 18), the Construction (Design and Management) Regulations 1984[10] and the Management of Health and Safety at Work Regulations

1999[11] apply, the enforcing authority generally being the Health and Safety Executive (HSE). Under these Acts, the employer has a duty to keep the work place in a safe condition without risk to health. This duty includes the provision and maintenance of means of escape and the provision of training, supervision and information to ensure health and safety. Employees must be conversant with fire drills and fire precautions. The HSE guide, *Fire safety in construction work*[3], identifies the appropriate enforcing authority.

Legislation regarding temporary buildings and general fire precautions at temporary accommodation units on construction sites[12] is addressed in the Fire Certificates (Special Premises) Regulations 1976[13] which are administered by the HSE. In effect, it calls for the same fire precautions to be provided in temporary accommodation as would be required under the Fire Precautions Act[7] once the premises are occupied. In enforcing the Regulations, the HSE issues certificates to qualifying structures.

Safety precautions for the special processes taking place during construction and for the storage and use of dangerous substances and materials are addressed in appropriate legislation including the Highly Flammable Liquids and Liquefied Petroleum Gases Regulations 1972[14] and the Petroleum (Consolidation) Act 1928[15].

12.5 Aspects to be considered in guidance documents

There are several aspects of fire precautions during construction which should be addressed in guidance documents, including:

— *The role of the designer*: (see also section 12.7) an appreciation of the fire hazards during construction should be part of the designer's brief. Fire precautions anticipated in the construction phase could then be incorporated in the design in the most economic manner and with the least disruption to the building process.

— *Fire strategy report*: the contractor should be made aware of the fire strategy for the completed building which would provide guidance on the intended fire precautions and highlight particular problems and provisions in the design. This knowledge would assist in providing fire precautions during construction by increasing the contractor's awareness of the fire control problems.

— *Performance requirements for site fire precautions*: fire risks during construction should be managed to avoid their being significantly increased. Contractors should produce manuals and work procedure documents to demonstrate their intentions to this effect, highlighting use of temporary measures and maximising the use during construction of provisions intended to protect the completed building.

— *Fire awareness*: the workforce must be made aware of the possibility of fire and be encouraged to increase their skills in dealing with it.

— *Revisions to conditions of contract*: contracts should address existing British Standards and other published guidance. They should include performance requirements for fire precautions and safety, method statements relative to planning of fire precautions, and intentions to appoint appropriately qualified fire wardens. Tender submissions and interviews should also address these issues.

Since publication of the first edition of this Guide, the HSE has produced its own guidance, *Fire safety in construction work*[3]. Many of the recommendations in this Guide have been incorporated into the HSE guidance.

12.6 Objectives of fire precautions during construction

12.6.1 Background

It is understandable and commendable that most of the guidance and legislation on fire precautions during construction is aimed at providing a safe environment for site staff and operatives during the works. That there have been no actual casualties in recent incidents suggests that existing provisions are probably adequate in terms of life safety. However, this situation will remain satisfactory only if the present standard of vigilance is maintained. It should be regarded as the minimum standard.

In terms of controlling overall fire damage, the situation is much less satisfactory and the fire precautions during construction need urgent attention.

12.6.2 The case for action

It is appreciated that there is a measure of awareness of the dangers from fire on building works. However, even with the unlikely assumption that existing building works have been protected to the standards anticipated by available guidance, fires within buildings undergoing works have happened and the resulting financial losses have been significant. Therefore it is clear that existing guidance is either being ignored or misunderstood, is inadequate, or does not address the issues that would prevent the large losses recently experienced. Addressing the issues with a view to improvement can be justified by the losses, both capital and consequential, particularly from smoke damage, from delays in completion and handover, and in lost business.

12.6.3 Temporary and permanent provision

The completed building will ideally incorporate suitable fire precautions such that, in the event of a fire, a controlled amount of damage can be anticipated. However, it must be remembered that statutory fire precautions are heavily weighted towards the preservation of life rather than property protection. Nonetheless, during the course of the building works, it would be advantageous to be able to rely as much as possible on the fire precautions provided for the protection of the final, occupied, building rather than having to introduce significant extra works to protect the building during construction or alteration. Although relying on the final provisions may add cost due to out of sequence working, this is often likely to be less than the cost of equivalent temporary provision. It is likely that some temporary provision will be inevitable but the aim should be to keep these to a minimum.

The intention would be to install the fire precautions as the work progresses, to preserve them during the works and leave them in good order upon completion. They would then assume their intended role of protecting the completed building. With this approach, there would be advantages in reducing programmes and subsequent time savings.

The alternative is to introduce extra fire precautions during the works and either leave them in the completed building or remove them before handover. However, it may be considered wasteful of resources to provide temporary facilities which later have to be removed.

It must be appreciated that the hazards in a completed building and one under construction or repair are not the same and it is generally accepted that they are greater before completion. This can be catered for by recognising the increased danger and increasing vigilance accordingly. If it is considered essential to provide additional temporary fire precautions, the maintenance and effectiveness of such measures is more likely to be ensured if they are active, such as detection and firefighting facilities, rather than structural (e.g. temporary partitions). Passive provisions are prone to damage although they can be easily inspected visually. Active systems are less prone to damage but need to be maintained appropriately.

12.6.4 Criteria for fire precautions

Based on the premise of maximising dependence on permanent, rather than temporary, measures, fires during construction may be considered using the same criteria as those anticipated for the completed building. These include:

— that suitable measures should be taken to avoid fires from starting

— the need to detect fires early in their development

— provision for raising the alarm and evacuating the building

— control of fire size by active or passive measures

— availability of access by fire services.

These provisions, all of which will be required in the finished building, can be incorporated early in the construction programme, to be addressed and maintained as the building work develops. The fire precautions required during building works can then be established based on an analysis of the various activities taking place during construction and the availability of the fire precautions measures intended for protection of the completed building.

Additional protection during the works may be necessary to reduce the risk to an acceptable level. In defining such a level, it would not be appropriate to attempt to quantify it rigorously by, for example, a statistical representation of time related to hazard. However, this should be borne in mind when evaluating proposals. For example, the storage of hazardous materials for a day or so may be allowed with strict management of a non-fire rated area. However, if such storage were over a period of several months, then the use of a secure, fire resisting room or compartment would be expected.

12.7 Designer's responsibility

12.7.1 HSE Guide: *Fire safety in construction work*

The HSE's own guidance, *Fire safety in construction work*[3], is a very thorough document and can be seen as sufficient in addressing the subject matter of this section. However, in addressing the responsibilities of all bodies associated with the construction site, emphasising the designer's role is appropriate in this Guide, which is mainly targeting the design team.

Addendum 3 of the HSE Guide is entitled '*Who does what?*' The designer's responsibility outlined in that addendum is summarised here.

12.7.2 How to stop fires occurring

Designers should be aware on the fire performance during storage, construction and use of their preferred materials. After such analysis, the use of hazardous materials or processes may not be appropriate if better is available. Suitable procedures to manage the choice of the more hazardous materials may be suitable.

12.7.3 Reducing ignition sources

A reduction in the need for hot work is the most crucial area; control of on-site ignition sources is more in the domain of the contractors. The need for welding on site may be reduced by using bolted rather than welded steel sections, and by the use of off-site fabrication. Another area would be the use of push- or threaded-fit plumbing rather than brazed jointing.

12.7.4 General fire precautions

Fire safety facilities required in the completed building can often be provided in the early stages of construction. If suitably fitted and made ready, they can begin to provide the advantage anticipated upon completion, but in the construction phase. Matters worthy of attention include:

— Wet or dry fire mains for firefighting. Suitable access to the inlets and for personnel and vehicles to the site would also be of great benefit.

— Compartmentation required in the finished building can probably be introduced, at least in part.

— Escape and firefighting stairs provided early will enhance escape, firefighting access and general circulation about the site.

— Fire doors, if shut during a fire, are very effective in controlling fire and smoke spread. Where they protect escape and firefighting stairs, their early installation would be beneficial.

— Alarm systems will provide great benefit by giving early warning of fire but should be suitable to cope with general builders' dust.

The early provision of these facilities, though conceptually possible, may have an impact on other design features. An appreciation of their benefits may allow their early provision if raised at a suitable stage in the design phase.

12.7.5   Emergency procedures

The provision and maintenance of first aid firefighting equipment and training regimes may be outside the scope of the designer's responsibility. But they can address the provision of suitable access to the site and within it for the fire brigade. A suitable route into the site and around it would be beneficial for general construction purposes, and could be kept suitably clear for firefighting access. Fire loads, their location, and general site access onto and around it are likely to be more hazardous than in the completed building. With higher risk projects, those below ground, and tall structures, particular attention to his aspect is justified.

12.7.6   Temporary accommodation units

Space should be allowed for these units when considering the general layout of the site and the location of the structure on it. Locating them outside the structure is preferable to within it but if this is not possible, the most suitable locations would include consideration for means of escape, fire spread beyond the unit, and firefighting access.

12.7.7   Sleeping accommodation

The advice of the fire prevention officer can be sought if there is any doubt about the specification or location of these units. High fire safety standards are justified for sleeping accommodation.

12.8   Building construction works

Method statements and works sequencing should consider and take account of the following fire safety issues.

12.8.1   Compartmentation

The need to provide and maintain compartmentation fire precautions at the early stages of construction should be emphasised. If self-closing fire doors that protect shafts and other vertical connections are vulnerable to damage, they should be provided with hold-open devices operated by the usual fire detection system.

The provision of compartmentation can be a major part of the fire strategy for the completed building. During construction, it may be provided only partially or not at all. For example, in the fire at Minster Court[16], compartmentation intended in the completed building was impaired with the result that fire spread up a protected shaft where doors were held or left open without a closing device. The atrium was not enclosed, as it would have been in the completed building, allowing fire and smoke to spread into it.

12.8.2   Ventilation

The control of smoke, as part of the means of escape provision, as assistance to the fire services in identifying a fire source or as a means of clearing a building, would normally form part of a project fire strategy. Again, in the Minster Court fire[16], smoke control systems were not operating; smoke spread up the atrium, accumulating at the top and causing considerable damage to upper floors, until the atrium roof failed, venting the smoke. The need to provide and maintain smoke ventilation at the early stages of construction should be considered.

12.8.3   Firefighting

12.8.3.1   Firefighting facilities

Firefighting facilities that will be provided in the completed building, including risers, hydrants and firefighting shafts, should become operable as early as possible during construction to maximise their usefulness. This issue is addressed in the LPC's *Joint Code*[2]. The provision and maintenance of these facilities in partially completed buildings is heavily dependent on management but is nonetheless considered possible and worthwhile.

12.8.3.2   Sprinklers

This issue is considered in the LPC's *Joint Code*[2]. The specification for the fire precautions for the completed building may anyway include a clause calling for conformity to the appropriate sprinkler standard (i.e. BS 5306: Part 2[17]). However, it has not been generally appreciated that clause 9.2 of this standard calls for the installation of functioning sprinklers as the building progresses. Decommissioning of sprinklers already installed must first be discussed with the owners and insurers of the building and with the fire authorities.

Active fire protection measures should be installed at the first opportunity and it will be of economic benefit if such measures also form part of the final provisions. This includes sprinklers if they form part of the final specification for the building in line with the recommendations of BS 5306: Part 2[17]. Damage to sprinklers during works is a matter for site management. However, in view of the concerns regarding such misuse, they could be guarded or be of a type that offers mechanical protection e.g. by being recessed. Special precautions would be required in exposed conditions during winter. Temporary alternative valve sets can be provided during construction and replaced at an appropriate time.

It is appreciated that provision of sprinklers to the relevant standard in a partially completed building poses considerable problems to the construction industry. However, if their importance in contributing to the reduction of fire damage during construction is appreciated, the design of the building could incorporate them at a much earlier stage.

If the building design does not include sprinklers, alternative precautions (probably passive) will be required.

12.8.3.3 First-aid firefighting

This issue is addressed in the LPC's *Joint Code*[2]. There is some evidence that first-aid firefighting facilities, including extinguishers, blankets and hosereels, are abused by site staff but their usefulness is otherwise generally accepted. That some fires are not extinguished by first-aid firefighting equipment may be due less to its not being available but more to a lack of skills in using the equipment or to the nature of the fire at the time of discovery relative to its development.

12.8.4 Detection

This issue is addressed in the LPC's *Joint Code*[2]. The early detection of fire in any circumstances is advantageous. On construction sites detection will alert those responsible for both first-aid firefighting and for alerting the fire services. The provision of fire detection during construction will require careful consideration of the problems of false alarms. This aspect must be considered to avoid early mistrust of the installation. Dust levels are likely to be much higher than in the finished building but this problem can be largely overcome by the choice of detector. Some detectors use a common base to which may be attached a head appropriate to the dust levels likely to occur during the particular building operation taking place.

12.8.5 Fire loads

Past incidents[18] clearly emphasise the need to address the increased fire load introduced by temporary works and the need to maintain the integrity of protected shafts. The use of less combustible materials for temporary works would reduce the risk of fire spread over combustible protective cladding, scaffold boards and staging. Nonetheless, automatic fire detection and control would reduce fire damage.

12.8.6 Building separation

Depending on certain factors, see section 3.2.5, the fire strategy for a project will consider the possibility of fire spread between buildings. The external elevations will be designed with the appropriate limits on unprotected areas. The contribution to limiting fire spread for this purpose will take into account the intended end use, compartmentation and the role of sprinklers. However, during construction, neither the sprinklers nor the compartmentation may be complete and the control of fire spread will accordingly be limited. Therefore the fire load may be temporarily higher than it will be upon completion. Furthermore, the design may provide for the external elevations themselves to include protected areas which, by being incomplete, can make little or no contribution to controlling fire spread.

Temporary measures in the form of fire resisting partitions, facades and/or enclosures for combustible materials, and the control of the quantities of combustibles may be required to avoid excessive fire load and exposure to adjoining property.

12.9 Management and communication

12.9.1 Management

Site management plays an important part in ensuring that fire precautions measures are pursued by all concerned. As a result of past incidents[18] they may need to ensure that site staff are more able to fight fires to complement their duties of implementing staff training, awareness and drills. Keeping the fire services informed of the development, in terms of access and firefighting facilities as well as the layout, form part of their duties. The importance of patrolling construction sites, particularly as the work nears the final stages, should be emphasised. Site management will play a leading role in guiding the attending fire services and in informing them of the details of the incident on their arrival. These issues are included in the LPC's *Joint Code*[2].

12.9.2 Fire wardens

This issue is addressed in the LPC's *Joint Code*[2] but there may still be a danger that the persons appointed will not be appropriately qualified. Their task is to ensure that fire precautions are being observed and they should be aware of the fire risks based on an understanding of fire, rather than merely as the application of rules. There needs to be a greater appreciation of the importance of the fire warden's role. Implementation of this recommendation should not result in the employment of a poorly qualified person doubling as the fire/safety officer. The better suited the person is to this role, the greater the reliance that fire precautions will be observed. The nature of the job and its responsibilities requires that safety measures must be implemented and the fire warden must receive full support from the site agent or project manager in any negotiations that may be required, whatever the contractual implications.

12.10   Motivation for provision and maintenance of fire precautions

12.10.1   Personal responsibility

An increased awareness of the possibility of fire and its tragic consequences is required. Despite past incidents[18], there is still a lack of belief that such events will happen again. The conflict between the need for fire precautions generally and their maintenance exists not only in completed buildings but is also apparent during construction. An effective way of increasing awareness is to impart responsibility for the outcome of failure to provide adequate fire precaution. Where it is unrealistic for individuals to bear that responsibility, it should be borne by their employers.

Contractors, at director level and with personal liability, should be made more responsible for the outcome of fires which occur in their area of work and as a result of processes under their control. One proven way of achieving this is to prepare contract documents that make clear the contractor's responsibilities for provision and maintenance of fire precautions for the various work packages. Fee-retention clauses relating to performance regarding site fire precautions could be included as well as to general construction performance.

12.10.2   General fire training and security

The building process is varied and complex and often conflicts with the need to provide and maintain fire precautions. A most effective form of detection and control, proven in health care premises particularly, is the presence of alert persons. Of the many fires which start in health care premises, few get out of hand because they are detected by persons trained to respond and are therefore tackled at a very early stage.

One solution to the need for provision and maintenance of fire precautions on building sites may be to employ trained persons to monitor the site and take appropriate action when fires are detected. This may be more cost-effective than stipulating temporary measures or over-specifying permanent ones to serve during construction. Such persons could be provided by private security contractors or, alternatively, suitably trained persons could be sought as part of the professional responsibility of the developer or contractor. That may be a role for a team of on-site professionals who could respond to major fire incidents.

General awareness of the risk of site fires would be increased by improved contractor training in firefighting. Contractors could then ensure that a minimum number of suitably trained operatives are on-site during construction. The initiative for this objective would need to be taken by the major contractors.

The availability of facilities to monitor the maintenance of fire precautions can be justified in view of the potential losses arising from inadequate provision. This is not a new concept; it is employed in certain hazardous industries and during national emergencies. The interests of the fire watchers to detect and control fires could be achieved by financial considerations, preferably backed by requirements from the Health and Safety Executive, the fire brigades and the building control authorities.

12.10.3   Life safety

The maintenance of the record of nil life loss in recent construction site fires is of primary importance. The provision and maintenance of means of escape is very important but may conflict with the normal activities taking place in the building during construction. Whilst the financial losses incurred from recent incidents are bad enough, the loss of life of operatives or firefighters must be avoided.

Many provisions and recommendations contribute to life safety and it would not be helpful to distinguish any as unique or of more importance than the others but particular items which should be addressed as part of the life safety are:

— escape routes

— detection and alarm

— ventilation to allow smoke to escape

— emergency lighting and signage.

Obviously the management and signage of escape routes is essential but emergency lighting on construction sites often fails to meet satisfactory standards. These issues are addressed in the LPC's *Joint Code*[2].

12.11   Built-in fire precautions

The concept of built-in, or 'hidden', fire precautions that cause minimal conflict with the building's use is not new. Such precautions are less likely to be misused or misunderstood. However, the more that they rely on continued management, the more likely they are to be ineffective when required. The dangers of having to use an escape route with which one is not familiar are well known and, in an emergency, it is often thought better to leave a building by the route through which it was entered.

The best fire precautions in completed buildings are those which are in harmony with the building's normal use. Good examples include health care buildings in which department boundaries coincide with compartmentation enclosures, and hotel bedrooms where fire-resisting doors provided for privacy and structural needs ensure sufficient mass to resist fire. There is no need to provide additional fire precautions for these specific areas since they are inherent in the building. Such fire precautions do not conflict with the normal operation of the building and will be effective when required.

The same considerations apply on construction sites and appropriate fire precautions, 'hidden' in the developing building, should be included where possible. The use of reinforced concrete, for example, provides fire resistance to the required value as soon as the formwork is removed.

The inherent fire resistance of steel may provide fire protection, but only for a much lower fire load than that for the finished building.

During the assessment of the fire at Broadgate Phase 8[19], the provision of oversized structural steel was discussed as a means of meeting the requirements for the site fire precautions. Where the finished building will anyway require a certain standard of fire protection, that provision may be capitalised upon during the construction phase to provide a cost-effective contribution to site fire safety. The more the final precautions can be provided during the construction process the less need there should be to make special provision during the building works.

References

1   New construction site code 'must succeed' *Fire Prevention* (252) 9 (September 1992)

2   *Fire Prevention on Construction Sites — The Joint Code of Practice on the Protection from Fire of Construction Sites and Buildings Undergoing Renovation* (London: Loss Prevention Council/Building Employers Confederation) (1992)

3   *Fire safety in construction work* HSG168 (London: HSE Books) (1997)

4   The Building Regulations 2000 Statutory Instruments 2000 No. 2531 (London: The Stationery Office) (2000)

5   The Building Standards (Scotland) Regulations 1990 Statutory Instruments 1990 No. 2179 (S. 187) (London: HMSO) (1990)

6   Building Regulations (Northern Ireland) 2000 Statutory Rules of Northern Ireland 2000 No. 389 (London: The Stationery Office) (2000)

7   The Fire Precautions Act 1971 (London: HMSO) (1971)

8   The Health and Safety at Work etc. Act 1974 (London: HMSO) (1974)

9   The Construction (Health, Safety and Welfare) Regulations 1996 Statutory Instruments 1996 No. 1592 (London: The Stationery Office) (1996)

10   The Construction (Design and Management) Regulations Statutory Instruments 1994 No. 3140 (London: HMSO) (1994)

11   The Management of Health and Safety at Work Regulations 1999 Statutory Instruments 1999 No. 3242 (London: The Stationery Office) (1999)

12   *General fire precautions at temporary accommodation units on construction sites* ID 404/23 (Sudbury: Health and Safety Executive) (1993)

13   Fire Certificates (Special Premises) Regulations 1976 Statutory Instrument Statutory Instruments 1976 No. 2003 (London: HMSO) (1976)

14   Highly Flammable Liquids and Liquefied Petroleum Gases Regulations 1972 Statutory Instruments 1972 No. 921 (London: HMSO) (1972)

15   Petroleum (Consolidation) Act 1928 (London: HMSO) (1928)

16   FPA casebook of fires *Fire Prevention* (248) 33 (April 1992)

17   BS 5306: *Fire extinguishing installations and equipment on premises*: Part 2: 1990: *Specification for sprinkler systems* (London: British Standards Institution) (1990)

18   Getting through construction *Fire Prevention* (248) 20 (April 1992)

19   *Investigation of the Broadgate Phase 8 fire* (Sunningdale: Steel Construction Institute) (1991)

Index

GUILDFORD **college**

Learning Resource Centre

Please return on or before the last date shown.
No further issues or renewals if any items are overdue.

Class: 696 CHA

Title: CIBSE Guide E: Fire Engineering

Author: CIBSE.